University Algebra

Prentice-Hall Mathematics Series

PRENTICE-HALL INTERNATIONAL, INC., *London*
PRENTICE-HALL OF AUSTRALIA, PTY. LTD., *Sydney*
PRENTICE-HALL OF CANADA, LTD., *Toronto*
PRENTICE-HALL OF INDIA (PRIVATE) LTD., *New Delhi*
PRENTICE-HALL OF JAPAN, INC., *Tokyo*

Preface

Abstract Algebra is now an integral part of the undergraduate mathematics curriculum of all universities and almost all colleges. This was not the case in 1953 when my book *First Course in Abstract Algebra* was published. In the intervening years, many topics of *First Course* have filtered down to more elementary courses. Then, too, the advent of Modern Mathematics in elementary and secondary school education has made the present-day student much more aware of algebraic structure. Such widespread curricular changes have made it imperative that *First Course* be revised, but at the same time made it almost impossible to salvage anything worthwhile from the book. Therefore, it was decided to write a new book to meet the algebraic needs of college and university students who plan on majoring in mathematics or related disciplines.

The basic theme of *University Algebra* is to define abstract concepts in as simple a setting as possible, and then carry them over to more complex systems. Thus, Cartesian products, homomorphisms, and quotient structures are first defined for Abelian groups and then extended to commutative rings, vector spaces, groups, and rings, in that order. Other examples of this procedure are: (1) Algebraic extensions of the rational field in the real field are considered prior to a general discussion of algebraic extensions of any field; (2) Factorization is studied in the rings of integers and polynomials before it is considered in principal ideal domains in general.

Chapters 0 and 1 are introductory, and should be covered as quickly as possible. For the teacher who wants an axiomatic approach to the integers, the Peano axioms are given in an Appendix. The first abstract algebraic system presented is the Abelian group in Chapter 2. This is followed by commutative rings in Chapters 3–5. The specialized topics of field extensions and factorization in integral domains are considered in Chapters 6 and 7. Vector spaces are studied in Chapter 8, in preparation for later studies of rings of linear transformations and matrices in Chapter 10 and linear equations and determinants in Chapter 11. Groups are presented in Chapter

v

9, and lattices in Chapter 12. A glossary of symbols and abbreviations follows the table of contents with a listing of pages on which the symbols first occur.

The book contains enough material for a three-hour undergraduate year course in abstract algebra. However, a more likely use of the book is in a semester course in abstract algebra in conjunction with a semester course in linear algebra. A possible outline for a three-hour, semester course is as follows: Chapters 0 and 1, 5 days; Chapter 2, 6 days; Chapters 3 and 4, 6 days; Chapter 5, 4 days (omitting Secs. 5 and 6 if necessary); Chapter 6, 4 days; Chapter 7, 3 days (omitting Secs. 4–6 if necessary); Chapter 8, 5 days (omitting Secs. 5 and 6 if necessary); Chapter 9, 5 days (omitting Sec. 7 if necessary); Chapter 10, 4 days. If vector spaces are already known, a few days can be spent on Chapter 12 in place of Chapter 8.

The exercises vary from simple computational ones to more difficult starred problems on theory. In addition, there are Theoretical Projects scattered throughout the book to challenge the superior students. Since some of the exercises are tricky, a separate pamphlet of selected answers has been prepared by the author and is available to the teacher from the publisher.

A bibliography of collateral reading is included at the end of the text. It is to be hoped that most of these books are readily available to the student in the library.

The author wishes to thank the many algebraists who have helped shape his views on algebra over the years; in particular, Professors N. Jacobson, N. H. McCoy, Y. Utumi, and C. E. Watts. Special thanks are due to Professors McCoy, I. H. Rose, and E. W. Swokowski, who were kind enough to read critically the final manuscript.

RICHARD E. JOHNSON

3. Cycles   173
4. Even and odd permutations   176
5. Normal subgroups and quotient groups   179
6. Homomorphisms   183
7. Existence of subgroups of a finite group   184

chapter 10   Rings   188

1. General remarks   188
2. Linear transformations   194
3. Matrix rings   200
4. The ring $L(V)$ 205

chapter 11   Linear Equations and Determinants   210

1. Linear equations over a field   210
2. The theory   218
3. The solution set of a system of linear equations   223
4. Determinants   226
5. Further properties of determinants   232
6. Determinants and systems of linear equations   236

chapter 12   Lattices   243

1. Posets   243
2. Lattices   245
3. Modular and complemented lattices   249
4. Distributive lattices   252

appendix   Natural Numbers and Integers   256

1. The natural numbers   256
2. Counting   260
3. The integers   261

Index   267

Glossary of Symbols and Abbreviations

Symbol	Meaning
iff	if and only if
■	end of proof
$\in$	is an element of, 1
$\notin$	is not an element of, 1
$\subset$	is contained in, 1
$\supset$	contains, 1
$\varnothing$	empty set, 2
$\cup$	union, 2
$\cap$	intersection, 2
$\{\ \mid\ \}$	set notation, 2
$\times$	Cartesian product, 3
$A \longrightarrow B$	mapping of A into B, 5
im f	image of f, 5
dom f	domain of mapping f, 5
$\mathscr{P}(S)$	set of all subsets of S, 6
$g \circ f$	composite of f and g, 7
$\#(S)$	number of elements in set S, 261
$\mathbb{N}$	set of natural numbers, 256
$\mathbb{Z}$	set of integers, 11
$\mathbb{Z}^{+}$	set of positive integers, 13
$\mathbb{Z}_n$	set of integers modulo n, 38
$\mathbb{Z}(p^{\infty})$	Prüfer group, 50
$\mathbb{Q}$	set of rational numbers, 20
$\mathbb{Q}/\mathbb{Z}$	set of rationals modulo 1, 39
$\mathbb{R}$	set of real numbers, 21
$\mathbb{C}$	set of complex numbers, 110

Symbol	Meaning
$\lvert a \rvert$	absolute value of a, 14
$\mid$	is a factor of, 16
(a,b)	ordered pair, 3
(a,b)	gcd of a and b, 16
gcd	greatest common divisor, 16
$[a,b]$	lcm of a and b, 16
lcm	least common multiple, 16
lub	least upper bound, 21
glb	greatest lower bound, 21
$\equiv$	congruence, 38
mod n	modulo n, 38
ker f	kernel of f, 46
C-ring	commutative ring, 53
ch R	characteristic of R, 61
deg $f(x)$	degree of $f(x)$, 79
$R[[x]]$	set of all formal power series, 97
$R[x]$	set of all polynomials, 76
$GF(p^n)$	Galois field, 108
$\bar{z}$	conjugate of z, 111
$T(z)$	trace of z, 111
$N(z)$	norm of z, 111
cis θ	$\cos \theta + i \sin \theta$, 115
ufd	unique factorization domain, 120
pid	principal ideal domain, 122
$V(F)$	vector space over F, 140
$\{\ \}^{\perp}$	independent set, 144
dim V	dimension of V, 151
δ_{ij}	Kronecker delta, 155
D_n	dihedral group, 171
S_n	symmetric group, 168
A_n	alternating group, 177
$L(V)$	set of linear transformations of V, 194
(a_{ij})	matrix, 201
$(F)_n$	set of all $n \times n$ matrices over F, 201
$r(f)$	rank of f, 205
$rr(A)$	row rank of A, 220
$cr(A)$	column rank of A, 220
det A	determinant of A, 226
sgn σ	sign of σ, 226
adj A	adjoint of A, 233
A^T	transpose of A, 227
poset	partially ordered set, 243

University Algebra

chapter 0

Basic Concepts

Abstract algebra is indebted to set theory for much of its language and notation. On the assumption that the reader is somewhat familiar with set theory, we shall only briefly sketch those parts of it that we shall need in this book.

I. Notation

We start with the primitive (undefined) notions of set and element. A set is made up of elements, although, again, the phrase "is made up of" is undefined. For the most part, sets will be denoted by italic capital letters such as $A, P, T, \ldots$, while elements of a set will be denoted by small italic letters such as $a, n, x, \ldots$. If x is an element of set A, we shall write

$$x \in A.$$

On the other hand, if x is not an element of set A, we shall write

$$x \notin A.$$

A stroke through a symbol always indicates a denial of that symbol.

The phrase "if and only if" is used so often in this book that we shall abbreviate it to "iff" in order to save some space.

Two sets S and T are called *equal*, and we write $S = T$, iff S and T are made up of the same elements. If every element of a set S is also an element of a set T, then S is called a *subset* of T and we write

$$S \subset T \quad \text{or} \quad T \supset S.$$

If $S \subset T$ and $S \neq T$, then S is called a *proper subset* of T. Evidently,

$$S = T \quad \text{iff} \quad S \subset T \quad \text{and} \quad T \subset S.$$

It is convenient to consider the existence of a set with no elements, the so-called *empty set*. The empty set is considered to be unique and is denoted by the symbol

$$\varnothing.$$

Clearly,

$$\varnothing \subset A$$

for every set A, since every element of $\varnothing$ (it contains none!) is also an element of A.

If S and T are both subsets of a set W, then the *union* of S and T, denoted by

$$S \cup T,$$

is the subset of W made up of the elements in either S or T (or both); and the *intersection* of S and T, denoted by

$$S \cap T,$$

is the subset of W made up of the elements in both S and T. Thus, for each $x \in W$,

$$x \in S \cup T \quad \text{iff} \quad x \in S \quad \text{or} \quad x \in T,$$
$$x \in S \cap T \quad \text{iff} \quad x \in S \quad \text{and} \quad x \in T.$$

Should it happen that S and T have no elements in common, then $S \cap T = \varnothing$. The union or intersection of any collection of subsets of W is defined analogously.

We shall often specify a subset of a set W by some condition on the elements of W. For example, if W is the set of all people living in Washington, D.C., and $C(x)$ is the condition "x works for the U.S. Government," then

$$A = \{x \in W \mid C(x)\}$$

denotes the set of all Federal employees in Washington. As another example, if N is the set of all natural numbers (see the Appendix), then

$$E = \{x \in N \mid x \text{ is even}\}$$

is the set of all even natural numbers. We can also describe E as below,

$$E = \{2n \mid n \in N\}.$$

If S is a set and $a,b \in S$, then $\{a,b\}$ is a two-element subset of S provided $a \neq b$. If $a = b$, then $\{a,b\} = \{a\}$ is a one-element subset of S.

If S and T are sets and $a \in S$, $b \in T$, then we can form the *ordered set*†

$$(a,b)$$

having first element a and second element b. The set of all such ordered pairs is called the *Cartesian product* of S and T and is denoted by

$$S \times T.$$

Thus,

$$S \times T = \{(a,b) \mid a \in S, b \in T\}.$$

For example, if

$$S = \{c,d\}, \qquad T = \{p,q,r\},$$

then

$$S \times T = \{(c,p),(c,q),(c,r),(d,p),(d,q),(d,r)\},$$

a set with six elements.

We can form the Cartesian product of three or more sets in the obvious way. For example, if A, B, and C are sets, then

$$A \times B \times C = \{(a,b,c) \mid a \in A, b \in B, c \in C\}.$$

2. Relations

Given a set S, a subset R of $S \times S$ is called a (binary) *relation* in S. It is common practice to write

$$a \, R \, b$$

iff $(a,b) \in R$.

For example, if M is the set of all men in Montana and F is the relation "is a father of," then $(m,n) \in F$ or, equivalently, $m \, F \, n$ if and only if m is the father of n. Another relation in M is S, where $(m,n) \in S$ or $m \, S \, n$ iff m has the same surname as n. Evidently $m \, F \, n$ implies $m \, S \, n$; that is, $F \subset S$.

A relation R in a set S is called *reflexive* iff $a \, R \, a$ for all $a \in S$, *symmetric* iff $b \, R \, a$ whenever $a \, R \, b$ for $a,b \in S$, and *transitive* iff $a \, R \, c$ whenever $a \, R \, b$ and $b \, R \, c$ for $a,b,c \in S$. If R is reflexive, symmetric, and transitive, then R is called an *equivalence relation* in S. Equality ($=$), defined to be identity, is always an equivalence relation, as is suggested by the similarity of the words "equals" and "equivalence." A relation R in S is called *antisymmetric* iff $a = b$ whenever $a \, R \, b$ and $b \, R \, a$ for $a,b \in S$.

In the example of the relation F ("is a father of") in the set M of all men in Montana, evidently F is far from an equivalence relation, being neither

---

† We can think of (a,b) as the (unordered) set $\{\{a\},\{a,b\}\}$. Since $\{a\} \subset \{a,b\}$, a is naturally the "first" element of the set. Note that $(b,a) = \{\{b\},\{a,b\}\}$ and $\{b\} \subset \{a,b\}$ so that b is naturally the "first" element of (b,a). It is easily shown that $(a,b) = (c,d)$ iff $a = c$ and $b = d$.

reflexive, symmetric, nor transitive. On the other hand, the relation S ("has the same surname as") evidently is an equivalence relation in M.

The common relation $\leq$ in the set Q of rational numbers is reflexive, transitive, and antisymmetric.

A set P made up of nonempty subsets of a set S is called a *partition* of S iff (i) the union of the subsets of S contained in P is S, and (ii) the intersection of any two subsets of S contained in P is $\varnothing$. For example, if

$$S = \{a,b,c,d,e,f,g\}$$

and

$$A = \{a,b\}, \qquad B = \{c,d,e,f\}, \qquad C = \{g\},$$

then

$$P = \{A,B,C\}$$

is a partition of S. Note that the elements of P are subsets of S.

Each partition P of a set S induces a relation R in S in an obvious way. Thus $(a,b) \in R$ if and only if a and b belong to the same element of the partition P. It is an easy exercise to prove that R is an equivalence relation in S.

It is true, conversely, that each equivalence relation R in a set S induces a partition of S in the following way. For each $a \in S$, let

$$a/R = \{b \in S \mid a \, R \, b\}.$$

Thus, each a/R is a subset of S. Since R is reflexive, $a \in a/R$. Therefore, if

$$S/R = \{a/R \mid a \in S\},$$

S/R is made up of subsets of S and the union of the subsets of S in S/R is S.

To prove that S/R is actually a partition of S, we need only show that $a/R \cap b/R = \varnothing$ for any two distinct subsets of S belonging to S/R. We shall do this by showing that if $a/R \cap b/R \neq \varnothing$, then $a/R = b/R$. If $c \in a/R \cap b/R$, then $a \, R \, c$ and $b \, R \, c$. Since R is symmetric and transitive, evidently $a \, R \, b$ and $b/R \subset a/R$. Clearly, $b \, R \, a$ also and $a/R \subset b/R$. Therefore, $a/R = b/R$ as desired.

For example, if M is the set of all men in Montana and S is the relation "has the same surname as," then M/S is a partition of M. Thus, $M/S = \{J,O,H, \ldots\}$, where J is the set of all men in Montana named Johnson, O is the set of all men named Olsen, H is the set of all men named Holter, and so forth.

3. Mappings

If S and T are sets and $f \subset S \times T$, then f is called a *mapping* or *function* of S into T iff for each element a of S there exists a unique element b of T

such that (a,b) is in f. We shall follow the usual practice of denoting by $f(a)$ the unique element of T corresponding to the element a of S. The notation

$$S \xrightarrow{f} T$$

is used to indicate that f is a mapping of set S into set T. Set S is called the *domain* of mapping f,

$$\operatorname{dom} f = S,$$

and $\{f(a) \mid a \in S\}$ is called the *image* of f,

$$\operatorname{im} f = \{f(a) \mid a \in S\}.$$

Thus, im f is a subset of T; it need not be all of T.

For example, let

$$S = \{a,b,c,d\}, \qquad T = \{r,s,t,u,v,w\},$$

and

$$f = \{(a,r),(b,t),(c,w),(d,r)\}.$$

Then $S \xrightarrow{f} T$ is a mapping such that

$$f(a) = r, \qquad f(b) = t, \qquad f(c) = w, \qquad f(d) = r.$$

Evidently dom $f = S$ and im $f = \{r,t,w\}$. The equations above may be said to *define f*.

As another example, if $\mathbb{N}$ is the set of natural numbers, then $\mathbb{N} \xrightarrow{s} \mathbb{N}$ defined by

$$s(x) = x^2 \quad \text{for every} \quad x \in \mathbb{N}$$

is a mapping of $\mathbb{N}$ into itself. The image of s is the set $\{0,1,4,9,16, \ldots\}$ of squares.

Two mappings f and g of set S into set T are *equal*, $f = g$, iff $f(x) = g(x)$ for all $x \in S$. Clearly equal mappings have equal domains and equal images.

A mapping $S \xrightarrow{f} T$ is called a

surjection if im $f = T$;
injection if $f(a) \neq f(b)$ whenever $a \neq b$, for $a,b \in S$;
bijection if f is a surjection and an injection.

A surjection $S \xrightarrow{f} T$ is often called a mapping of S *onto T*, while a bijection is frequently called a 1-1 *mapping of S onto T*.

Associated with every mapping $S \xrightarrow{f} T$ is a surjection $S \xrightarrow{f'} \operatorname{im} f$ defined by $f'(x) = f(x)$ for all $x \in S$. Thus, f' and f map the same way but f' is forced to be a surjection.

For example, the mapping

$$\mathbb{N} \xrightarrow{s} \mathbb{N} \quad \text{defined by} \quad s(x) = x^2 \quad \text{for all} \quad x \in \mathbb{N}$$

is an injection but not a surjection (and hence not a bijection). If we let $S = \{0,1,4,9,16, \ldots\}$, the set of squares, then the mapping

$$\mathbb{N} \xrightarrow{\;s'\;} S \quad \text{defined by} \quad s'(x) = x^2 \quad \text{for all} \quad x \in \mathbb{N}$$

is a surjection, and hence a bijection. If $E = \{2x \mid x \in \mathbb{N}\}$, then the mapping

$$\mathbb{N} \xrightarrow{\;h\;} E \quad \text{defined by} \quad h(x) = 2x \quad \text{for all} \quad x \in \mathbb{N}$$

is a bijection.

As another example, if

$$S = \{a,b,c,d\}, \qquad T = \{r, s\},$$

and $S \xrightarrow{\;f\;} T$ is defined by

$$f(a) = r, \qquad f(b) = s, \qquad f(c) = s, \qquad f(d) = r,$$

then f is a surjection but not an injection (and hence not a bijection).

In defining a mapping $S \xrightarrow{\;f\;} T$, we shall often do so by telling what $f(x)$ is for all $x \in S$. We need not include the statement "for all $x \in S$" in this definition if we assume that the domain of the variable x is the natural one, namely set S. For example, we gave above the example $\mathbb{N} \xrightarrow{\;s\;} \mathbb{N}$ defined by $s(x) = x^2$.

Associated with each set S is the set $\mathscr{P}(S)$ of all subsets of S. We call $\mathscr{P}(S)$ the *power set* of S. For example, if

$$S = \{a,b,c\},$$

then

$$\mathscr{P}(S) = \{\,\varnothing,\{a\},\{b\},\{c\},\{a,b\},\{a,c\},\{b,c\},\{a,b,c\}\},$$

a set with eight elements.

Each surjection $S \xrightarrow{\;f\;} T$ has associated with it an *inverse mapping*

$$T \xrightarrow{\;f^{-1}\;} \mathscr{P}(S)$$

defined as follows,

$$f^{-1}(b) = \{a \in S \mid f(a) = b\} \quad \text{for every} \quad b \in T.$$

Thus, for each $b \in T, f^{-1}(b)$ is the subset of all elements of S that are mapped into b by f. Clearly,

$$\{f^{-1}(b) \mid b \in T\}$$

is a partition of S.

For example, if

$$S = \{a,b,c,d,e,g\}, \qquad T = \{r,s,t\},$$

and

$$f(a) = r, \; f(b) = s, \; f(c) = t, \; f(d) = t, \; f(e) = s, \; f(g) = s,$$

then the mapping $T \xrightarrow{f^{-1}} \mathcal{P}(S)$ is defined by

$$f^{-1}(r) = \{a\}, \quad f^{-1}(s) = \{b,e,g\}, \quad f^{-1}(t) = \{c,d\}.$$

Note that

$$\{\{a\},\{b,e,g\},\{c,d\}\}$$

is a partition of S.

If $S \xrightarrow{f} T$ is a mapping and A is a subset of S, then it is convenient to let

$$f(A) = \{f(a) \mid a \in A\}.$$

That is, $f(A)$ is the image of set A in T under the mapping f. Similarly, if $S \xrightarrow{f} T$ is a surjection and B is a subset of T, then we shall let

$$f^{-1}(B) = \{a \in S \mid f(a) \in B\}.$$

Thus, $f^{-1}(B)$ is the inverse image of B in set S.

For the special case in which $S \xrightarrow{f} T$ is a bijection, $f^{-1}(b)$ is a one-element subset of S for every $b \in T$. It is conventional in this case to consider f^{-1} as a mapping of T into S rather than of T into the set of one-element subsets of S. Evidently $T \xrightarrow{f^{-1}} S$ is again a bijection.

For example, the bijection $\mathbb{N} \xrightarrow{h} E$ defined by $h(x) = 2x$ has inverse $E \xrightarrow{h^{-1}} \mathbb{N}$ defined by $h^{-1}(y) = \frac{1}{2}y$.

Given mappings

$$S \xrightarrow{f} T, \quad T \xrightarrow{g} U,$$

there is defined in a natural way a mapping

$$S \xrightarrow{p} U.$$

Thus, each $a \in S$ is mapped into $f(a) \in T$ and, in turn, $f(a) \in T$ is mapped into $g(f(a)) \in U$. That is, p is defined by

$$p(a) = g(f(a)), \quad a \in S.$$

We call p the *composite* of f and g and denote it by $g \circ f$ or, on occasion, by gf. That is, the mapping

$$S \xrightarrow{g \circ f} U \quad \text{is defined by} \quad (g \circ f)(a) = g(f(a)), \quad a \in S.$$

If we have three mappings

$$S \xrightarrow{f} T, \quad T \xrightarrow{g} U, \quad U \xrightarrow{h} V,$$

then a mapping $S \xrightarrow{p} V$ is defined in a natural way:

$$p(a) = h(g(f(a))) \quad \text{for every} \quad a \in S.$$

Clearly this is the composite of the mappings

$$S \xrightarrow{g \circ f} U, \quad U \xrightarrow{h} V$$

or of the mappings

$$S \xrightarrow{f} T, \quad T \xrightarrow{h \circ g} V.$$

That is,

$$p = h \circ (g \circ f) = (h \circ g) \circ f.$$

As we shall presently see, this equation shows that the composite is an *associative operation*.

For any set S, the mapping $S \xrightarrow{e} S$ defined by

$$e(a) = a, \quad a \in S$$

is called the *identity mapping* in S. We shall on occasion designate the identity mapping in a set S by e_S to show its association with set S. It is easily verified that for every mapping $S \xrightarrow{f} T$,

$$f \circ e_S = e_T \circ f = f.$$

If f is a bijection, then

$$f^{-1} \circ f = e_S, \quad f \circ f^{-1} = e_T.$$

4. Operations

The word "operation" is used in mathematics to indicate a special kind of mapping. If S is a set, then each mapping $S \times S \xrightarrow{\alpha} S$ is called a (binary) *operation*† in S. We shall follow the usual custom of indicating the element of S corresponding to the ordered pair $(a,b) \in S \times S$ by

$$a \; \alpha \; b$$

rather than by $\alpha(a,b)$.

For example, addition and multiplication in the set S of numbers used in elementary arithmetic and algebra are operations. Thus, to each pair (a,b) of numbers corresponds a unique number $a + b$, and to each pair (a,b) of numbers corresponds a unique number $a \cdot b$.

Another quite different example of an operation is the following. Let S be the set of all points in a Euclidean plane. For each pair $(a,b) \in S \times S$, with

---

† More generally, if S, T, and U are sets then a mapping $S \times T \xrightarrow{\alpha} U$ is called a (binary) operation of $S \times T$ into U. Since we shall have very little use for this extended definition of an operation, it suffices to limit the meaning of operation to the case $S = T = U$.

$a \neq b$, let $a \alpha b$ be the point of trisection nearer a of the segment connecting a to b. Also, let $a \alpha a = a$. Then the mapping $S \times S \xrightarrow{\alpha} S$ is an operation in S (see Figure 0.1).

We saw an example of an operation in the preceding section—namely, the composition of mappings. Rather than considering mappings of a set S into another set T, let us consider mappings of a set S into itself. Let M be the set of all mappings of S into S, and, for $f,g \in M$, let $f \circ g$ be the composition of f and g. Thus, $S \xrightarrow{f} S$ and $S \xrightarrow{g} S$ are mappings, and $S \xrightarrow{f \circ g} S$ is the mapping defined by

$$f \circ g(a) = f(g(a)), \qquad a \in S.$$

Since to each pair $(f,g) \in M \times M$ there corresponds a unique element $f \circ g \in M$, $\circ$ is an operation in M.

If S is a set and α is an operation in S, then α is said to be *associative* if

$$a \alpha (b \alpha c) = (a \alpha b) \alpha c \quad \text{for all} \quad a,b,c \in S.$$

If

$$a \alpha b = b \alpha a \quad \text{for all} \quad a,b \in S,$$

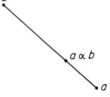

Figure 0.1

then the operation α is said to be *commutative*. The operations of addition and multiplication in elementary algebra are both associative and commutative. The operation of composition of mappings is associative, as we saw in the preceding section.

We call $e \in S$ an *identity element* of the operation α in S if

$$e \alpha a = a \quad \text{and} \quad a \alpha e = a \quad \text{for all} \quad a \in S.$$

An identity element, if it exists, is necessarily unique; for if e and f are identity elements of a, then $e \alpha f = e$ or $e \alpha f = f$ depending on whether we consider f or e as the identity element. Hence, $e \alpha f = e = f$. If M is the set of all mappings of set T into itself and $\circ$ is the operation of composition in M, then the identity mapping e is the identity element of the operation $\circ$ in M; i.e.,

$$h \circ e = e \circ h = h \quad \text{for all} \quad h \in M.$$

If α is an operation in a set S and α has an identity element e, then α is called an *inversive operation* iff for every $a \in S$ there exists some $b \in S$ such that

$$a \alpha b = e \quad \text{and} \quad b \alpha a = e.$$

An element b such that $a \alpha b = b \alpha a = e$ is called an *inverse* of a. Of course, a is also an inverse of b.

It is easy to construct examples of operations in a finite set S, for we need only write down "multiplication" tables at random. For example, if

$$S = \{e,u,v\},$$

then the table below defines an operation α in S. To find $a \, \alpha \, b$ by this

α	e	u	v
e	e	u	v
u	u	e	v
v	v	e	e

table, look for a in the column below α and b in the row to the right of α. Then $a \, \alpha \, b$ is the element of the table directly to the right of a and below b. Thus,

$$u \, \alpha \, v = v, \qquad v \, \alpha \, u = e, \qquad e \, \alpha \, v = v, \qquad v \, \alpha \, e = v.$$

Any filling in of the nine entries of the table with elements of S yields an example of an operation in S. Thus, it is clear that there are 3^9 different operations definable in S.

The operation α defined in the table above is not commutative, since $u \, \alpha \, v \neq v \, \alpha \, u$, and it is not associative since

$$u \, \alpha \, (v \, \alpha \, u) = u \, \alpha \, e = u, \qquad (u \, \alpha \, v) \, \alpha \, u = v \, \alpha \, u = e,$$

and $u \neq e$. The element e is an identity element of α. Finally, α is inversive since

$$e \, \alpha \, e = e, \qquad u \, \alpha \, u = e, \qquad v \, \alpha \, v = e.$$

Thus, each element is its own inverse.

Given two operations α and γ in a set S, α is said to be *distributive* with respect to γ iff

$$a \, \alpha \, (b \, \gamma \, c) = (a \, \alpha \, b) \, \gamma \, (a \, \alpha \, c), \qquad (b \, \gamma \, c) \, \alpha \, a = (b \, \alpha \, a) \, \gamma \, (c \, \alpha \, a)$$

for all $a,b,c \in S$. For example, multiplication is distributive with respect to addition in the number system of elementary algebra; i.e.,

$$a \cdot (b + c) = a \cdot b + a \cdot c, \qquad (b + c) \cdot a = b \cdot a + c \cdot a$$

for all numbers a, b, and c.

chapter I

The Real
Number System

A set together with the operations and relations defined in it is called an *algebraic system*. Modern algebra is concerned with properties of the common algebraic systems of mathematics. Historically, modern algebra is a by-product of late nineteenth and twentieth century mathematics. The algebra preceding modern algebra, which we shall call *elementary algebra*, was principally concerned with solutions of equations and factorization problems involving real and complex numbers. We shall start this book with a brief description of some of the basic number systems of elementary algebra.

1. The System of Integers

The system of integers consists of a set

$$\mathbb{Z} = \{\ldots, -3, -2, -1, 0, 1, 2, 3, \ldots\},$$

the operations of addition $(+)$ and multiplication $(\cdot)$, and a relation $\geq$. An axiomatic development of $\mathbb{Z}$ may be found in Appendix 1. As shown there, addition and multiplication have the following properties.

1.1 Addition is associative. $a + (b + c) = (a + b) + c$ for all $a, b, c \in \mathbb{Z}$.

1.2 Addition is commutative. $a + b = b + a$ for all $a, b \in \mathbb{Z}$.

1.3   0 is the additive identity. $a + 0 = a$ and $0 + a = a$ for all $a \in \mathbb{Z}$.

1.4   Addition is inversive. For every $a \in \mathbb{Z}$ there exists $-a \in \mathbb{Z}$ such that

$$a + (-a) = 0 \quad \text{and} \quad (-a) + a = 0.$$

1.5   Multiplication is associative. $a \cdot (b \cdot c) = (a \cdot b) \cdot c$ for all $a,b,c \in \mathbb{Z}$.

1.6   Multiplication is commutative. $a \cdot b = b \cdot a$ for all $a,b \in \mathbb{Z}$.

1.7   1 is the multiplicative identity. $a \cdot 1 = a$ and $1 \cdot a = a$ for all $a \in \mathbb{Z}$.

1.8   The multiplicative cancellation law holds. If $a \cdot c = b \cdot c$ or $c \cdot a = c \cdot b$ for some $a,b,c \in \mathbb{Z}$, with $c \neq 0$, then $a = b$.

1.9   Multiplication is distributive with respect to addition. $a \cdot (b + c) = a \cdot b + a \cdot c$ and $(b + c) \cdot a = b \cdot a + c \cdot a$ for all $a,b,c \in \mathbb{Z}$.

Since addition and multiplication are commutative, we need have stated only one of the equations in 1.3, 1.4, 1.7, 1.8, and 1.9. However, we have stated each property so as to make it independent of the other properties.

The many other properties of addition and multiplication in $\mathbb{Z}$ that come to mind can be derived from the nine basic properties above. Some of the more useful of these are listed below.

1.10   The additive cancellation law. If $a + c = b + c$ or $c + a = c + b$ for some $a,b,c \in \mathbb{Z}$, then $a = b$.

1.11 $a \cdot 0 = 0$ and $0 \cdot a = 0$ for all $a \in \mathbb{Z}$.

1.12 $-(a \cdot b) = (-a) \cdot b = a \cdot (-b)$ for all $a,b \in \mathbb{Z}$.

Proof of 1.10: If $a + c = b + c$, then

$$(a + c) + (-c) = (b + c) + (-c)$$

and

$$a + [c + (-c)] = b + [c + (-c)]$$

by 1.1. Hence, $a + 0 = b + 0$ by 1.4 and $a = b$ by 1.3.   ∎

We omit the proofs of 1.11 and 1.12.

The operation of *subtraction* $(-)$ is defined in $\mathbb{Z}$ as follows:

$$a - b = a + (-b) \quad \text{for all} \quad a,b \in \mathbb{Z}.$$

Clearly subtraction is neither associative nor commutative. It is easily shown that subtraction has the following properties: For all $a,b,c \in \mathbb{Z}$,

$$a - b = -(b - a),\ a \cdot (b - c) = a \cdot b - a \cdot c,\ a - (b - c) = (a - b) + c.$$

Another set of properties of $\mathbb{Z}$ has to do with the order relation "greater than or equal to" ($\geq$). These are listed below:

1.13 $\geq$ *is reflexive.* $a \geq a$ for all $a \in \mathbb{Z}$.

1.14 $\geq$ *is antisymmetric.* If $a \geq b$ and $b \geq a$, then $a = b$.

1.15 $\geq$ *is transitive.* If $a \geq b$ and $b \geq c$, then $a \geq c$.

1.16 $\geq$ *is a linear ordering.* Either $a \geq b$ or $b \geq a$ for all $a,b \in \mathbb{Z}$.

1.17 $a \geq b$ iff $a + c \geq b + c$ for some $c \in \mathbb{Z}$.

1.18 $a \geq b$ iff $a \cdot c \geq b \cdot c$ for some $c > 0$, $c \in \mathbb{Z}$.

The relation $>$ is defined in $\mathbb{Z}$ as follows:

$$a > b \quad \text{iff} \quad a \geq b \quad \text{and} \quad a \neq b.$$

The other relations $\leq$ and $<$ are defined as usual: $a \leq b$ iff $b \geq a$ and $a < b$ iff $b > a$. Each of the properties 1.13–1.18 has a *dual* which is also true and is obtained by replacing $\geq$ by its dual relation $\leq$.

The nonzero integers are separated into two sets,

$$\mathbb{Z}^+ = \{x \in \mathbb{Z} \mid x > 0\},$$

the set of *positive integers*, and

$$\mathbb{Z}^- = \{x \in \mathbb{Z} \mid x < 0\},$$

the set of *negative integers*.

Using 1.17 and 1.18, it may be shown that $\mathbb{Z}^+$ is *closed* under addition and multiplication; i.e., $a + b$, $a \cdot b \in \mathbb{Z}^+$ for all $a,b \in \mathbb{Z}^+$. If $a \in \mathbb{Z}^+$, then $-a \in \mathbb{Z}^-$ since $a > 0$ and $0 = -a + a > -a$ by 1.17. Similarly, if $a \in \mathbb{Z}^-$, then $-a \in \mathbb{Z}^+$. The set $\mathbb{Z}^-$ is closed under addition but not under multiplication. In fact,

1.19 $a \cdot b \in \mathbb{Z}^+$ for all $a,b \in \mathbb{Z}^-$.

Proof: If $a,b \in \mathbb{Z}^-$, then $-a,-b \in \mathbb{Z}^+$. Since $a \cdot b = (-a) \cdot (-b)$ and $\mathbb{Z}^+$ is closed under multiplication, evidently $a \cdot b \in \mathbb{Z}^+$. ∎

By our remarks above,

$$\mathbb{Z} = \mathbb{Z}^+ \cup \mathbb{Z}^- \cup \{0\}, \qquad \mathbb{Z}^+ \cap \mathbb{Z}^- = \varnothing.$$

That is $\{\mathbb{Z}^+, \mathbb{Z}^-, \{0\}\}$ is a partition of $\mathbb{Z}$.

While we feel certain that $1 \in \mathbb{Z}^+$, this is not given as a basic property (1.13–1.18). However, $a^2 > 0$ if $a \neq 0$ by 1.19 and the fact that $\mathbb{Z}^+$ is closed under multiplication. Hence, $1 \in \mathbb{Z}^+$ since $1 = 1^2$.

Associated with each integer x is its *absolute value* $|x|$ defined as follows:

$$|x| = x \quad \text{if} \quad x \geq 0; \qquad |x| = -x \quad \text{if} \quad x < 0.$$

By the definition, $|x| \geq 0$ for all $x \in \mathbb{Z}$. It may be proved that

$$|x + y| \leq |x| + |y|, \qquad |x \cdot y| = |x| \cdot |y| \quad \text{for all} \quad x, y \in \mathbb{Z}.$$

A final property of the integers has to do with the set

$$\mathbb{N} = \{x \in \mathbb{Z} \mid x \geq 0\}$$

of natural numbers.

1.20   Principle of mathematical induction. If $S \subset \mathbb{N}$, if $0 \in S$, and if $n + 1 \in S$ whenever $n \in S$, then $S = \mathbb{N}$.

From 1.20, we may derive the following useful property of $\mathbb{Z}$:

1.21 $\mathbb{N}$ is well-ordered. That is, every nonempty subset A of $\mathbb{N}$ has a least element.

A proof of 1.21 may be found on p.260.

We may easily prove that 1 is the least positive integer, i.e., 1 is the least element of $\mathbb{Z}^+$. By 1.21, $\mathbb{Z}^+$ has a least element $k \leq 1$. If $k < 1$, then $k^2 < k$ by the dual of 1.18. This is not possible, however, since $k^2 \in \mathbb{Z}^+$.

Exercises

1. Prove that $\mathbb{Z}^+$ is closed under addition and multiplication.

2. An element $u \in \mathbb{Z}$ is called a *unit* if $u \cdot v = 1$ for some $v \in \mathbb{Z}$. Prove that 1 and -1 are the only units of $\mathbb{Z}$.

3. Let $k \in \mathbb{Z}$ and $T \subset \{x \in \mathbb{Z} \mid x \geq k\}$, $T \neq \varnothing$. Prove that T contains a least element.

*4. Prove that if S is a nonempty proper subset of $\mathbb{Z}$ which has the property that $n + 1 \in S$ whenever $n \in S$, then S has a least element k and $S = \{x \in \mathbb{Z} \mid x \geq k\}$.

2. Arithmetic of the Integers

We turn now to the development of some of the elementary factorization properties of the integers, the so-called "arithmetic" of the integers. The basic division process familiar to all of us comes first. This states roughly that an integer a can be "divided" by a positive integer b, yielding a "quotient" q and a nonnegative "remainder" r smaller than b. For example,

$$39 = 5 \cdot 7 + 4;$$

that is, 39 divided by 5 gives a quotient of 7 and a remainder of 4 ($0 \leq 4 < 5$). We state this process as follows:

1.22 Division process. For every pair (a,b) of integers, with $b > 0$, there exist unique integers q and r such that

$$a = b \cdot q + r \quad \text{and} \quad 0 \leq r < b.$$

The integer q is called the *quotient* and r the *remainder* on dividing a by b.

Proof of 1.22: Let $S = \{a - b \cdot x \mid a - b \cdot x \geq 0, x \in \mathbb{Z}\}$. We assert that $S \neq \varnothing$; for if $a \geq 0$ then $a = a - b \cdot 0 \in S$, whereas if $a < 0$ then $-a > 0$ and, since $b \geq 1$, $b \cdot (-a) \geq -a$, $a - b \cdot a \geq 0$, and $a - b \cdot a \in S$. By the well-ordering property, S has a least element $r \geq 0$. Since $r \in S$, $r = a - b \cdot q$ for some $q \in \mathbb{Z}$ and $a = b \cdot q + r$.

To prove that $r < b$, we note that $r - b = a - b \cdot (q + 1)$, that is, $r - b$ has the correct form to be in S if $r - b \geq 0$. However, $r - b < r$ and r is the least element of S. Therefore, $r - b \notin S$, $r - b < 0$, and $r < b$.

All that remains to be proved in 1.22 is that q and r are unique. If

$$a = b \cdot q + r \quad \text{and} \quad 0 \leq r < b$$

and also

$$a = b \cdot q' + r' \quad \text{and} \quad 0 \leq r' < b,$$

then either $r \leq r'$ or $r' \leq r$. If $r \leq r'$, then

$$r' - r = b \cdot (q - q') \geq 0.$$

Evidently $r' - r \leq r' < b$, and hence $b \cdot (q - q') < b$ and $q - q' < 1$. Since $0 \leq q - q' < 1$ and 1 is the least positive integer, clearly $q - q' = 0$ and $q = q'$. Therefore, $r' = r$ also. ∎

We shall assume the reader is familiar with the "long-division process" for finding the quotient and remainder on dividing a by b.

An integer a is called a *factor*, or *divisor*, of integer b if $b = a \cdot x$ for some $x \in \mathbb{Z}$. If a is a factor of b, then b is called a *multiple* of a. The notation

$$a \mid b$$

is commonly used to indicate that a is a factor of b. The relation "is a factor of" ($\mid$) in $\mathbb{Z}$ is easily shown to be reflexive and transitive. Since $\mid$ is not symmetric, it is not an equivalence relation.

Every integer may be factored as $a = a \cdot 1$ and $a = (-a) \cdot (-1)$. Thus, $1, -1, a$, and $-a$ are always factors of a. An integer p, different from $0, 1$, and -1, is called a *prime number* iff $1, -1, p$, and $-p$ are the only factors of p. Certainly 2 and 3 are prime; 4 is not prime since $2 \mid 4$; 5 is prime; 6 is not prime since $3 \mid 6$; 7 is prime; 403 is not prime since $13 \mid 403$; and so on.

An integer c is called a *greatest common divisor* (gcd) of the integers a and b iff:

(i) $c \mid a$ and $c \mid b$ and (ii) whenever $x \mid a$ and $x \mid b$ for some $x \in \mathbb{Z}$, then $x \mid c$.

Dually, an integer d is called a *least common multiple* (lcm) of the integers a and b iff:

(ii) $a \mid d$ and $b \mid d$ and (ii) whenever $a \mid x$ and $b \mid x$ for some $x \in \mathbb{Z}$, then $d \mid x$.

For example, 8 is a gcd of 24 and 32, and 96 is a lcm of 24 and 32. Note that -8 is also a gcd and -96 a lcm of 24 and 32.

The reader may easily show that if the integers a and b have a gcd (or lcm) c, then c and $-c$ are the only gcd's (or lcm's) of a and b. Hence, a and b have a unique positive gcd (or lcm) if, indeed, they have one.

If the integers a and b have a gcd, then the unique positive gcd of a and b is denoted by

$$(a,b).$$

Similarly, the unique positive lcm of a and b, if it exists, is denoted by

$$[a,b].$$

Since $n \mid 0$ for every integer n, it is clear that the integers 0 and 0 do not have a gcd. If $a \neq 0$, then evidently $(a,0) = |a|$. Since $0 \mid n$ iff $n = 0$, evidently 0 is the unique lcm of 0 and a for all $a \in \mathbb{Z}$. These are special cases which are of no interest in what follows.

For convenience, we shall henceforth let

$$\mathbb{Z}' = \{a \in \mathbb{Z} \mid a \neq 0\}.$$

That any two elements of $\mathbb{Z}'$ have a gcd and a lcm is proved below.

1.23   Theorem. Any two elements of $\mathbb{Z}'$ have a gcd. Furthermore, for all $a,b \in \mathbb{Z}'$ there exist $u,v \in \mathbb{Z}$ such that

$$(a,b) = a \cdot u + b \cdot v.$$

Outline of proof: Let $S = \{a \cdot x + b \cdot y \mid x,y \in \mathbb{Z}, a \cdot x + b \cdot y > 0\}$. Clearly $S \neq \varnothing$, and hence S has a least element c of the form $c = a \cdot u + b \cdot v$ for some $u,v \in \mathbb{Z}$. By 1.22, there exist $q,r \in \mathbb{Z}$ such that $a = c \cdot q + r$ and $0 \leq r < c$. Now

$$r = a \cdot (1 - u \cdot q) + b \cdot (-v \cdot q) \quad \text{and} \quad r \notin S;$$

therefore $r = 0$. Hence, $c \mid a$ and, similarly, $c \mid b$. It is easily shown that if $x \mid a$ and $x \mid b$, then $x \mid c$. ■

We shall leave the proof of the existence of $[a,b]$ for all $a,b \in \mathbb{Z}'$ as an exercise. However, we point out that the general theory of factorization is studied in detail in Chapter 7.

If $a,b \in \mathbb{Z}'$ are such that $(a,b) = 1$, then a and b are called *relatively prime* integers.

1.24   Theorem. If $a,b,p \in \mathbb{Z}'$ and p is a prime, then

$$p \mid a \cdot b \quad \text{iff} \quad p \mid a \quad \text{or} \quad p \mid b.$$

Proof: If $p \mid a$ or $p \mid b$, then clearly $p \mid a \cdot b$. Conversely, if $p \mid a \cdot b$ but $p \nmid a$ (p is not a factor of a), then $(p,a) = 1$ and $1 = a \cdot u + p \cdot v$ for some $u,v \in \mathbb{Z}$ by 1.23. By assumption, $a \cdot b = p \cdot c$ for some $c \in \mathbb{Z}'$. Hence, $b = a \cdot b \cdot u + p \cdot b \cdot v = p \cdot (c \cdot u + b \cdot v)$ and $p \mid b$. ■

Every integer a different from 0, 1, and -1 has at least one prime factor, for the least element of $\{x \in \mathbb{Z} \mid x > 1, x \mid a\}$ clearly is a prime. Not only does a have one prime factor; it can also be expressed as a product of primes according to the following result, often called the *fundamental theorem of arithmetic*.

1.25   Theorem. Every integer $a > 1$ has a unique factorization (except for the order of the factors)

$$a = p_1 \cdot p_2 \cdot \ldots \cdot p_n$$

into a product of positive prime numbers.

Outline of proof: If $p_1 \mid a$, p_1 a positive prime, then $a = p_1 \cdot a_1$ for some integer $a_1 \geq 1$. If $a_1 > 1$, then $p_2 \mid a_1$ for some positive prime p_2 and $a = p_1 \cdot p_2 \cdot a_2$ for some integer $a_2 \geq 1$. Continuing this process, we obtain primes $p_1, p_2, \ldots, p_k, \ldots$ and integers $a_1 > a_2 > \ldots > a_k > \ldots$ such that $a = p_1 \cdot p_2 \cdot \ldots \cdot p_k \cdot a_k$ for $k = 1, 2, \ldots$. Let a_n be the least element of the set $\{a_1, a_2, \ldots, a_k, \ldots\}$. Necessarily $a_n = 1$, for otherwise $a_n = p_{n+1} \cdot a_{n+1}$

for some prime p_{n+1} and some positive integer $a_{n+1} < a_n$. Hence,

$$a = p_1 \cdot p_2 \cdot \ldots \cdot p_n.$$

We shall postpone the proof of the uniqueness of the factorization until Chapter 7. ∎

If $b \in \mathbb{Z}$, $b < -1$, then $-b > 1$ and $-b$ has a unique factorization $-b = q_1 \cdot q_2 \cdot \ldots \cdot q_k$ into a product of positive primes. Hence

$$b = -q_1 \cdot q_2 \cdot \ldots \cdot q_k.$$

It is apparent that the gcd and lcm of integers a and b may be easily found once a and b have been factored into primes. For example, $24 = 2 \cdot 2 \cdot 2 \cdot 3$ and $32 = 2 \cdot 2 \cdot 2 \cdot 2 \cdot 2$; therefore, since the factorization is unique, $(24,32) = 2 \cdot 2 \cdot 2 = 8$ and $[24,32] = 2 \cdot 2 \cdot 2 \cdot 2 \cdot 2 \cdot 3 = 96$. In general, if $p_1, p_2, \ldots, p_n$ are the distinct positive prime factors of the positive integers a and b, then

$$a = p_1^{k_1} \cdot p_2^{k_2} \cdot \ldots \cdot p_n^{k_n}, \qquad b = p_1^{l_1} \cdot p_2^{l_2} \cdot \ldots \cdot p_n^{l_n}$$

for some integers $k_i \geq 0$ and $l_i \geq 0$, $i = 1, \ldots, n$. If

$$r_i = \min \{k_i, l_i\}, \qquad s_i = \max \{k_i, l_i\}, \qquad i = 1, \ldots, n,$$

then

$$(a,b) = p_1^{r_1} \cdot p_2^{r_2} \cdot \ldots \cdot p_n^{r_n}, \qquad [a,b] = p_1^{s_1} \cdot p_2^{s_2} \cdot \ldots \cdot p_n^{s_n}.$$

From these equations, it is evident that

$$a \cdot b = (a,b) \cdot [a,b].$$

The study of factorization properties of the integers is contained in a branch of mathematics known as *number theory*. For countless centuries, both amateur and professional mathematicians have been fascinated by problems in number theory. One such problem is that of finding a rule for determining prime numbers. The greatest of the amateurs was Fermat, a French lawyer of the seventeenth century. After computing

$$F_n = 2^{2^n} + 1$$

for $n = 0$, 1, 2, 3, and 4 and showing it to be prime in each case, Fermat conjectured that F_n is a prime for every integer $n > 0$. This conjecture was proved to be false by the Swiss mathematician Euler, who showed in 1732 that $641 \mid F_5$. Many more Fermat numbers have been examined, some by modern computing machines, but no Fermat prime F_n, $n > 4$, has been found as yet.

Perhaps the greatest of the professionals in number theory was the nine-teenth-century German mathematician and astronomer, Gauss. As a young man, he solved a problem extant since the time of Euclid—that of determining all constructible regular polygons. Curiously enough, he proved that a regular polygon with a prime number p of sides is constructible (with straight edge and compass) if and only if p is a Fermat prime. Thus, it was discovered for the first time that a regular polygon with $17 (= F_2)$ sides is constructible. This and many other problems of number theory are solved in Gauss' book, *Disquisitiones Arithmeticae*, published in 1801 when he was twenty-four.

Exercises

In each of Exercises 1–5, find the desired integer.

1. (4,284, 14,586).

2. (18,336, 29,412).

3. [78, 143].

4. [5,809, 11,729].

5. (125,836, 47,527).

6. Prove that if $a,b,c \in \mathbb{Z}^+$ and $c \mid ab, (c,a) = 1$, then $c \mid b$.

7. If $n \geq 2$ and p is a prime such that $p \mid (n! + 1)$, then prove that $p > n$. Use this fact to prove that there are infinitely many primes.

8. Prove that if $a,m \in \mathbb{Z}^+$, $a > 1$, and $a^m + 1$ is prime, then necessarily a is even and $m = 2^n$ for some integer n.

9. Prove that if $a,m \in \mathbb{Z}$, with $a > 1$ and $m > 1$, and $a^m - 1$ is prime, then $a = 2$ and m is a prime. Such primes are called *Mersenne primes*. Find some.

10. If $a,b \in \mathbb{Z}^+$ and $(a,b) = 1$, then prove that $(a + b, a - b) = 1$ or 2.

*11. Prove that $(F_n, F_{n+k}) = 1$ if $k > 0$. [*Hint:* Prove that $F_n \mid (F_{n+k} - 2)$.] Use this fact to prove that there are infinitely many primes.

*12. Let $r_0, r_1 \in \mathbb{Z}^+$ and r_2 be the remainder on dividing r_0 by r_1, r_3 the remainder on dividing r_1 by r_2, r_4 the remainder on dividing r_2 by r_3, and so on. Prove that $r_n \neq 0$, $r_{n+1} = 0$, for some integer $n > 0$. Prove that

$$(r_0, r_1) = r_n.$$

This process of successive divisions for finding the gcd of two integers is known as *Euclid's algorithm*. Use Euclid's algorithm in working Exercises 1 and 2 above.

3. The Rational Number System

We recall that numbers of the form m/n, where $m,n \in \mathbb{Z}$ with $n \neq 0$, are called *rational numbers*. Since $m = m/1$, every integer is a rational number also. The set of all rational numbers will be denoted by

$$\mathbb{Q}$$

throughout this book. As we saw above,

$$\mathbb{Q} \supset \mathbb{Z}.$$

The operations of addition and multiplication in $\mathbb{Z}$ may be extended to $\mathbb{Q}$ as follows: For all $a,b,c,d \in \mathbb{Z}$, with $b \neq 0$ and $d \neq 0$,

$$\frac{a}{b} + \frac{c}{d} = \frac{a \cdot d + b \cdot c}{b \cdot d}, \qquad \frac{a}{b} \cdot \frac{c}{d} = \frac{a \cdot c}{b \cdot d}.$$

It may be shown that properties 1.1–1.12 hold in $\mathbb{Q}$ as well as in $\mathbb{Z}$. An additional property of multiplication in $\mathbb{Q}$ is as follows.

1.26   Each nonzero $a \in \mathbb{Q}$ has a *multiplicative inverse* a^{-1}; i.e.,

$$a \cdot a^{-1} = 1 \quad \text{and} \quad a^{-1} \cdot a = 1.$$

For example, $\frac{1}{2}$ is the multiplicative inverse of 2, and $(-3)/4$ of $4/(-3)$. We shall also call the multiplicative inverse of a the *reciprocal* of a and denote it by $1/a$.

The order relation $\geq$ is defined in $\mathbb{Q}$ as well as in $\mathbb{Z}$ and has properties 1.13–1.18. The set $\mathbb{Q}^+$ of positive rational numbers may be defined by

$$\mathbb{Q}^+ = \left\{ \frac{a}{b} \,\middle|\, a,b \in \mathbb{Z}, \, a \cdot b > 0 \right\},$$

and similarly, the set of negative rational numbers by

$$\mathbb{Q}^- = \left\{ \frac{a}{b} \,\middle|\, a,b \in \mathbb{Z}, \, a \cdot b < 0 \right\}.$$

Evidently

$$\mathbb{Q} = \mathbb{Q}^+ \cup \mathbb{Q}^- \cup \{0\}, \qquad \mathbb{Q}^+ \cap \mathbb{Q}^- = \varnothing.$$

There is no property of $\mathbb{Q}$ corresponding to the induction property 1.20 of $\mathbb{Z}$. Another difference between $\mathbb{Z}$ and $\mathbb{Q}$ is that there exist consecutive integers n and $n + 1$, but there do not exist consecutive rational numbers. To prove this, let $a,b \in \mathbb{Q}$ with $a > b$. Then

$$a + a > a + b > b + b$$

by two applications of 1.17; that is, $2a > a + b > 2b$. On multiplying each member of this inequality by the positive rational number $\frac{1}{2}$, we obtain by 1.18

$$a > \frac{a + b}{2} > b.$$

Thus, the arithmetic average of two unequal rational numbers is always strictly between them.

4. The Real Number System

The rational number system is contained in a still larger system, called the *real number system*. We shall designate the set of all real numbers by

$$\mathbb{R}$$

throughout this book. Thus, $\mathbb{R} \supset \mathbb{Q} \supset \mathbb{Z}$.

Operations of addition and multiplication and the order relation $\geq$ are defined in $\mathbb{R}$ and possess properties 1.1–1.18 and 1.26 given previously. An additional property of $\mathbb{R}$ is its completeness relative to the order relation $\geq$. We shall state this property after making the following definitions.

A real number r is called a *lower bound* of a subset A of $\mathbb{R}$ if $r \leq x$ for every $x \in A$. Similarly, a real number s is called an *upper bound* of a subset B of $\mathbb{R}$ if $s \geq y$ for every $y \in B$. Of course, a set of real numbers does not necessarily have a lower bound or an upper bound.

If subset A of $\mathbb{R}$ has at least one lower bound, then the set

$$A' = \{ r \in \mathbb{R} \mid r \leq x \quad \text{for every} \quad x \in A \}$$

is nonempty. The greatest element of A', if it exists, is called the *greatest lower bound* (abbreviated "glb") of set A. Dually, if B is a subset of $\mathbb{R}$ and

$$B' = \{ s \in \mathbb{R} \mid s \geq y \quad \text{for} \quad \text{every} \quad y \in B \}$$

is nonempty, then the least element of B', if it exists, is called the *least upper bound* (abbreviated "lub") of set B. It is evident, for example, that the interval $I = \{ x \in \mathbb{R} \mid 0 < x < 1 \}$ has 0 as its glb and 1 as its lub. Clearly a glb or a lub of a set, if its exists, is unique.

1.27 Completeness property. Every nonempty subset of $\mathbb{R}$ which has an upper bound has a lub, and every nonempty subset which has a lower bound has a glb.

From the basic properties of $\mathbb{R}$ stated above, we can prove the following important property.

1.28   Archimedean property. For each real number r there exists an integer n such that $n > r$.

Proof: Assume that the property is false; that is, there exists a real number r such that $n \leq r$ for every $n \in \mathbb{Z}$. This means that the set $\mathbb{Z}$ has an upper bound in $\mathbb{R}$. Hence, by the completeness property, $\mathbb{Z}$ has a lub k in $\mathbb{R}$. Since $n \leq k$ for every $n \in \mathbb{Z}$, and $n + 1 \in \mathbb{Z}$ whenever $n \in \mathbb{Z}$, evidently $n + 1 \leq k$ for every $n \in \mathbb{Z}$. However, then

$$n \leq k - 1 \quad \text{for every} \quad n \in \mathbb{Z}$$

and $k - 1$ is an upper bound of $\mathbb{Z}$ less than the lub of $\mathbb{Z}$. Since the assumption that the property is false leads to a contradictory statement, the property must be true. ∎

A dual argument shows that for every $r \in \mathbb{R}$ there exists an $n \in \mathbb{Z}$ such that $n < r$.

We may use the Archimedean property to prove that $\mathbb{Q}$ is dense in $\mathbb{R}$, as stated below.

1.29   Theorem. The set $\mathbb{Q}$ of rational numbers is *dense* in the set $\mathbb{R}$; that is, if $a,b \in \mathbb{R}$ with $a < b$, then there exists an $r \in \mathbb{Q}$ such that

$$a < r < b.$$

Outline of proof: Select $k \in \mathbb{Z}$ such that $k \leq a < k + 1$. Also select $n \in \mathbb{Z}$ such that $n > 1/(b - a)$. Then

$$a < k + \frac{m}{n} < b$$

for some positive integer $m \leq n$. Hence, $r = k + m/n$ is a rational number with the desired property. ∎

If k is a real number and

$$S = \{r \in \mathbb{Q} \mid r < k\},$$

then

$$\text{lub } S = k.$$

For k is an upper bound of S whereas no real number $a < k$ is an upper bound of S, since $a < r < k$ for some $r \in \mathbb{Q}$ by the theorem above. Thus, *every real number is the* lub *of a set of rational numbers.*

We shall not prove it at this time, but it may be shown that if a is a positive real number and n is an integer, $n > 1$, then

$$b = \text{lub } \{r \in \mathbb{Q} \mid r > 0, r^n < a\}$$

is an nth root of a; that is, $b^n = a$ and therefore

$$b = \sqrt[n]{a}.$$

Consequently, every positive real number has a unique positive nth root for each integer $n > 1$. It follows readily that every negative real number has a unique negative nth root for each odd integer $n > 1$.

Real numbers which are not rational are commonly called *irrational numbers*.

Exercises

1. Prove that the lub of a set $A \subset \mathbb{R}$, if it exists, is unique.

2. If set $A \subset \mathbb{R}$ has a lub, then prove that set $-A = \{-x \mid x \in A\}$ has a glb, and vice versa.

3. Prove that it is enough in 1.27 to state that every set $A \subset \mathbb{R}$ which has an upper bound has a lub.

4. Give examples of sets of real numbers which contain their lub and sets which do not; do the same for glb.

5. If $S = \left\{ \dfrac{1}{n} \,\middle|\, n \in \mathbb{Z}^+ \right\}$, prove that $0 = \text{glb } S$.

6. If $S = \left\{ \dfrac{n}{n+1} \,\middle|\, n \in \mathbb{Z}^+ \right\}$, prove that $1 = \text{lub } S$.

7. If $a \in \mathbb{R}$, $a > 1$, then prove that the set $\{a^n \mid n \in \mathbb{Z}^+\}$ has no lub.

8. Let $k \in \mathbb{R}$, with $k > 1$. Prove that the inequalities

(i) $1 + \dfrac{n}{k} < \left(1 + \dfrac{1}{k}\right)^n < 1 + \dfrac{2^n - 1}{k}$,

(ii) $1 - \dfrac{n}{k} < \left(1 - \dfrac{1}{k}\right)^n < 1 - \dfrac{1}{k}$,

are true for every integer $n > 1$.

9. If $n \in \mathbb{Z}^+$ and $r, x \in \mathbb{R}^+$ are such that $x^n < r$, then prove that there exists some $y \in \mathbb{R}^+$ such that $x^n < y^n < r$. [*Hint:* Let $y = x(1 + 1/k)$ and prove that for some number $k > 1$, $y^n < r$. Use Exercise 8.]

10. If $n \in \mathbb{Z}^+$ and $r, x \in \mathbb{R}^+$ are such that $x^n > r$, then prove that there exists some $y \in \mathbb{R}^+$ such that $x^n > y^n > r$. [*Hint:* Let $y = x(1 - 1/k)$ and continue as in Exercise 9.]

*11. Using Exercises 9 and 10, prove that every $r \in \mathbb{R}^+$ has a positive nth root for each integer $n > 1$.

[*Hint:* Let $\sqrt[n]{r} = \text{lub } S$, where $S = \{x \in R^+ \mid x^n < r\}$.]

12. Do negative real numbers ever have real nth roots? Prove your answer.

5. Real Fields

A subset F of $\mathbb{R}$ is called a *real field* iff:

(i) F is closed under addition and multiplication,
(ii) $0, 1 \in F$,
(iii) $-a$ and $1/a$ are in F for every nonzero $a \in F$.

If F is a real field, then clearly the properties 1.1–1.18 hold for F since they hold for $\mathbb{R}$. Since $1 \in F$ and also $n + 1 \in F$ whenever $n \in F$, evidently $\mathbb{Z}^+ \subset F$ by 1.20. Hence, $\dfrac{m}{n} = m \cdot \dfrac{1}{n}$ is in F for all $m, n \in \mathbb{Z}^+$ by (i)–(iii) above, and therefore

1.30 $\mathbb{Q} \subset F$.

Clearly $\mathbb{Q}$ is a real field; in fact, $\mathbb{Q}$ is the *least real field* by 1.30. Also, $\mathbb{R}$ is a real field. There are many other real fields between $\mathbb{Q}$ and $\mathbb{R}$, as we shall indicate below.

Integers greater than 1 such as 2, 3, 5, 6, 7, 10, 11, 13, 14, 15, and so on, which have no perfect-square factors other than 1 are called *positive square-free* integers.

For each positive square-free integer n, let

1.31 $\mathbb{Q}[\sqrt{n}] = \{a + b\sqrt{n} \mid a, b \in \mathbb{Q}\}$.

We claim that $\mathbb{Q}[\sqrt{n}]$ is a real field. That $\mathbb{Q}[\sqrt{n}]$ is closed under addition and multiplication is shown below.

$$(a + b\sqrt{n}) + (c + d\sqrt{n}) = (a + c) + (b + d)\sqrt{n},$$
$$(a + b\sqrt{n}) \cdot (c + d\sqrt{n}) = (ac + bdn) + (ad + bc)\sqrt{n}.$$

Next,

$$0 = 0 + 0\sqrt{n}, \qquad 1 = 1 + 0\sqrt{n},$$

so that $0,1 \in \mathbb{Q}[\sqrt{n}]$. Finally, if $a + b\sqrt{n} \neq 0$, then $a - b\sqrt{n} \neq 0$ and $c = a^2 - nb^2 \neq 0$. Hence, $-(a + b\sqrt{n})$ and $(a + b\sqrt{n})^{-1}$ are in $\mathbb{Q}[\sqrt{n}]$ by the following calculations:

$$-(a + b\sqrt{n}) = (-a) + (-b)\sqrt{n}, \qquad (a + b\sqrt{n})^{-1} = \frac{a}{c} - \frac{b}{c}\sqrt{n}.$$

The real field $\mathbb{Q}[\sqrt{n}]$ defined in 1.31 is called a *quadratic field*. For example,

$$\mathbb{Q}[\sqrt{2}] = \{a + b\sqrt{2} \mid a,b \in \mathbb{Q}\}$$

is a quadratic field.

We shall not go into the details, but there are cubic, quartic, quintic, and so on, real fields defined in an analogous way. For example,

$$\mathbb{Q}[\sqrt[3]{2}] = \{a + b\sqrt[3]{2} + c\sqrt[3]{4} \mid a,b,c \in \mathbb{Q}\}$$

is a cubic field. Such fields are studied in detail in Chapter 6.

Exercises

1. If F_1 and F_2 are real fields, is $F_1 \cap F_2$ also a real field? Extend this result to any number of real fields.

2. In what way or ways does $\mathbb{Z}[\sqrt{2}] = \{a + b\sqrt{2} \mid a,b \in \mathbb{Z}\}$ fail to be a real field?

*3. Prove that $\mathbb{Q}[\sqrt[3]{2}]$ is a real field. [*Hint:* You may assume that $a + b\sqrt[3]{2} + c\sqrt[3]{4} = 0$ iff $a = b = c = 0$.]

*4. Do you think that $\{a + b\sqrt{2} + c\sqrt{3} + d\sqrt{6} \mid a,b,c,d \in \mathbb{Q}\}$ is a real field? Give reasons for your remarks.

*5. We call $u \in \mathbb{Z}[\sqrt{2}]$ a unit if there exists some $v \in \mathbb{Z}[\sqrt{2}]$ such that $u \cdot v = 1$. Discuss the units of $\mathbb{Z}[\sqrt{2}]$. Exhibit an infinite set of units of $\mathbb{Z}[\sqrt{2}]$.

6. The Field of Constructible Numbers

We recall from analytic geometry that $\mathbb{R}$ may be used as a set of co-ordinates on a line. Thus, a regular scale may be put on a line in such a way that each point has a real-number coordinate and each real number is the coordinate of some point on the line.

The scale may be constructed in part by the instruments of Euclidean geometry—namely, a compass and a straight edge. Thus, given points O and I to which we assign the numbers 0 and 1, respectively, we can mark off equispaced points on both sides of O with our compass and assign the rest of the integers to these points (Figure 1.1).

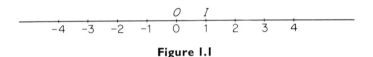

Figure 1.1

In turn, each unit segment joining consecutive integers can be divided into n equal parts for every integer $n > 0$. The obvious rational numbers are assigned to these points. For example, the segment [3,4] is divided into fourths as shown in Figure 1.2. Thus, four equispaced points are marked off on a line AB and are joined to points on the segment [3,4] by parallel lines.

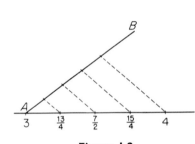

Figure 1.2

The set S of all real numbers whose corresponding points on the line can be constructed, starting from points O and I and using only a compass and a straight edge, is called the set of *constructible numbers*. From our remarks above,

$$S \supset \mathbb{Q}.$$

1.32   Theorem. The set S of constructible numbers is a real field. Furthermore, $\sqrt{x} \in S$ for each positive $x \in S$.

Outline of proof: If $a \in S$, $a > 0$, then $-a \in S$ as we see by using a circle of radius a with center at O (Figure 1.3). If $a,b \in S$, $b > 0$, then $a + b$, $a - b \in S$ for reasons shown in Figure 1.4. If $a,b \in S$, $a > 0$ and $b > 0$, then

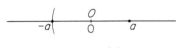

Figure 1.3

Figure 1.4

$a \cdot b, a/b \in S$ for reasons shown in Figures 1.5 and 1.6. These remarks make it clear that S is a real field.

If $a \in S$, $a > 1$, then we can construct a segment of length $\sqrt{a}$ as shown

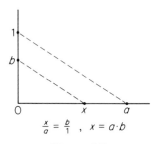

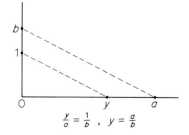

Figure 1.5   **Figure 1.6**

in Figure 1.7. If $0 < a < 1$, then $1/a > 1$ and $\sqrt{1/a} \in S$. Hence, $\sqrt{a} = 1/\sqrt{1/a} \in S$ also. ∎

According to Theorem 1.32, each of the numbers

$$\sqrt[4]{2} = \sqrt{\sqrt{2}}, \quad \sqrt{1 + \sqrt{5}}, \quad \frac{\sqrt{7}}{3 - \sqrt{\sqrt{11} - 3}}$$

is constructible. Evidently $\sqrt[n]{a} \in S$ if $a \in S$ as long as n is a positive integral power of 2.

There are three famous construction problems of antiquity: one is to construct a cube having a volume twice that of a given cube; another, to "square the circle"—that is, to construct a square having the same area as a given circle; the third, to trisect any angle. In each of these problems, we are supposed to use only a compass and a straight edge.

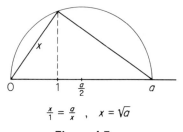

Figure 1.7

If we take an edge of the given cube to be 1 unit length, then each edge of the cube with twice the volume will have length $\sqrt[3]{2}$ units. Thus, the problem of duplicating the cube is equivalent to that of constructing the number $\sqrt[3]{2}$. Although we shall not do so, it may be proved that only square roots, fourth roots, eighth roots, and so on, are constructible. Hence, $\sqrt[3]{2}$ is not a constructible number and a cube cannot be duplicated.

If a circle has a radius of 1 unit, then its area is π. Thus, we are asked in the circle-squaring problem to construct a square of area π. Clearly we can do this iff π is a constructible number. While we cannot do so in the context of this book, it may be proved that π is not a constructible number. Thus, this problem is also impossible.

The problem of trisecting any angle may be shown to be impossible for similar reasons.

Exercises

1. Look up the history of the three famous construction problems of antiquity.

2. Using a compass and a straight edge, actually construct:

(i) $\sqrt{5}$,   (ii) $\sqrt[4]{2}$,   (iii) $\dfrac{\sqrt{3}}{1+\sqrt{5}}$.

chapter 2

Abelian Groups

The primary purpose of Chapter 1 was to develop examples for the purpose of illustrating the various types of algebraic systems encountered in modern mathematics. We chose as our set of elements the set of real numbers of elementary algebra.

In this and succeeding chapters, the nature of the elements of an algebraic system will be of little importance. Rather, we shall concentrate on algebraic systems defined by specified properties, such as associative, commutative, and distributive laws. Our problem will be to derive as many additional properties as we can from those that are stated.

One of the simplest and most common algebraic systems of mathematics is the Abelian group to be studied in the present chapter.

1. Abelian Groups

An algebraic system

$$\{G;\alpha\}$$

consisting of a set G and a (binary) operation α is called an *Abelian*† (or, *commutative*) *group* iff

2.1 α is associative.

2.2 α is commutative.

---

† Niels Henrik Abel was a brilliant Norwegian mathematician of the early nineteenth century. He used groups in connection with his work on solving polynomial equations.

2.3   There exists an identity element for α.

2.4 α is inversive.

Later on, in Chapter 9, we shall study *groups*, which are algebraic systems with one operation having all the properties above except the commutative law.

We have at hand several examples of Abelian groups contained in the real number system. Thus,

$$\{\mathbb{Z};+\}, \qquad \{\mathbb{Q};+\}, \qquad \{\mathbb{R};+\}$$

are Abelian groups. If we let $\mathbb{Q}'$ denote the set of nonzero elements of $\mathbb{Q}$, and similarly for $\mathbb{R}'$, then

$$\{\mathbb{Q}';\cdot\}, \qquad \{\mathbb{R}';\cdot\}$$

are also Abelian groups. However, $\{\mathbb{Z}';\cdot\}$ is not an Abelian group since multiplication is not inversive in $\mathbb{Z}'$.

It is customary to use addition $(+)$ as the operation when discussing Abelian groups in general, and to denote the additive identity element of each group by 0 (zero). It is also customary to speak of the Abelian group G rather than $\{G;+\}$, the operation of addition being implicitly understood.

Other useful properties of an Abelian group G may be derived from 2.1–2.4. For example, the following *cancellation law* holds:

2.5   If $a + c = b + c$ or $c + a = c + b$ for some $a,b,c \in G$, then $a = b$.

Proof: If $a + c = b + c$ and d is an inverse of c, then

$$\begin{aligned}
(a + c) + d &= (b + c) + d, \\
a + (c + d) &= b + (c + d) && \text{(by 2.1)}, \\
a + 0 &= b + 0 && \text{(by 2.4)}, \\
a &= b && \text{(by 2.3)}.
\end{aligned}$$

If $c + a = c + b$, then $a + c = b + c$ by 2.2 and $a = b$ by the proof above. ∎

A consequence of 2.5 is that each $a \in G$ has a unique inverse; for if $a + b = 0$ and $a + c = 0$, then $a + b = a + c$ and $b = c$ by 2.5. We shall denote the inverse of $a \in G$ by $-a$ and call $-a$ the *negative* of a. Since $a + (-a) = 0$, a and $-a$ are inverses of each other. Hence,

2.6 $-(-a) = a$ for all $a \in G$.

How is the negative of $a + b$ related to $-a$ and $-b$? To answer this question, we note that

$$(a + b) + (-b) = a + [b + (-b)] = a.$$

Therefore,

$$(a + b) + [(-b) + (-a)] = [(a + b) + (-b)] + (-a) = a + (-a) = 0.$$

This proves that $(-b) + (-a)$ is the inverse of $a + b$; i.e.,

2.7 $\qquad\qquad -(a + b) = (-b) + (-a)$ for all $a,b \in G.$

An interesting feature of our proof of 2.7 is that we never use the commutative law. Hence, 2.7 holds for any group, Abelian or not. Since $(-b) + (-a) = (-a) + (-b)$ in an Abelian group, we can express 2.7 in the following form for an Abelian group G:

2.8 $\qquad\qquad -(a + b) = (-a) + (-b)$ for all $a,b \in G.$

A (binary) operation of *subtraction* $(-)$ may be defined in an Abelian group G as follows:

2.9 $\qquad\qquad a - b = a + (-b)$ for all $a,b \in G.$

Subtraction is neither associative nor commutative in general. Furthermore, there is generally no identity element relative to subtraction. The reader may easily verify the following properties of subtraction in G.

2.10 $\quad -(a - b) = b - a, a - (b - c) = (a - b) + c$ for all $a,b,c \in G.$

For convenience, we write $a + b + c$ in place of $(a + b) + c, a + b + c + d$ in place of $[(a + b) + c] + d$, and so on in an Abelian group G. More precisely, if $(a_1, a_2, \ldots, a_n, \ldots)$ is a sequence† of elements of G, then we define $a_1 + a_2 + \ldots + a_n$ for every $n \in \mathbb{Z}^+$ "recursively" as follows. We define

$$a_1 = a_1, \quad a_1 + a_2 = a_1 + a_2, \quad a_1 + a_2 + a_3 = (a_1 + a_2) + a_3,$$

and, in general,

$$a_1 + a_2 + \ldots + a_{n+1} = (a_1 + a_2 + \ldots + a_n) + a_{n+1}$$

for all $n \in \mathbb{Z}^+$. That such sums are well-defined follows from the recursion theorem (p.257). With this definition, addition may be considered to be an n-ary operation for any integer $n \geq 2$. That is, corresponding to each ordered set $(a_1, a_2, \ldots, a_n)$ of n elements of G is a unique element $a_1 + a_2 + \ldots + a_n$ of G. As an n-ary operation for every $n \geq 2$, addition has the following properties in an Abelian group G.

---

† Any mapping $\mathbb{Z}^+ \overset{f}{\longrightarrow} G$ defines an ordered set, called a *sequence*, of elements of G. The elements of the sequence, in order, are $a_1, a_2, \ldots, a_n, \ldots$, where $a_1 = f(1), a_2 = f(2), \ldots, a_n = f(n), \ldots$.

2.11 General associative law. For every ordered set $(a_1, a_2, \ldots, a_n)$ of elements of G and every integer i, $1 \le i < n$,

$$(a_1 + \ldots + a_i) + (a_{i+1} + \ldots + a_n) = a_1 + a_2 + \ldots + a_n.$$

2.12 General commutative law. For every ordered set $(a_1, a_2, \ldots, a_n)$ of elements of G and every permutation $(i_1, i_2, \ldots, i_n)$ of $(1, 2, \ldots, n)$,

$$a_{i_1} + a_{i_2} + \ldots + a_{i_n} = a_1 + a_2 + \ldots + a_n.$$

Proof of 2.11: Let $S = \{n \in \mathbb{Z}^+ \mid 2.11 \text{ is true for every ordered set of } n$ elements of $G\}$. Since $a_1 = a_1$, $a_1 + a_2 = a_1 + a_2$, and

$$a_1 + (a_2 + a_3) = (a_1 + a_2) + a_3 = a_1 + a_2 + a_3,$$

evidently $1, 2, 3 \in S$. Assume that $n \in S$ and let $(a_1, a_2, \ldots, a_{n+1})$ be an ordered set of $n + 1$ elements of G. If

$$b_i = (a_1 + \ldots + a_i) + (a_{i+1} + \ldots + a_{n+1}), \qquad i = 1, 2, \ldots, n,$$

then $b_n = a_1 + a_2 + \ldots + a_{n+1}$ by definition. If $i < n$, then

$$
\begin{aligned}
b_i &= (a_1 + \ldots + a_i) + [(a_{i+1} + \ldots + a_n) + a_{n+1}] \\
&= [(a_1 + \ldots + a_i) + (a_{i+1} + \ldots + a_n)] + a_{n+1} \\
&= (a_1 + a_2 + \ldots + a_n) + a_{n+1} \\
&= a_1 + a_2 + \ldots + a_{n+1}.
\end{aligned}
$$

Hence, $n + 1 \in S$. The theorem now follows by mathematical induction. ∎

The proof of 2.12 is left as an exercise.

The familiar notation for such sums as $a + a$, $a + a + a$, and so on will be used in an Abelian group G. Thus,

$$\overbrace{a + a + \ldots + a}^{n \text{ terms}}$$

is denoted by na for every $n \in \mathbb{Z}^+$. For example,

$$1a = a, \qquad 2a = a + a, \qquad 3a = a + a + a,$$

and, recursively, $(n + 1)a = na + a$ for every $n \in \mathbb{Z}^+$. We call na a *multiple* of a. It must be realized that na does not mean "n times a," since there is no operation of multiplication associated with G. However, we might recall that multiplication was defined in $\mathbb{Z}$ in terms of multiples (Appendix 1).

It is convenient to define

$$0a = 0$$

and

$$(-n)a = -(na) \text{ for all } n \in \mathbb{Z}^+.$$

In this way, ka is defined for all $k \in \mathbb{Z}$.

Some of the useful properties of multiples are listed below.

2.13 $\qquad (m + n)a = ma + na$ for all $a \in G$, $m,n \in \mathbb{Z}$.

2.14 $\qquad m(na) = (m \cdot n)a$ for all $a \in G$, $m,n \in \mathbb{Z}$.

2.15 $\qquad m(a + b) = ma + mb$ for all $a,b \in G$, $m \in \mathbb{Z}$.

A special case of 2.14, with $m = -1$, is as follows:

2.16 $\qquad -(na) = (-n)a$ for all $a \in G$, $n \in \mathbb{Z}$.

If $n \geq 0$, this follows by definition. If $n < 0$, then $-n > 0$, $-(-n) = n$, and $na = [-(-n)]a = -[(-n)a]$. Hence $-(na) = (-n)a$ once again.

Outline of proof of 2.13: This follows immediately from 2.11 if $m,n \in \mathbb{Z}^+$. If $m = 0$, $n = 0$, or $m + n = 0$, 2.13 is easily proved. If $m < 0$ and $n < 0$, then

$$(m + n)a = -([(-m) + (-n)]a) = -[(-m)a + (-n)a] = ma + na$$

by 2.16. If $m < 0$, $n > 0$, and $m + n = k$, $k > 0$, then

$$(m + n)a = ma + (-m)a + ka = ma + (-m + k)a = ma + na.$$

Similar remarks may be made if $k < 0$. ∎

The proofs of 2.14 and 2.15 are by induction. For a given $n \in \mathbb{Z}$ and $a \in G$, let $S = \{m \in \mathbb{Z}^+ \mid m(na) = (m \cdot n)a\}$. Clearly $1 \in S$. If $k \in S$, then it is not hard to show that $k + 1 \in S$ also. We leave the details for the reader to supply.

Exercises

1. Which of the properties 2.1–2.4 are satisfied by each of the following algebraic systems?

(a) $\{\mathbb{Z}^+;+\}$. 　　　　　　　　(b) $\{\mathbb{N};+\}$.
(c) $\{\mathbb{Z}^+;\cdot\}$. 　　　　　　　　(d) $\{\mathbb{Q}^+;\cdot\}$.
(e) $\{\mathbb{Q}^-;+\}$. 　　　　　　　　(f) $\{G;+\}$, where $G = \left\{\dfrac{n}{p^k} \,\middle|\, n,k \in \mathbb{Z}\right\}$,

$\qquad\qquad\qquad\qquad\qquad$ p a prime number.

(g) $\{\mathbb{Z};\alpha\}$, where $\quad a \alpha b = a + b + a \cdot b$.
(h) $\{\mathbb{R};\circ\}$, where $\quad a \circ b = \sqrt{a^2 + b^2}$.
(i) $\{\mathbb{R};\gamma\}$, where $\quad a \gamma b = \sqrt[3]{a^3 + b^3}$.
(j) $\{\mathbb{Q};\delta\}$, where $\quad a \delta b = |a + b|$.

2. Prove 2.10.

*3. Prove 2.12.

4. Prove 2.14.

5. Prove 2.15.

6. If $\{G;+\}$ is an Abelian group, is $\{G \times G;+\}$ also an Abelian group if addition is defined in $G \times G$ by

$$(a_1,a_2) + (b_1,b_2) = (a_1 + b_1, a_2 + b_2)?$$

7. Generalize Exercise 6 to the case of two Abelian groups $\{G;+\}$ and $\{H;+\}$ and the associated algebraic system $\{G \times H;+\}$.

8. An algebraic system $\{S;\alpha\}$ has two distinct elements a and b such that $a \, \alpha \, a = a$ and $b \, \alpha \, b = b$. Can S be an Abelian group? Prove your answer.

9. Let $\{G;+\}$ be an Abelian group, $S \subset G$, and $a \in G$. Prove that the mapping $S \xrightarrow{f} G$ defined by $f(x) = a + x$, $x \in S$, is an injection.

10. If $\{G;+\}$ is an Abelian group, is the mapping $G \xrightarrow{h} G$ defined by $h(x) = -x$, $x \in G$, a bijection? Prove your answer.

11. Let $\{G;+\}$ be a group; i.e., it satisfies 2.1, 2.3, and 2.4. Prove that G is an Abelian group if either of the following properties holds:
    (i) $-a = a$ for all $a \in G$,
    (ii) $2(a + b) = 2a + 2b$ for all $a,b \in G$.

*12. If S is a set, $\{G;+\}$ is an algebraic system with a binary operation $+$, and M is the set of all mappings of S into G, then $\{M;+\}$ is an algebraic system with a binary operation $+$ defined by:

$$(f + g)(x) = f(x) + g(x) \text{ for all } x \in S \text{ and all } f,g \in M.$$

If $\{G;+\}$ satisfies any or all of properties 2.1–2.4, does $\{M;+\}$ satisfy the same properties? Prove your answers.

2. Subgroups and Quotient Groups

A nonempty subset H of an Abelian group $\{G;+\}$ is called a *subgroup* of G if $\{H;+\}$, with operation borrowed from G, is itself an Abelian group. Clearly H is a subgroup of G iff (1) H is closed under addition, (2) $0 \in H$, and (3) $-a \in H$ for each $a \in H$. The associative and commutative laws automatically hold in H since they hold in the larger set G. The additive identity element of a subgroup H must be the same as that of G, since $a + a = a$ in G (or H) iff $a = 0$.

It is immediate that $\{0\}$ and G are subgroups of G according to the definition. We call a subgroup H of G a *proper subgroup* if $H \neq \{0\}$ and $H \neq G$. For example, $\{\mathbb{Z}\,;+\}$ is a proper subgroup of $\{\mathbb{Q}\,;+\}$ and $\{\mathbb{Q}'\,;\cdot\}$ is a proper subgroup of $\{\mathbb{R}'\,;\cdot\}$.

An interesting problem is to describe all the subgroups of $\{\mathbb{Z}\,;+\}$. Let

$$k\mathbb{Z} = \{kn \mid n \in \mathbb{Z}\}$$

for each $k \in \mathbb{Z}$. We can think of kn either as a multiple of n (as defined in Section 1) or as $k \cdot n$, since these two concepts coincide in $\mathbb{Z}$. We claim that $k\mathbb{Z}$ is a subgroup of $\{\mathbb{Z}\,;+\}$ for every $k \in \mathbb{Z}$. To show this, observe first of all that $k\mathbb{Z}$ is closed under addition:

$$kn + km = k(n + m) \text{ for all } k,m,n \in \mathbb{Z}.$$

Next, $0 \in k\mathbb{Z}$ since $0 = k0$. Finally, $-(km) \in \mathbb{Z}$ for each $km \in \mathbb{Z}$, since $-(km) = k(-m)$. Thus, $k\mathbb{Z}$ is a subgroup of $\{\mathbb{Z}\,;+\}$.

If H is any proper subgroup of $\{\mathbb{Z}\,;+\}$, then H contains some nonzero element a. Since $-a \in H$ and either a or $-a$ is in $\mathbb{Z}^+$, evidently H contains positive integers. Hence, H contains a least positive integer k by the well-ordering of $\mathbb{Z}$ (1.21). Since $k \in H$ and since whenever $kn \in H$ for $n \in \mathbb{Z}^+$ then also $k(n + 1) = kn + k \in H$, clearly $k\mathbb{Z} \subset H$ by mathematical induction. For every $a \in H$, there exist $q,r \in \mathbb{Z}$ such that

$$a = k \cdot q + r \quad \text{and} \quad 0 \leq r < k$$

by 1.22. Now $r = a + (-kq)$, a sum of two elements of H, and therefore $r \in H$. Since $r \geq 0$ and r is less than the least positive element of H, necessarily $r = 0$. Hence, $a = kq \in k\mathbb{Z}$. We conclude that $H \subset k\mathbb{Z}$. Consequently, $H = k\mathbb{Z}$ and the following theorem is proved:

2.17 Theorem. $\{H;+\}$ is a subgroup of $\{\mathbb{Z}\,;+\}$ iff $H = k\mathbb{Z}$ for some $k \in \mathbb{Z}$.

For example,

$$3\mathbb{Z} = \{\ldots,-9,-6,-3,0,3,6,9,\ldots\},$$
$$16\mathbb{Z} = \{\ldots,-48,-32,-16,0,16,32,48,\ldots\},$$

$0\mathbb{Z} = \{0\}$, and $1\mathbb{Z} = \mathbb{Z}$ are subgroups of $\{\mathbb{Z}\,;+\}$.

If G is an Abelian group and H is a subgroup of G, let us define

$$a + H = \{a + x \mid x \in H\}$$

for each $a \in G$. Thus, $a + H$ is a subset of G called a *coset* of H.

The coset $a + H$ is often called a *translation* of H by a for the reason illustrated below by the group $\{\mathbb{Z};+\}$ and its subgroup $3\mathbb{Z}$. If we represent $\mathbb{Z}$ by a set of equispaced points on a line, then $3\mathbb{Z}$ is represented by the circled points in Figure 2.1. The coset $1 + 3\mathbb{Z}$ is obtained from the subgroup $3\mathbb{Z}$ by translating the points in $3\mathbb{Z}$ one unit to the right, as indicated in Figure 2.1. Thus,

$$1 + 3\mathbb{Z} = \{\ldots, -5, -2, 1, 4, 7, \ldots\}.$$

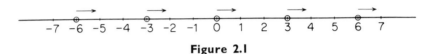

Figure 2.1

If we translate the points in $3\mathbb{Z}$ two units to the right, we obtain the coset

$$2 + 3\mathbb{Z} = \{\ldots, -4, -1, 2, 5, 8, \ldots\}.$$

Is it not clear that

$$\{3\mathbb{Z}, 1 + 3\mathbb{Z}, 2 + 3\mathbb{Z}\}$$

is a partition of $\mathbb{Z}$? That is,

$$\mathbb{Z} = 3\mathbb{Z} \cup (1 + 3\mathbb{Z}) \cup (2 + 3\mathbb{Z})$$

and

$$3\mathbb{Z} \cap (1 + 3\mathbb{Z}) = \varnothing, \quad 3\mathbb{Z} \cap (2 + 3\mathbb{Z}) = \varnothing, \quad (1 + 3\mathbb{Z}) \cap (2 + 3\mathbb{Z}) = \varnothing.$$

To return to an Abelian group G and a subgroup H of G, let us show that if $a + H$ and $b + H$ are two cosets of H, then:

2.18   Either $a + H = b + H$ or $(a + H) \cap (b + H) = \varnothing$.

Evidently we need only show that if $(a + H) \cap (b + H) \neq \varnothing$, then $a + H = b + H$. If $c \in (a + H) \cap (b + H)$, then $c = a + u = b + v$ for some $u, v \in H$. Hence,

$$a + x = b + (v - u) + x \text{ for all } x \in H,$$

and therefore $a + H \subset b + H$. Interchanging the roles of a and b, we easily prove that $b + H \subset a + H$. Consequently, $a + H = b + H$ and 2.18 is proved.

We leave to the reader to prove that if H is a subgroup of G and $a, b \in G$, then:

2.19 $a + H = b + H$ iff $b - a \in H$.

The subgroup H of G is a coset of itself, since $0 + H = H$. By 2.19, $b + H = H$ iff $b \in H$. Since H is the only coset of H in G which contains the identity element 0 of G, H is the only coset which is a subgroup of G.

Every element a of G is in some coset of H, since $a = a + 0 \in a + H$. Consequently, the union of all the cosets of H is G. This remark, along with 2.18, constitutes a proof of the following result.

2.20 Theorem. If G is an Abelian group and H is a subgroup of G, then $\{a + H \mid a \in G\}$ is a partition of G.

The notation G/H is commonly used for the partition of G induced by H,

$$G/H = \{a + H \mid a \in G\}.$$

We must remember that the *elements of G/H are subsets* of G. For example,

$$\mathbb{Z}/3\mathbb{Z} = \{3\mathbb{Z}, 1 + 3\mathbb{Z}, 2 + 3\mathbb{Z}\}.$$

If G is an Abelian group and H is a subgroup, then there is a natural way to define an operation of addition in G/H, as we shall presently show. If A and B are any subsets of G, then we define

$$A + B = \{x + y \mid x \in A, y \in B\}.$$

In particular, the sum of two cosets of H in G is given by

$$(a + H) + (b + H) = \{(a + h_1) + (b + h_2) \mid h_1, h_2 \in H\}.$$

Since each element of the above set has the form $a + b + h$, $h \in H$, evidently $(a + H) + (b + H) \subset (a + b) + H$. On the other hand, each element $a + b + h \in (a + b) + H$ has the form $(a + 0) + (b + h)$ and therefore $(a + b) + H \subset (a + H) + (b + H)$. Consequently,

2.21 $(a + H) + (b + H) = (a + b) + H$ for all $a + H, b + H \in G/H$.

2.22 Theorem. If G is an Abelian group and H is a subgroup of G, then $\{G/H; +\}$ with addition as defined in 2.21 is an Abelian group.

Outline of proof: Since
$$(a + H) + (b + H) = (a + b) + H = (b + a) + H = (b + H) + (a + H),$$
addition is commutative. A similar computation shows that addition is associative. Since $(a + H) + H = a + H$, H is the identity element of addition in G/H. Finally, $(-a) + H$ is easily seen to be the inverse of $a + H$ in G/H, i.e.,

$$-(a + H) = (-a) + H \quad \text{for all} \quad a + H \in G/H.$$

Thus, $+$ is inversive. ∎

If G is an Abelian group and H is a subgroup of G, then the Abelian group G/H is called the *quotient group* of G by H.

The quotient group of $\{\mathbb{Z};+\}$ by the subgroup $n\mathbb{Z}$ will be denoted by $\mathbb{Z}_n$ throughout the book,

$$\mathbb{Z}_n = \mathbb{Z}/n\mathbb{Z}.$$

Since $\mathbb{Z}_0 = \{a + 0\mathbb{Z} \mid a \in \mathbb{Z}\} = \{\{a\} \mid a \in \mathbb{Z}\}$, $\mathbb{Z}_0$ is essentially $\mathbb{Z}$. Clearly $\mathbb{Z}_1 = \{\mathbb{Z}\}$, a group with one element. Since $n\mathbb{Z} = (-n)\mathbb{Z}$ for all $n \in \mathbb{Z}$, evidently $\mathbb{Z}_n = \mathbb{Z}_{-n}$. Thus, the interesting quotient groups of $\mathbb{Z}$ are those of the form $\mathbb{Z}_n$ for $n > 1$.

If $n > 1$, then the n elements of $\mathbb{Z}_n$,

$$n\mathbb{Z}, \quad 1 + n\mathbb{Z}, \quad 2 + n\mathbb{Z}, \quad \ldots, \quad (n-1) + n\mathbb{Z},$$

are distinct. For if $0 \le a < b < n$, then $0 < b - a < n$ and $b - a$ cannot be a multiple of n. Hence, $b - a \notin n\mathbb{Z}$ and $a + n\mathbb{Z} \ne b + n\mathbb{Z}$ by 2.19. Let us prove that these are the only cosets of $n\mathbb{Z}$ in $\mathbb{Z}$, i.e., that

2.23 $$\mathbb{Z}_n = \{n\mathbb{Z}, 1 + n\mathbb{Z}, \ldots, (n-1) + n\mathbb{Z}\}.$$

Thus, we wish to prove that $\mathbb{Z} = n\mathbb{Z} \cup (1 + n\mathbb{Z}) \cup \ldots \cup [(n-1) + n\mathbb{Z}]$. To this end, let $m \in \mathbb{Z}$. Then,

$$m = n \cdot q + r \quad \text{and} \quad 0 \le r < n$$

for some $q, r \in \mathbb{Z}$ by 1.22. Hence, $m \in r + n\mathbb{Z}$ and m is in one of the cosets listed in 2.23. Therefore, $\mathbb{Z}_n$ is a set with n elements as listed in 2.23.

The Abelian group $\mathbb{Z}_n$, $n > 1$, having n elements is called the *group of integers modulo n*.

Besides the infinite Abelian groups $\mathbb{Z}$, $\mathbb{Q}$, and $\mathbb{R}$, we now have examples of Abelian groups with any finite number of elements. We shall describe all possible finite Abelian groups in Theorem 8.42.

Since $\mathbb{Z}_n$ in 2.23 is a partition of $\mathbb{Z}$, it induces an equivalence relation in $\mathbb{Z}$ called *congruence modulo n*, which is denoted by $\equiv \pmod{n}$. Thus, we write $a \equiv b \pmod{n}$ iff integers a and b are congruent modulo n. By 2.19,

2.24 $$a \equiv b \pmod{n} \quad \text{iff} \quad b - a \in n\mathbb{Z}.$$

Each integer m is congruent modulo n to a unique nonnegative integer $k < n$. Since $\mathbb{Z}_n$ is an Abelian group with addition defined by 2.21, we have

2.25 If $a_1 \equiv b_1$ and $a_2 \equiv b_2 \pmod{n}$, then $a_1 + a_2 \equiv b_1 + b_2 \pmod{n}$.

For example, $12 \equiv 3$ and $22 \equiv 4 \pmod{9}$. Hence, $12 + 22 \equiv 3 + 4$ or $34 \equiv 7 \pmod{9}$. It is also true, as we shall show in the next chapter, that $12 \cdot 22 \equiv 3 \cdot 4 \pmod{9}$; i.e., $12 \cdot 22 \equiv 3 \pmod{9}$.

Each of the Abelian groups $\{\mathbb{Z}_n;+\}$, $n \ge 1$, is finite and therefore can be exhibited by a table. If, for convenience, we denote the element $a + n\mathbb{Z}$ by

a, where $0 \leq a < n$, then $\mathbb{Z}_n = \{0, 1, \ldots, n - 1\}$. We have used this notation in the groups $\mathbb{Z}_2, \mathbb{Z}_3$, and $\mathbb{Z}_4$ given below.

$$\mathbb{Z}_2$$

+	0	1
0	0	1
1	1	0

$$\mathbb{Z}_3$$

+	0	1	2
0	0	1	2
1	1	2	0
2	2	0	1

$$\mathbb{Z}_4$$

+	0	1	2	3
0	0	1	2	3
1	1	2	3	0
2	2	3	0	1
3	3	0	1	2

    Another interesting quotient group is $\mathbb{Q}/\mathbb{Z}$, called the group of *rationals modulo 1*. In describing this group, it is convenient to use the notation $[a]$ for the *greatest integer* $n \leq a$. For example, $[\frac{5}{2}] = 2$, $[\frac{1}{5}] = 0$, $[7] = 7$, and $[-\frac{12}{5}] = -3$. Thus, $[a] \in \mathbb{Z}$ and $0 \leq a - [a] < 1$ for every $a \in \mathbb{Q}$. Since

$$a + \mathbb{Z} = (a - [a]) + \mathbb{Z} \text{ for all } a + \mathbb{Z} \in \mathbb{Q}/\mathbb{Z},$$

evidently every coset $a + \mathbb{Z}$ is equal to a unique coset of the form $b + \mathbb{Z}$ where $0 \leq b < 1$. If we identify $b + \mathbb{Z}$ with b, then $\mathbb{Q}/\mathbb{Z}$ has the form

$$\mathbb{Q}/\mathbb{Z} = \{b \in \mathbb{Q} \mid 0 \leq b < 1\},$$

with addition modulo 1 its operation. That is, if $x, y \in \mathbb{Q}/\mathbb{Z}$, then $x + y \in \mathbb{Q}/\mathbb{Z}$ is the ordinary sum of x and y if this sum is less than 1, and is 1 less than the ordinary sum if this sum is greater than or equal to 1. For example,

$$\tfrac{1}{5} + \tfrac{2}{3} = \tfrac{13}{15}, \qquad \tfrac{2}{3} + \tfrac{1}{3} = 0, \qquad \tfrac{3}{4} + \tfrac{5}{6} = \tfrac{7}{12}$$

in $\mathbb{Q}/\mathbb{Z}$. Clearly $\mathbb{Q}/\mathbb{Z}$ is an infinite Abelian group.

    If G is a finite Abelian group and H is a subgroup of G, then† $\#(H) = \#(a + H)$ for every $a \in G$ since the mapping $H \xrightarrow{f} a + H$ defined by $f(x) = a + x$, $x \in H$, is a bijection. Now $\{a + H \mid a \in G\}$ is a partition of G, and if $H_1, H_2, \ldots, H_k$ are the distinct subsets of this partition then

$$\#(G) = \#(H_1) + \#(H_2) + \ldots + \#(H_k) = k \cdot \#(H).$$

This proves the following famous theorem of group theory:

2.26 Lagrange's theorem. ‡ If G is a finite Abelian group and H is a subgroup of G, then

$$\#(G) = \#(H) \cdot \#(G/H).$$

---

† See glossary for meaning of $\#$.

‡ Lagrange, an eighteenth-century mathematician, was born in Italy but spent most of his life in Germany and France. He is considered by many to be one of the greatest mathematicians of all time.

The number of elements of a finite group G is called the *order* of G. According to 2.26, the order of a finite Abelian group is divisible by the order of each of its subgroups.

Exercises

1. Make tables for the Abelian groups $\mathbb{Z}_5$ and $\mathbb{Z}_6$. Find all subgroups of these groups.

2. Each of the Abelian groups $\mathbb{Z}_4$ and $\mathbb{Z}_2 \times \mathbb{Z}_2$ (see Exercise 6, p. 34) has four elements. Are they essentially the same group or are they quite different? Find all subgroups of these groups.

3. If p is a prime number, describe the set of all subgroups of $\mathbb{Z}_p$, of $\mathbb{Z}_{p^2}$.

4. If H and K are subgroups of an Abelian group G, then prove that $H \cap K$ and $H + K$ are also subgroups of G.

5. If H and K are subgroups of an Abelian group G, then prove that $A = \{x + H \mid x \in K\}$ is a subgroup of G/H. Under what conditions on K is A a proper subgroup?

6. If H is a subgroup of an Abelian group G and A is a subgroup of G/H, then prove that $K = \{x \in G \mid x + H \in A\}$ is a subgroup of G. Under what conditions on A is K a proper subgroup?

7. Prove 2.19.

8. Under what conditions on integers m and n is $m\mathbb{Z} \subset n\mathbb{Z}$? Is $m\mathbb{Z} + n\mathbb{Z} = \mathbb{Z}$? Is $m\mathbb{Z} \cap n\mathbb{Z} = \{0\}$?

9. If $a,b,m,n \in \mathbb{Z}^+$ are such that $m\mathbb{Z} + n\mathbb{Z} = a\mathbb{Z}$ and $m\mathbb{Z} \cap n\mathbb{Z} = b\mathbb{Z}$, how are a and b related to m and n?

10. Prove that every subgroup of $\mathbb{Z}_n$ has the form $k\mathbb{Z}/n\mathbb{Z}$ for some factor k of n.

11. Describe all Abelian groups which have no proper subgroups.

3. Homomorphisms

A mapping $G \xrightarrow{f} K$ of an Abelian group G into an Abelian group K is called a *homomorphism* provided

$$f(a + b) = f(a) + f(b) \text{ for all } a,b \in G.$$

A homomorphism $G \xrightarrow{f} K$ is called an

epimorphism iff f is a surjection;
monomorphism iff f is an injection;
isomorphism iff f is a bijection.

An example of a homomorphism that comes to mind immediately is the mapping $\mathbb{Z} \xrightarrow{f} \mathbb{Z}_n$ defined by

$$f(a) = a + n\mathbb{Z} \text{ for all } a \in \mathbb{Z}.$$

It is a homomorphism since (by 2.21)

$$f(a + b) = (a + b) + n\mathbb{Z} = (a + n\mathbb{Z}) + (b + n\mathbb{Z}) = f(a) + f(b)$$

for all $a,b \in \mathbb{Z}$. Actually, since f is a surjection, f is an epimorphism. If $n > 0$, then f is not an isomorphism for the simple reason that $\mathbb{Z}$ is an infinite set whereas $\mathbb{Z}_n$ is a finite set.

More generally, if G is an Abelian group and H is a subgroup of G, then the mapping $G \xrightarrow{f} G/H$ defined by

$$f(a) = a + H \text{ for all } a \in G$$

is an epimorphism. It is an isomorphism iff $H = \{0\}$.

It is worthwhile observing that if G is an Abelian group, $\{K;\alpha\}$ is an algebraic system with a binary operation α, and $G \xrightarrow{f} K$ is a surjection such that

$$f(a + b) = f(a) \, \alpha \, f(b) \text{ for all } a,b \in G,$$

then necessarily $\{K;\alpha\}$ is an Abelian group. The verification of 2.1–2.4 for K is purely routine. For example,

$$[f(a) \, \alpha \, f(b)] \, \alpha \, f(c) = f(a + b) \, \alpha \, f(c) = f[(a + b) + c],$$
$$f(a) \, \alpha \, [f(b) \, \alpha \, f(c)] = f(a) \, \alpha \, f(b + c) = f[a + (b + c)].$$

Since $(a + b) + c = a + (b + c)$, we have

$$[f(a) \, \alpha \, f(b)] \, \alpha \, f(c) = f(a) \, \alpha \, [f(b) \, \alpha \, f(c)]$$

for all $f(a), f(b), f(c) \in K$. This proves that α is an associative operation. The proof that α is commutative is similar, and hence is omitted. Clearly $f(0)$ is the identity element of K, since $f(0) \, \alpha \, f(a) = f(0 + a) = f(a)$ for all $f(a) \in K$. Finally,

$$f(a) \, \alpha \, f(-a) = f(a + (-a)) = f(0) \text{ for all } f(a) \in K,$$

and therefore $f(-a)$ is the inverse of $f(a)$ in K, i.e.,

$$-f(a) = f(-a) \text{ for all } f(a) \in K.$$

Hence, $\{K;\alpha\}$ is an Abelian group. It may be proved by mathematical induction that

2.27 $f(na) = nf(a)$ for all $a \in G$, $n \in \mathbb{Z}$.

If we recall that $K = \{f(a) \mid a \in G\}$ is called the *image* of f, then our remarks above can be stated in the following compact form:

2.28   Theorem. Every homomorphic image of an Abelian group is an Abelian group.

This theorem can be used to prove that G/H is an Abelian group for every Abelian group G and subgroup H. Thus, the natural mapping $G \overset{f}{\longrightarrow} G/H$ defined by $f(a) = a + H$ is a homomorphism by 2.21, and therefore G/H is an Abelian group by 2.28.

If $G \overset{f}{\longrightarrow} K$ is a homomorphism, but not necessarily a surjection, then all we can say from 2.28 is that $\operatorname{im} f = \{f(a) \mid a \in G\}$ is an Abelian group. The algebraic system $\{K;\alpha\}$ need not be an Abelian group, as is easily shown.

If G and K are Abelian groups and $G \overset{f}{\longrightarrow} K$ is a homomorphism, then

$$f(H) = \{f(x) \mid x \in H\}$$

is a subgroup of K for every subgroup H of G by 2.28. Furthermore,

$$f^{-1}(J) = \{a \in G \mid f(a) \in J\}$$

is a subgroup of G for every subgroup J of K. The proof of this fact is left as an exercise.

In the special case of an isomorphism $G \overset{f}{\longrightarrow} K$, the inverse mapping $K \overset{f^{-1}}{\longrightarrow} G$ defined by $f^{-1}(b) = a$ iff $f(a) = b$, where $a \in G$ and $b \in K$, is also an isomorphism. Since f^{-1} is known to be a bijection, all that needs to be proved is that f^{-1} is a homomorphism. This follows from the calculations below. For all $a,b \in G$,

$$f^{-1}[f(a) + f(b)] = f^{-1}[f(a + b)] = a + b = f^{-1}[f(a)] + f^{-1}[f(b)].$$

Exercises

1. For each $k \in \mathbb{Z}$, discuss the mapping $\mathbb{Z} \overset{f}{\longrightarrow} \mathbb{Z}$ defined by $f(n) = kn$. Is it a homomorphism? If your answer is "yes," tell under what conditions on k the mapping f is an epimorphism; a monomorphism; an isomorphism.

2. For each nonzero $r \in \mathbb{Q}$, discuss the mapping $\mathbb{Q} \xrightarrow{h} \mathbb{Q}$ defined by $h(x) = r \cdot x$. Consider the two Abelian groups $\{\mathbb{Q};+\}$ and $\{\mathbb{Q}';\cdot\}$.

3. Let G and K be Abelian groups and $G \xrightarrow{f} K$ be a homomorphism. Prove 2.27 for f.

4. If G and K are Abelian groups and $G \xrightarrow{f} K$ is an epimorphism, prove that $f^{-1}(J)$ is a subgroup of G for every subgroup J of K.

5. Consider the groups $\{\mathbb{Z};+\}$ and $\{\mathbb{Q}^+;\cdot\}$ and the mapping $\mathbb{Z} \xrightarrow{f} \mathbb{Q}^+$ defined by $f(n) = 2^n$. Prove that f is a monomorphism. Generalize.

*6. Let $k,m,n \in \mathbb{Z}^+$ be such that $kn \in m\mathbb{Z}$. Prove that the mapping $\mathbb{Z}_n \xrightarrow{f} \mathbb{Z}_m$, $f(a + n\mathbb{Z}) = ka + m\mathbb{Z}$, is well-defined and is a homomorphism. Under what conditions on k, m, and n is f an epimorphism? a monomorphism? an isomorphism?

4. Cartesian Products

If $G_1, G_2, \ldots, G_n$ are Abelian groups, then so is their Cartesian product

$$P = G_1 \times G_2 \times \ldots \times G_n$$

if we define addition in P coordinatewise; that is,

2.29 $(a_1, a_2, \ldots, a_n) + (b_1, b_2, \ldots, b_n) = (a_1 + b_1, a_2 + b_2, \ldots, a_n + b_n)$

for all $a_i, b_i \in G_i$, $i = 1, \ldots, n$. The identity element of P clearly is

$$0 = (0_1, 0_2, \ldots, 0_n),$$

where 0_i is the identity element of G_i, $i = 1, \ldots, n$. It is evident that addition is both associative and commutative in P. Finally, the negative of each element of P is given by

$$-(a_1, a_2, \ldots, a_n) = (-a_1, -a_2, \ldots, -a_n).$$

A special case of the Cartesian product above is obtained if the groups $G_1, G_2, \ldots, G_n$ are equal. The resulting group

$$\overbrace{G \times G \times \ldots \times G}^{n \text{ fold}}$$

is called the nth *power group* of G and is denoted by G^n.
    For example,

$$\mathbb{R}^3 = \mathbb{R} \times \mathbb{R} \times \mathbb{R} = \{(a_1, a_2, a_3) \mid a_i \in \mathbb{R}\}$$

is the cube of $\mathbb{R}$. We know from analytic geometry that $\mathbb{R}^3$ may be used to represent the set of all points, or the set of all vectors emanating from the origin, in a 3-dimensional Cartesian coordinate system. If

$$u = (a_1, a_2, a_3), \qquad v = (b_1, b_2, b_3)$$

are points in $\mathbb{R}^3$, then $u + v$ may be described geometrically by the parallelogram law as shown in Figure 2.2.

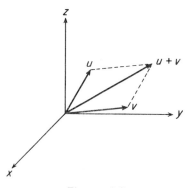

Figure 2.2

As a second example of a Cartesian product of Abelian groups, consider

$$P = \mathbb{Z}_2 \times \mathbb{Z}_3.$$

If $\mathbb{Z}_2 = \{0_1, 1_1\}$ and $\mathbb{Z}_3 = \{0_2, 1_2, 2_2\}$, where $0_1 = 0 + 2\mathbb{Z}$, $0_2 = 0 + 3\mathbb{Z}$, and so on, then P is an Abelian group with six elements,

$$P = \{(0_1, 0_2), (0_1, 1_2), (0_1, 2_2), (1_1, 0_2),$$
$$(1_1, 1_2), (1_1, 2_2)\}.$$

We know of another Abelian group with six elements, namely $\mathbb{Z}_6$. Are the groups P and $\mathbb{Z}_6$ isomorphic? If $\mathbb{Z}_6 = \{0,1,2,3,4,5\}$ and $\mathbb{Z}_6 \xrightarrow{f} P$ is to be an isomorphism, then necessarily $f(0) = (0_1, 0_2)$. If $f(1) = a$ in P, then $f(2) = f(1+1) = f(1) + f(1) = 2a$, $f(3) = 3a$, $f(4) = 4a$, and $f(5) = 5a$. Hence, P must equal $\{0, a, 2a, 3a, 4a, 5a\}$ if f is to be an isomorphism. There are only two elements of P whose multiples generate P—namely, $(1_1, 1_2)$ and $(1_1, 2_2)$. If we take $a = (1_1, 1_2)$, then

$$f(0) = (0_1, 0_2), \qquad f(1) = (1_1, 1_2), \qquad f(2) = (0_1, 2_2),$$
$$f(3) = (1_1, 0_2), \qquad f(4) = (0_1, 1_2), \qquad f(5) = (1_1, 2_2).$$

As we shall see in Section 6, f is actually an isomorphism. Incidentally, it would also have been an isomorphism if we had taken $a = (1_1, 2_2)$. Thus, the Abelian groups $\mathbb{Z}_6$ and $\mathbb{Z}_2 \times \mathbb{Z}_3$ are isomorphic.

If

$$P = G_1 \times G_2 \times \ldots \times G_n$$

is a Cartesian product of Abelian groups, as above, then there is a natural surjection $P \xrightarrow{p_k} G_k$ defined by

$$p_k(a_1, a_2, \ldots, a_n) = a_k, \qquad (a_1, a_2, \ldots, a_n) \in P$$

for each $k = 1,2, \ldots ,n$. Since

$$p_k[(a_1,a_2, \ldots ,a_n) + (b_1,b_2, \ldots ,b_n)]$$
$$= p_k(a_1 + b_1, a_2 + b_2, \ldots , a_n + b_n)$$
$$= a_k + b_k$$
$$= p_k(a_1,a_2, \ldots ,a_n) + p_k(b_1,b_2, \ldots ,b_n),$$

evidently p_k is an epimorphism. We call p_k the *projection* of P into its kth component G_k.

For example, the projection $\mathbb{R}^3 \xrightarrow{p_k} \mathbb{R}$, $k = 1,2,3$ can be considered to be projections of 3-dimensional space onto a coordinate line. Thus, if $u = (a_1,a_2,a_3)$, then $p_1(u) = a_1, p_2(u) = a_2$, and $p_3(u) = a_3$.

While the Abelian groups $G_1,G_2, \ldots ,G_n$ are not subgroups (or even subsets) of $P = G_1 \times G_2 \times \ldots \times G_n$, isomorphic images of $G_1,G_2, \ldots ,G_n$ are contained in P. Thus, if

$$G_k' = \{(0_1, \ldots ,0_{k-1},a_k,0_{k+1}, \ldots ,0_n) \mid a_k \in G_k\}, \qquad k = 1,2, \ldots , n,$$

then each G_k' is a subgroup of P isomorphic to G_k under the mapping $G_k \xrightarrow{s_k} G_k'$ defined by

$$s_k(a_k) = (0_1, \ldots ,0_{k-1},a_k,0_{k+1}, \ldots ,0_n) \text{ for all } a_k \in G_k.$$

For example, the mappings s_1, s_2, and s_3 associated with $\mathbb{R}^3$ are mappings of $\mathbb{R}$ onto the x-, y-, and z-axes. Thus,

$$s_1(a) = (a,0,0) \text{ for all } a \in \mathbb{R}$$

is a mapping of $\mathbb{R}$ onto the x-axis, and so forth.

The composites of p_k and s_k associated with $P = G_1 \times G_2 \times \ldots \times G_n$ are of some interest. If $G_k \xrightarrow{e_k} G_k$ is the identity mapping, then it is easily shown that

$$p_k \circ s_k = e_k, \qquad k = 1,2, \ldots ,n.$$

On the other hand, $s_k \circ p_k$ maps P into G_k' in the obvious way,

$$s_k \circ p_k(a_1,a_2, \ldots ,a_n) = (0_1, \ldots ,0_{k-1},a_k,0_{k+1}, \ldots ,0_n).$$

For example, $s_1 \circ p_1$, $s_2 \circ p_2$, and $s_3 \circ p_3$ are the perpendicular projections of $\mathbb{R}^3$ onto the x-axis, the y-axis, and the z-axis, respectively. Thus,

$$s_1 \circ p_1(a_1,a_2,a_3) = (a_1,0,0),$$

and so on.

Exercises

1. Prove that $\mathbb{Z}_2 \times \mathbb{Z}_2$ is not isomorphic to $\mathbb{Z}_4$, Generalize.

2. Is the mapping $\mathbb{Z} \xrightarrow{f} \mathbb{Z} \times \mathbb{Z}$ defined by $f(n) = (n,n)$ a homomorphism? If so, tell whether f is an epimorphism, monomorphism, or isomorphism.

3. Are the projection mappings of $\mathbb{R}^3$ into the coordinate planes isomorphisms? Describe them algebraically.

4. Consider the groups $\{\mathbb{Z};+\}$ and $\{\mathbb{Q}^+;\cdot\}$ and the positive integers a and b. Is the mapping $\mathbb{Z} \times \mathbb{Z} \xrightarrow{h} \mathbb{Q}^+$ defined by $h(m,n) = a^m \cdot b^n$ a homomorphism? If so, tell under what conditions on a and b it is a monomorphism. Generalize to a mapping $\mathbb{Z}^k \to \mathbb{Q}^+$, $k > 2$.

5. An Isomorphism Theorem

If G and K are Abelian groups and $G \xrightarrow{f} K$ is an epimorphism, then

$$\{f^{-1}(b) \mid b \in K\}$$

is a partition of G. Since $\{0\}$ is a subgroup of K, $f^{-1}(0)$ is a subgroup of G. The subgroup $f^{-1}(0)$ is called the *kernel* of f and is denoted by "ker f"; thus,

$$\ker f = \{a \in G \mid f(a) = 0\}.$$

Each $b \in K$ has the form $b = f(a)$ for some $a \in G$. If $x \in f^{-1}(b)$, so that $f(x) = b$, then
$$f(x - a) = f(x) - f(a) = b - b = 0.$$

Hence, $x - a \in \ker f$ and $x \in a + \ker f$. In other words,

(1) $$f^{-1}(b) \subset a + \ker f.$$

On the other hand, if $u \in \ker f$, then

$$f(a + u) = f(a) + f(u) = b + 0 = b$$

and $a + u \in f^{-1}(b)$. Therefore,

(2) $$a + \ker f \subset f^{-1}(b).$$

Putting (1) and (2) together, we have

$$f^{-1}(b) = a + \ker f \quad \text{if} \quad b = f(a).$$

Hence, the partition $\{f^{-1}(b) \mid b \in K\}$ of G is simply the partition of G into cosets of the subgroup ker f.

We are now in a position to prove the following basic result.

2.30 Isomorphism theorem. If G is an Abelian group and K is a homomorphic image of G under the mapping $G \xrightarrow{f} K$, then K is isomorphic to the quotient group $G/\ker f$ under the mapping $G/\ker f \xrightarrow{h} K$ defined by

$$h(a + \ker f) = f(a) \text{ for all } a \in G.$$

Proof: We first ask if h is well-defined; i.e., if $a + \ker f = a' + \ker f$, then is $f(a) = f(a')$? The answer is "yes," for if $a' - a \in \ker f$, then

$$f(a' - a) = f(a') - f(a) = 0.$$

Next, we prove that h is a homomorphism:

$$\begin{aligned}
h[(a + \ker f) + (b + \ker f)] &= h[(a + b) + \ker f] \\
&= f(a + b) = f(a) + f(b) \\
&= h(a + \ker f) + h(b + \ker f).
\end{aligned}$$

To prove that h is an epimorphism we need only observe that f is one. Finally, to prove that h is an isomorphism, assume that $h(a + \ker f) = h(b + \ker f)$ for some $a,b \in G$. Then $f(a) = f(b)$, $a - b \in \ker f$, and $a + \ker f = b + \ker f$. Hence, h is an injection and, consequently, an isomorphism. ∎

If $\ker f = \{0\}$ in 2.30, then h and f are equal; that is, f is an isomorphism. Conversely, if f is an isomorphism then $\ker f = \{0\}$.

According to 2.30, every epimorphism $G \xrightarrow{f} K$ of an Abelian group G can be realized in the following way:

$$G \xrightarrow{g} G/H \xrightarrow{h} K,$$

where H is a subgroup of $G (H = \ker f)$, g is the natural mapping $g(a) = a + H$, and h is an isomorphism. Thus,

$$f = h \circ g,$$

where h is an isomorphism and g is a natural homomorphism of G onto one of its quotient groups.

Isomorphic Abelian groups are algebraically the same—they can differ only in the nature of their elements. That is, the operations in the groups have identical properties. For example, if $3a = 0$ for every a in one of the groups, then necessarily $3b = 0$ for every b in the other group. Since we are interested only in algebraic properties and not in the nature of the elements involved, isomorphic groups are indistinguishable to us. Thus, up to isomorphisms, *the only homomorphic images of an Abelian group are its quotient groups* according to 2.30.

For example, the only homomorphic images (up to isomorphisms) of $\{\mathbb{Z} ;+\}$ are the groups $\{\mathbb{Z}_n;+\}$, $n \geq 0$. In fact, all the homomorphic images of $\mathbb{Z}$, excepting isomorphic images, are finite Abelian groups.

6. Cyclic Groups

If G is an Abelian group, then for every $b \in G$ there is a natural mapping

$$\mathbb{Z} \xrightarrow{f} G \text{ defined by } f(n) = nb \text{ for all } n \in \mathbb{Z}.$$

Since

$$f(m + n) = (m + n)b = mb + nb = f(m) + f(n),$$

f is a homomorphism, and the image of f,

$$\operatorname{im} f = \{nb \mid n \in \mathbb{Z}\},$$

is a subgroup of G. We call the order of $\operatorname{im} f$, i.e., $\#(\operatorname{im} f)$, the *order of b* in G. In case $\operatorname{im} f = G$, so that every element of G is a multiple of b, we call G a *cyclic group* and the element b a *generator* of G.

For example, consider the mapping

$$\mathbb{Z} \xrightarrow{f} \mathbb{Z}_{12} \text{ defined by } f(n) = n(3) \text{ for all } n \in \mathbb{Z}.$$

Then $\operatorname{im} f$ consists of all multiples of 3 in $\mathbb{Z}_{12}$, i.e.,

$$\operatorname{im} f = \{0, 3, 6, 9\}.$$

Thus, 3 has order $4 = \#(\operatorname{im} f)$ in $\mathbb{Z}_{12}$. Although $\operatorname{im} f \neq \mathbb{Z}_{12}$, this does not mean that $\mathbb{Z}_{12}$ is not cyclic; all it means is that 3 is not a generator of $\mathbb{Z}_{12}$. Actually, $\mathbb{Z}_{12}$ is cyclic since $\{n(1) \mid n \in \mathbb{Z}\} = \mathbb{Z}_{12}$. That is, the element 1 is a generator of $\mathbb{Z}_{12}$. Other generators of $\mathbb{Z}_{12}$ are 5, 7, and 11.

It is very easy to characterize all cyclic groups; for if G is cyclic with generator b, then $\mathbb{Z} \xrightarrow{f} G$ defined by $f(n) = nb$ for all $n \in \mathbb{Z}$ is an epimorphism. Hence, by 2.30, G is isomorphic to some quotient group of $\mathbb{Z}$. However, the only quotient groups of $\mathbb{Z}$ are $\mathbb{Z}_n$ for all $n \geq 0$. Clearly all $\mathbb{Z}_n$, $n \geq 0$, are cyclic with generator 1. Thus, we have the following result.

2.31   Theorem. A group G is cyclic iff G is isomorphic to $\mathbb{Z}$ or to $\mathbb{Z}_n$ for some integer $n > 0$.

This theorem states, in effect, that $\mathbb{Z}$ is the only infinite cyclic group and the $\mathbb{Z}_n$, $n = 1, 2, \ldots$, are the only finite cyclic groups.

Every subgroup of $\{\mathbb{Z}; +\}$ is cyclic, being of the form $k\mathbb{Z}$ for some $k \geq 0$. Since every subgroup of $\mathbb{Z}_n$ is a homomorphic image of a subgroup of $\mathbb{Z}$, and the homomorphic image of a cyclic group is cyclic, evidently every subgroup of $\mathbb{Z}_n$ is also cyclic. Thus, we have proved the following result.

2.32 **Theorem.** Every subgroup of a cyclic group is cyclic.

It is an easy matter to list the subgroups of $\mathbb{Z}_n$ in view of 2.32: we simply list the sets of multiples of the various elements of $\mathbb{Z}_n$. For example, the subgroups of $\mathbb{Z}_{12}$ are as follows:

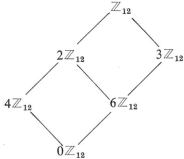

Thus, $2\mathbb{Z}_{12} = \{0,2,4,6,8,10\}$, $3\mathbb{Z}_{12} = \{0,3,6,9\}$, $4\mathbb{Z}_{12} = \{0,4,8\}$, $6\mathbb{Z}_{12} = \{0,6\}$ and $0\mathbb{Z}_{12} = \{0\}$. We have arranged the subgroups in a lattice-like formation; the sets below a given set that are connected to it by descending lines are subsets. The elements 1, 5, 7, and 11 generate $\mathbb{Z}_{12}$, 8 generates $4\mathbb{Z}_{12}$, 9 generates $3\mathbb{Z}_{12}$, and 10 generates $2\mathbb{Z}_{12}$.

Number-theoretic methods of determining all subgroups of $\mathbb{Z}_n$ are given in the exercises.

Exercises

1. List the subgroups of $\mathbb{Z}_8$ in a lattice-like formation. What effect does the fact that 8 is a power of a prime have on this formation? Generalize.

2. List the subgroups of $\mathbb{Z}_{36}$ in a lattice-like formation.

3. Let G be a finite Abelian group. Prove that the order of each $b \in G$ is the least positive integer k such that $kb = 0$. If b has order k, then prove that $nb = 0$ iff $k \mid n$.

4. If $n,b \in \mathbb{Z}^+$, prove that the order of $b + n\mathbb{Z}$ in $\mathbb{Z}_n$ is $n/(b,n)$. Also prove that $k\mathbb{Z}_n = (n,k)\mathbb{Z}_n$ for all $k \in \mathbb{Z}$. How many subgroups does $\mathbb{Z}_n$ have? Which elements of $\mathbb{Z}_n$ are generators of $\mathbb{Z}_n$? Under what conditions on a and b is $a\mathbb{Z}_n = b\mathbb{Z}_n$?

5. Each element of the group $\mathbb{Q}/\mathbb{Z}$ of rationals modulo 1 is of finite order. Describe the order of each element.

6. Describe all Abelian groups with 4 elements; with 6 elements; with 8 elements.

7. If p is a prime number and $n > 0$, describe all Abelian groups with p^n elements in which every nonzero element has order p.

8. If p and q are distinct prime numbers, describe all Abelian groups with pq elements.

*9. Let p be a prime number and $G = \{a/p^n \mid a,n \in \mathbb{Z}\}$. Prove that $\{G;+\}$ is an Abelian group, $\mathbb{Z} \subset G \subset \mathbb{Q}$. The group $G/\mathbb{Z}$ is called the *Prüfer* p^∞-*group* and is denoted by $\mathbb{Z}(p^\infty)$. Prove that $\mathbb{Z}(p^\infty)$ is not cyclic but that every proper subgroup of $\mathbb{Z}(p^\infty)$ is a finite cyclic group. Describe the set of subgroups of $\mathbb{Z}(p^\infty)$.

10. If G and K are Abelian groups and $G \xrightarrow{\ f\ } K$ is an epimorphism, show that there is a natural bijection of the set of subgroups of K into the set of subgroups of G containing $\ker f$.

THEORETICAL PROJECT 1

Complete the proofs of the following theorems, in each of which G is an Abelian group.

2.33   Theorem. If $x \in G$ has order $n > 1$, then kx has order $n/(k,n)$ for every $k \in \mathbb{Z}^+$.

Proof: On the one hand, $[n/(k,n)]kx = [k/(k,n)]nx = 0$. On the other hand, if $m(kx) = 0$ for some $m \in \mathbb{Z}^+$, then $n \mid mk$ and $[n/(k,n)] \mid m$. ∎

2.34   Theorem. If $x,y \in G$ have finite orders m and n, respectively, and $(m,n) = 1$, then $x + y$ has order mn.

Proof: If $x + y$ has order k, then $k \mid mn$. By 2.33, $n(x + y)$ has order $k/(n,k)$. Hence, nx has order $k/(n,k)$ and also order $m/(m,n)$. ∎

2.35   Theorem. If $z \in G$ has order mn, where $(m,n) = 1$, then $z = x + y$ for some unique $x,y \in G$ of orders m and n, respectively.

Proof: By assumption, $mr + ns = 1$ for some $r,s \in \mathbb{Z}$. Clearly $(r,n) = (m,s) = 1$. Let $x = nsz$ and $y = mrz$. ∎

2.36   Theorem. If $p_1, \ldots, p_t$ are distinct prime numbers and $x \in G$ has order $p_1^{k_1} \cdot p_2^{k_2} \cdot \ldots \cdot p_t^{k_t}$, where each $k_i > 0$, then there exist unique $y_1, \ldots, y_t \in G$ such that

$$x = y_1 + \cdots + y_t$$

and the order of y_i is $p_i^{t_i}$, $i = 1, \ldots, t$.

Proof: Follows from 2.35 by induction. ∎

2.37 Theorem. If $x, y \in G$ have finite orders m and n, respectively, then some $z \in G$ has order $[m,n]$.

Proof: Use the theorems above. ∎

THEORETICAL PROJECT 2

Complete the proof of the following theorem, in which G is an Abelian group.

2.38 Theorem. G is isomorphic to a Cartesian product of Abelian groups
$$G_1 \times G_2 \times \ldots \times G_n$$
iff there exist subgroups $H_1, H_2, \ldots, H_n$ of G such that

   (i) G_i is isomorphic to H_i, $i = 1, \ldots, n$,

   (ii) $G = H_1 + H_2 + \ldots + H_n$, and

   (iii) $H_i \cap (H_1 + \ldots + H_{i-1} + H_{i+1} + \ldots + H_n) = \{0\}$, $i = 1, \ldots, n$.

Proof: If G is isomorphic to $G_1 \times G_2 \times \ldots \times G_n$, then let $H_i = G'_i$ as defined on p.45. Conversely, if G has subgroups satisfying (i)–(iii), then show that each $g \in G$ has a unique representation $g = h_1 + h_2 + \ldots + h_n$ for some $h_i \in H_i$. Hence, prove that the mapping $G \overset{f}{\longrightarrow} H_1 \times H_2 \times \ldots \times H_n$ defined by $f(g) = (h_1, h_2, \ldots, h_n)$ is an isomorphism. ∎

THEORETICAL PROJECT 3

An Abelian group $\{G; +\}$ is called *divisible* iff for every $x \in G$ and every nonzero $n \in \mathbb{Z}$ there exists some $y \in G$ such that $ny = x$.

1. Prove that every homomorphic image of a divisible group is divisible.

2. Which of the additive groups of $\mathbb{Z}, \mathbb{Q}, \mathbb{R}, \mathbb{Q}/\mathbb{Z}$, and $\mathbb{Z}(p^\infty)$ are divisible?

3. Is either of the groups $\{\mathbb{Q}^+; \cdot\}$ or $\{\mathbb{R}^+; \cdot\}$ divisible? [*Hint:* Remember, the analogue of a multiple in additive notation is a power in the multiplicative notation.]

4. Is a subgroup of a divisible group necessarily divisible?

5. Prove that the sum of a set of divisible subgroups of an Abelian group G is divisible. Hence, conclude that G has a maximal divisible subgroup.

6. Prove that no finite group, other than $\{0\}$, is divisible.

chapter 3

Commutative Rings

The real number system and its subsystems of the rationals and integers have two operations whereas an Abelian group has only one. Furthermore, these systems are not simply Abelian groups with respect to each operation. For example, $\{R; \cdot\}$ is not an Abelian group since 0 has no multiplicative inverse. Then, too, the distributive law involves both operations simultaneously. These observations lead us to consider a ring—an algebraic system with two operations having many of the properties of the systems of reals, rationals, and integers.

I. Rings

An algebraic system

$$\{R; +, \cdot\}$$

consisting of a set R and two binary operations of addition ($+$) and multiplication ($\cdot$) is called a *ring* iff it has the following three properties:

3.1 $\{R; +\}$ is an Abelian group.

3.2   Multiplication is associative.

3.3   Multiplication is distributive with respect to addition.

52

The properties above were chosen as a minimum set from 1.1–1.9 for which there exist examples of useful algebraic systems. Such examples will be given in this and succeeding chapters.

We shall commonly speak of a ring R, mentioning only the set R and not the operations of R. In this case, it is always understood that the operations are addition and multiplication as above. We shall also follow the custom of indicating the product of a and b by ab as well as by $a \cdot b$.

A ring R is called a *commutative ring* (abbreviated *C-ring*) iff it has the following additional property:

3.4   Multiplication is commutative.

A ring R with more than one element is called a *ring with unity* iff in addition to 3.1–3.3 it has the following property:

3.5   There exists a multiplicative identity element.

The rings $\mathbb{Z}$, $\mathbb{Q}$, and $\mathbb{R}$ of Chapter 1 are all C-rings with unity. We shall postpone examples of noncommutative rings until Chapter 10. Some new examples of C-rings are given below.

3.6 Example. Let $C(\mathbb{R})$ be the set of all continuous functions (mappings) of $\mathbb{R}$ into $\mathbb{R}$. Thus, each $f \in C(\mathbb{R})$ has $\mathbb{R}$ as its domain and a subset of $\mathbb{R}$ as its range. Furthermore, f is continuous. If $f, g \in C(\mathbb{R})$, then $f + g$ and $f \cdot g$ are defined as usual:

$$(f + g)(x) = f(x) + g(x), \quad (f \cdot g)(x) = f(x) \cdot g(x) \text{ for all } x \in \mathbb{R}.$$

Since $f + g$ and $f \cdot g$ are continuous, $\{C(\mathbb{R}); +, \cdot\}$ is an algebraic system. It is easily verified that $C(\mathbb{R})$ is a C-ring with unity. The additive identity is the constant function $0: 0(x) = 0$ for all $x \in \mathbb{R}$, whereas the multiplicative identity (i.e., the unity) is the function $I: I(x) = 1$ for all $x \in \mathbb{R}$. The negative of each $f \in C(\mathbb{R})$ is defined by: $(-f)(x) = -f(x)$ for all $x \in \mathbb{R}$. We leave the other details to the reader.

3.7 Example. Let S be a nonempty set and $\mathscr{P}(S)$ be the set of all subsets of S. Operations of addition $(+)$ and multiplication $(\cdot)$ are defined in $\mathscr{P}(S)$ as follows: For all $A, B \in \mathscr{P}(S)$,

$$A + B = \{x \in S \mid x \in A \cup B, x \notin A \cap B\}, \quad A \cdot B = A \cap B.$$

If we denote the complement of A in S by $\bar{A}$, then

$$A + B = (\bar{A} \cap B) \cup (A \cap \bar{B}),$$

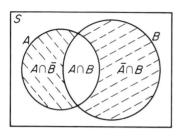

Figure 3.1

the shaded region of Figure 3.1. It is simple set theory to verify that $\{\mathscr{P}(S); +, \cdot\}$ is a C-ring with unity. The empty set $\varnothing$ is the additive identity and S is the unity of $\mathscr{P}(S)$. This ring has the interesting properties

$$A + A = \varnothing,$$

$$A \cdot A = A \text{ for all } A \in \mathscr{P}(S).$$

Hence, $-A = A$ for all $A \in \mathscr{P}(S)$. A C-ring with these two additional properties is called a *Boolean ring*.

The properties of addition in a ring R are as given in the preceding chapter. Other useful properties of R involving both addition and multiplication are given below.

3.8 $a \cdot 0 = 0, \ 0 \cdot a = 0 \text{ for all } a \in R.$

3.9 $-(a \cdot b) = (-a) \cdot b = a \cdot (-b) \text{ for all } a, b \in R.$

Proof of 3.8: We must use the distributive law since we are asked to prove something about the product of a by the additive identity element 0. The distributive law is the only property of a ring that relates addition to multiplication. In brief, the proof is as follows:

$$0 + a \cdot 0 = a \cdot 0 = a \cdot (0 + 0) = a \cdot 0 + a \cdot 0.$$

Hence, by the additive cancellation law, $0 = a \cdot 0$. ∎

Outline of proof of 3.9: $a \cdot b + (-a) \cdot b = (a - a) \cdot b = 0 \cdot b = 0$. Hence $(-a) \cdot b$ is the negative of $a \cdot b$. ∎

We define the product of three or more elements of a ring R just as we did the sum of three or more elements in an Abelian group. Thus, we define $a_1 \cdot a_2 \cdot a_3 = (a_1 \cdot a_2) \cdot a_3$ and, recursively,

$$a_1 \cdot a_2 \cdot \ldots \cdot a_{n+1} = (a_1 \cdot a_2 \cdot \ldots \cdot a_n) \cdot a_{n+1}$$

for every integer $n \geq 2$. A general associative law, analogous to 2.11, holds for multiplication. The general commutative law (2.12) also holds if R is a commutative ring. We state a general distributive law below, leaving its proof as an exercise. In this law, we use the conventional Σ-notation

$$\sum_{i=1}^{n} c_i = c_1 + c_2 + \ldots + c_n.$$

3.10 General distributive law. For all $a_1, a_2, \ldots, a_m$, $b_1, b_2, \ldots, b_n$ in a ring R,

$$\sum_{i=1}^{m} a_i \cdot \sum_{j=1}^{n} b_j = \sum_{i=1}^{m} \sum_{j=1}^{n} a_i b_j.$$

Corresponding to the concept of multiple in an Abelian group is that of *power* in the multiplicative system $\{R; \cdot\}$ of a ring R. In this notation, $a^1 = a$, $a^2 = a \cdot a$, and, recursively,

$$a^{n+1} = a^n \cdot a$$

for every $a \in R$ and every integer $n \geq 2$. If R has a unity 1, then we define

$$a^0 = 1.$$

No meaning is given to a^n, $n < 0$, in a general ring. However, we are able to give a meaning in this case if R is a field (Chapter 4). Useful properties of powers in a ring R are as follows:

3.11 $\qquad\qquad a^m \cdot a^n = a^{m+n}$ for all $a \in R$, $m, n \in \mathbb{Z}^+$.

3.12 $\qquad\qquad (a^m)^n = a^{mn}$ for all $a \in R$, $m, n \in \mathbb{Z}^+$.

Furthermore, if R is assumed to be a C-ring, we have:

3.13 $\qquad\qquad (a \cdot b)^m = a^m \cdot b^m$ for all $a, b \in R$, $m \in \mathbb{Z}^+$.

Since these properties relative to multiplication are identical with the additive properties 2.13–2.15, their proofs are also identical.

We should see why 3.13 does not necessarily hold for a noncommutative ring R. If $a, b \in R$, with $a \cdot b \neq b \cdot a$, then

$$(a \cdot b)^2 = (a \cdot b) \cdot (a \cdot b) = a \cdot (b \cdot a) \cdot b$$

whereas $a^2 \cdot b^2 = a \cdot (a \cdot b) \cdot b$. It seems clear that $a \cdot (b \cdot a) \cdot b \neq a \cdot (a \cdot b) \cdot b$ in general.

Exercises

1. Make addition and multiplication tables for the Boolean ring of all subsets of a two-element set $\{a, b\}$.

2. Show that there exist nonzero $f, g \in C(\mathbb{R})$ such that $f \cdot g = 0$. If $f \in C(\mathbb{R})$, $f \neq 0$, is $f^n \neq 0$ for every positive integer n?

3. Let S be a set, R a ring, and M the set of all mappings of S into R. Is M a ring if operations are defined in M as in 3.6?

4. For any set S, we can form the algebraic system $\{\mathcal{P}(S); \cup, \cap\}$. Is this a ring? If your answer is "no," tell precisely which properties of a ring it does not possess.

5. Let R be a C-ring with unity 1. An element $x \in R$ is called a *unit* iff $x \cdot y = 1$ for some $y \in R$. If G is the set of all units of R, describe the algebraic system $\{G; \cdot\}$. Is the sum of two units necessarily a unit? Can the sum of two nonunits be a unit? Can the product of two nonunits be a unit?

6. Describe the set G of all units of the ring $C(\mathbb{R})$.

7. Describe the set G of all units of the Boolean ring $\mathcal{P}(S)$ associated with a set S; of any Boolean ring R with unity.

8. Prove 3.10.

9. If R is a ring, S is a set, and $R \xrightarrow{f} S$ is a bijection, then describe how S might be made into a ring. Illustrate in case $R = \mathbb{Z}, S = 2\mathbb{Z}$, and $f(x) = 2x$.

10. Show that the mapping $\mathbb{Z} \xrightarrow{h} \mathbb{Z}$ defined by $h(x) = 1 - x$ is a bijection. Imagining h as a mapping of *ring* $\mathbb{Z}$ into *set* $\mathbb{Z}$, we can define operations $\oplus$ and $\odot$ in set $\mathbb{Z}$ corresponding to the operations $+$ and $\cdot$ in ring $\mathbb{Z}$. Describe the relationship between the operations $\oplus$ and $\odot$ and the operations $+$ and $\cdot$ in $\mathbb{Z}$.

11. Carry through the same procedure as in Exercise 10 for the mapping $\mathbb{R} \xrightarrow{g} \mathbb{R}$ defined by $g(x) = \sqrt[3]{x}$.

*12. An interesting ring in analysis is the *convolution ring*† $\{C; +, *\}$, where C is the set of all continuous, real-valued functions having $[0, \infty) = \{x \in \mathbb{R} \mid x \geq 0\}$ as domain. Addition is the ordinary functional addition of 3.6 and $*$ is the convolution operation

$$(f * g)(x) = \int_0^x f(t)g(x - t)\, dt.$$

Show that C is a C-ring. [*Hint:* The change of variable $u = x - t$ will prove that $*$ is commutative. An interchange of the order of integration will prove that $*$ is associative; i.e.,

$$\int_0^x \left(\int_0^t f(u)g(t - u)\, du \right) h(x - t)\, dt = \int_0^x \left(\int_u^x f(u)g(t - u)h(x - t)\, dt \right) du.$$

Then change variables $v = t - u$.]

---

† For a full discussion of this ring, see A. Erdélyi, *Operational Calculus and Generalized Functions* (New York: Holt, Rinehart & Winston, Inc., 1962), chap. 2.

2. Subrings and Ideals

For simplicity, in the remainder of this chapter we shall restrict our remarks to C-rings. This is not much of a restriction at this time, since all the examples of rings we have given so far are commutative.

If a nonempty subset S of a C-ring R is a subgroup of $\{R; +\}$ and is closed under multiplication, then clearly $\{S; +, \cdot\}$ is a C-ring. We call S a *subring* of R. Two trivial subrings of R are $\{0\}$ and R itself. If $S \neq \{0\}$ and $S \neq R$, then S is called a *proper subring* of R.

For example, $\mathbb{Z}$ is a subring of $\mathbb{Q}$ and $\mathbb{R}$. We recall that S is a subgroup of $\{\mathbb{Z}; +\}$ iff $S = n\mathbb{Z}$ for some $n \in \mathbb{Z}$. Since $(nx) \cdot (ny) = n(nx \cdot y)$, evidently $n\mathbb{Z}$ is closed under multiplication and hence is a subring of $\mathbb{Z}$. Thus, S is a subring of $\mathbb{Z}$ iff $S = n\mathbb{Z}$ for some $n \in \mathbb{Z}$. Other examples of subrings are given below.

3.14 Example. Let $C(\mathbb{R})$ be the ring of continuous functions defined in 3.6 and P be the set of all polynomial functions. Thus, each $f \in P$ is defined by an equation of the form

$$f(x) = a_0 + a_1 x + \ldots + a_n x^n \text{ for all } x \in \mathbb{R},$$

where $n \geq 0$ and $a_0, a_1, \ldots, a_n \in \mathbb{R}$. Clearly $P \subset C(\mathbb{R})$, $f + g$ and $f \cdot g$ are in P for all $f, g \in P$, $0 \in P$, and $-f \in P$ for all $f \in P$. Hence, P is a subring of $C(\mathbb{R})$.

As another example of a subring of $C(\mathbb{R})$, let

$$C_r = \{f \in C(\mathbb{R}) \mid f(r) = 0\}$$

for each $r \in \mathbb{R}$. The reader may easily verify that C_r is a subring.

3.15 Example. If $\mathbb{Z}[\sqrt{n}] = \{a + b\sqrt{n} \mid a, b \in \mathbb{Z}\}$ for each square-free positive integer n, then it is evident that $\mathbb{Z}[\sqrt{n}]$ is a subring of the quadratic field $\mathbb{Q}[\sqrt{n}]$.

3.16 Example. Let $\mathscr{P}(S)$ be the Boolean ring of all subsets of an infinite set S and

$$\mathscr{F}(S) = \{A \in \mathscr{P}(S) \mid \#(A) < \infty\}.$$

Since $A + B$ and $A \cdot B$ are finite sets whenever A and B are, evidently $\mathscr{F}(S)$ is a proper subring of $\mathscr{P}(S)$.

A subring S of a C-ring R is called an *ideal* if $ar \in S$ for all $a \in S$ and $r \in R$. The trivial subrings $\{0\}$ and R are clearly ideals of R. An ideal I of a C-ring R is called a *proper ideal* if $I \neq \{0\}$ and $I \neq R$. We shall discover as we progress in this book that ideals are of fundamental importance in ring theory.

Each subring $n\mathbb{Z}$ of $\mathbb{Z}$ is actually an ideal, since $(nx) \cdot y = n(x \cdot y) \in n\mathbb{Z}$ for all $nx \in n\mathbb{Z}$ and $y \in \mathbb{Z}$.

More generally, if R is a C-ring and $a \in R$, then

$$aR = \{a \cdot x \mid x \in R\}$$

is easily shown to be an ideal of R. Such an ideal is called a *principal ideal* of R. If R has a unity 1, then $a \in aR$ since $a = a \cdot 1$.

The subring P of all polynomial functions of $C(\mathbb{R})$ given in 3.14 is not an ideal. For example, the sine function is in $C(\mathbb{R})$ but the product of the sine and a nonzero polynomial function may be shown to be a nonpolynomial function. On the other hand, the subring C_r of $C(\mathbb{R})$ defined in 3.14 is an ideal. For if $f \in C_r$ and $g \in C(\mathbb{R})$, then

$$(fg)(r) = f(r) \cdot g(r) = 0$$

and therefore $fg \in C_r$.

We may easily show that $\mathbb{Z}[\sqrt{n}]$ of 3.15 is not an ideal of $\mathbb{Q}[\sqrt{n}]$ just as $\mathbb{Z}$ is not an ideal of $\mathbb{Q}$.

Is the subring $\mathscr{F}(S)$ of $\mathscr{P}(S)$, defined in 3.16, an ideal? That is, if $A \in \mathscr{F}(S)$ and $B \in \mathscr{P}(S)$, then is $A \cdot B \in \mathscr{F}(S)$? Since $A \cdot B = A \cap B$, $A \cdot B$ is a subset of a finite set A and hence is itself finite. Therefore, $A \cdot B \in \mathscr{F}(S)$ and $\mathscr{F}(S)$ is an ideal of $\mathscr{P}(S)$.

Exercises

1. Is the set of all differentiable functions a subring of $C(\mathbb{R})$? An ideal of $C(\mathbb{R})$?

2. Describe the principal ideals of $\mathscr{P}(S)$.

3. Prove that an Abelian group $\{G; +\}$ can be made into a ring by defining multiplication as follows: $a \cdot b = 0$ for all $a, b \in G$. A ring R is called a *zero ring* iff $a \cdot b = 0$ for all $a, b \in R$.

4. For each subset A of a C-ring R, let $I(A) = \{x \in R \mid x \cdot a = 0$ for all $a \in A\}$. Prove that $I(A)$ is an ideal of R.

5. If A and B are ideals of a C-ring R, prove that $A \cap B$ and $A + B = \{a + b \mid a \in A, b \in B\}$ are also ideals of R. Is the intersection of an infinite set of ideals of R an ideal?

6. Let A and B be ideals of a C-ring R with unity and $C = \{x \in R \mid xa \in B$ for all $a \in A\}$. Prove that C is an ideal of R containing B. Describe C in case $A = B$; in case $A = R$.

7. If $R_1, R_2, \ldots, R_n$ are rings and $R = R_1 \times R_2 \times \ldots \times R_n$, prove that R is a ring if the operations of R are defined coordinatewise [i.e.,

$$(a_1, a_2, \ldots, a_n) \cdot (b_1, b_2, \ldots, b_n) = (a_1 \cdot b_1, a_2 \cdot b_2, \ldots, a_n \cdot b_n),$$

and similarly for addition]. Show that R is commutative iff every R_i is and that R has a unity iff every R_i has one. If R has a unity, what are the units of R? Can all the nonzero elements of R be units?

*8. Let R be a C-ring which is not a zero ring and which has no proper ideals. Prove that R has a unity 1. Prove that every nonzero element of R is a unit.

3. Quotient Rings and Homomorphisms

If R is a C-ring and I is an ideal of R, then $\{I; +\}$ is a subgroup of $\{R; +\}$. Therefore, we can form the quotient group

$$R/I = \{a + I \mid a \in R\}.$$

Can R/I be made into a ring? A natural way to try to define multiplication in R/I is as follows:

3.17 $(a + I) \cdot (b + I) = a \cdot b + I$ for all $a + I, b + I \in R/I$.

Is multiplication well-defined by 3.17? That is, if $a + I = a' + I$ and $b + I = b' + I$, does $a \cdot b + I = a' \cdot b' + I$? To answer this question, note that $a' - a = u$ and $b' - b = v$ for some $u, v \in I$. Therefore,

$$a' \cdot b' = (a + u) \cdot (b + v) = a \cdot b + (ub + av + uv).$$

Now I is an ideal, and hence ub, av, and uv are in I as is their sum. Consequently, $a' \cdot b' - a \cdot b \in I$ and $a \cdot b + I = a' \cdot b' + I$ by 2.19. Thus, multiplication is well-defined by 3.17.

A mapping $R \xrightarrow{f} S$ of a ring R into a ring S is called a *homomorphism* iff

$$f(a + b) = f(a) + f(b), \quad f(a \cdot b) = f(a) \cdot f(b) \text{ for all } a, b \in R.$$

We shall use the words "epimorphism," "monomorphism," and "isomorphism" in the same way they were used with Abelian groups. For example, a homomorphism $R \xrightarrow{f} S$ is an epimorphism iff the image of R is S, im $R = S$.

If $\{R; +, \cdot\}$ is a ring, $\{S; +, \cdot\}$ is an algebraic system, and $R \xrightarrow{f} S$ is an epimorphism, then necessarily S is a ring. The proof of this fact is similar to that given for Abelian groups and hence is omitted.

To return to a C-ring R and an ideal I, we know that the mapping

$$R \xrightarrow{f} R/I \text{ defined by } f(a) = a + I \text{ for all } a \in R$$

is an epimorphism. Therefore, R/I is itself a C-ring. If R has a unity 1, then $1 + I$ is the unity of R/I.

For example, $n\mathbb{Z}$ is an ideal of $\mathbb{Z}$ for every integer $n \geq 0$, and therefore $\mathbb{Z}_n = \mathbb{Z}/n\mathbb{Z}$ is not only an Abelian group but also a C-ring with unity. Multiplication is carried out modulo n in $\mathbb{Z}_n$ just as is addition. For example, $5 \cdot 6 \equiv 2 \pmod{7}$, and therefore $5 \cdot 6 = 2$ in $\mathbb{Z}_7$.

The multiplication table for $\mathbb{Z}_4$ is shown below. We see from the table that $\{1,3\}$ is the group of units of $\mathbb{Z}_4$.

$\cdot$	0	1	2	3
0	0	0	0	0
1	0	1	2	3
2	0	2	0	2
3	0	3	2	1

As another example, consider the ring $C(\mathbb{R})$ of continuous functions and the ideal $C_r = \{f \in C(\mathbb{R}) \mid f(r) = 0\}$. Since $C(\mathbb{R})$ is a C-ring with unity, so is $S = C(\mathbb{R})/C_r$. For each $c \in \mathbb{R}$, the constant function $\bar{c}$ defined by $\bar{c}(x) = c$ for all $x \in \mathbb{R}$ is in $C(\mathbb{R})$. There is a mapping $\mathbb{R} \xrightarrow{h} S$ defined by

$$h(c) = \bar{c} + C_r \text{ for all } c \in \mathbb{R}.$$

Since $\overline{c + d} = \bar{c} + \bar{d}$ and $\overline{c \cdot d} = \bar{c} \cdot \bar{d}$, clearly h is a homomorphism. Actually, h is an epimorphism. For if $g \in C(\mathbb{R})$ and $g(r) = c$, then $h(c) = g + C_r$ since $(g - \bar{c})(r) = g(r) - \bar{c}(r) = c - c = 0$ and $g - \bar{c} \in C_r$. Is h an isomorphism, i.e., is $\ker h = \{0\}$? If $h(c) = C_r$, then $\bar{c} \in C_r$, $\bar{c}(r) = 0$, and $c = 0$. Hence, $\ker h = \{0\}$ and h is an isomorphism. We conclude that the ring $C(\mathbb{R})/C_r$ is isomorphic to the ring $\mathbb{R}$.

If R and S are rings and $R \xrightarrow{f} S$ is a homomorphism, then

$$\ker f = \{x \in R \mid f(x) = 0\}$$

is known to be an Abelian group. Let us show that $\ker f$ is an ideal of R. If $a \in \ker f$ and $r \in R$, then

$$f(a \cdot r) = f(a) \cdot f(r) = 0 \cdot f(r) = 0$$

and therefore $a \cdot r \in \ker f$. Hence, *$\ker f$ is an ideal of R.*

The isomorphism theorem for Abelian groups (2.30) applies equally well to rings.

3.18 Isomorphism theorem. If R and S are rings and $R \overset{f}{\longrightarrow} S$ is an epimorphism, then the mapping $R/\ker f \overset{h}{\longrightarrow} S$ defined by $h(a + \ker f) = f(a)$ is an isomorphism.

Consequently, except for isomorphisms, the only homomorphic images of a ring R are the rings R/I, I an ideal of R.

Exercises

1. Give the multiplication table for $\mathbb{Z}_3$, $\mathbb{Z}_5$, and $\mathbb{Z}_6$. Find the group of units in each case.

2. If I and J are ideals of the C-rings R and S, then prove that $I \times J$ is an ideal of $R \times S$. Is $(R \times S)/(I \times J)$ isomorphic to $(R/I) \times (S/J)$?

3. Let R be a C-ring which contains two ideals A and B such that $A \cap B = \{0\}$ and $A + B = R$. Prove that R is isomorphic to $A \times B$.

4 Let R be a C-ring which contains two ideals A and B such that $A \cap B = \{0\}$. Prove that R is isomorphic to $(R/A) \times (R/B)$. State and prove a similar theorem in case $A \cap B \neq \{0\}$.

5. If $m, n \in \mathbb{Z}^+$ and $n \mid m$, then $m\mathbb{Z}$ is an ideal of the C-ring $n\mathbb{Z}$. Describe the ring $n\mathbb{Z}/m\mathbb{Z}$.

4. The Characteristic

It is common practice in ring theory to use the word "characteristic" in describing the order of an element in the Abelian group of a ring. To be more specific, if R is a ring, $b \in R$, and $B = \{nb \mid n \in \mathbb{Z}\}$, then the *characteristic* of b is denoted by "ch b" and is defined as follows:

ch $b = \#(B)$ if B is a finite set, ch $b = 0$ if B is an infinite set.

In other words, if $kb = 0$ for some $k \in \mathbb{Z}^+$, then ch b is the least positive integer n such that $nb = 0$; and if $kb \neq 0$ for all $k \in \mathbb{Z}^+$, then ch $b = 0$. Note that ch $0 = 1$.

The ring R itself is said to have *characteristic* $n > 0$, ch $R = n$, if n is the least positive integer such that $nb = 0$ for all $b \in R$. If no such positive integer n exists, we say that ch $R = 0$.

For example, in the ring $\mathbb{Z}_6$ we have

$$\text{ch } 0 = 1, \text{ ch } 1 = 6, \text{ ch } 2 = 3, \text{ ch } 3 = 2, \text{ ch } 4 = 3, \text{ ch } 5 = 6.$$

Hence, ch $\mathbb{Z}_6 = 6$. This example illustrates the following theorem:

3.19 Theorem. If ring R has a unity 1, then ch $R = $ ch 1.

Proof: If ch $1 = 0$, then clearly ch $R = 0$ also. If ch $1 = n$, $n \in \mathbb{Z}^+$, then $nb = n(1 \cdot b) = (n \cdot 1) \cdot b = 0 \cdot b = 0$ for all $b \in R$. Since $nb = 0$ for all $b \in R$ and n is the least positive integer such that $n1 = 0$, evidently ch $R = n$. ▮

Because of 3.19, we see that ch $\mathbb{Z}_n = n$ for every $n \in \mathbb{Z}^+$.

If R is a ring with unity, which we denote by e to destinguish it from the unity 1 of $\mathbb{Z}$, then the mapping

$$\mathbb{Z} \xrightarrow{\ h\ } R \text{ defined by } h(n) = ne \text{ for all } n \in \mathbb{Z}$$

is a homomorphism, since $h(m + n) = (m + n)e = me + ne$ and $h(m \cdot n) = (m \cdot n)e = (m \cdot n)(e \cdot e) = (me) \cdot (ne)$ for all $m,n \in \mathbb{Z}$. Evidently ker $h = n\mathbb{Z}$ where $n = $ ch $e = $ ch R. Therefore, the mapping

$$\mathbb{Z}_n \xrightarrow{\ f\ } R \text{ defined by } f(k + n\mathbb{Z}) = ke \text{ for all } k \in \mathbb{Z}$$

is a monomorphism by 3.18. Since the image of f,

$$\text{im } f = \{ke \mid k \in \mathbb{Z}\},$$

is isomorphic to $\mathbb{Z}_n$, and since we are only interested in the algebraic properties of R and not in the nature of the elements of R, we may replace im f by $\mathbb{Z}_n$ in R. If we consider $\mathbb{Z}_n = \{0, 1, \ldots, n - 1\}$, then

$$\mathbb{Z}_n \subset R,$$

1 is the unity of R, and $ka = k \cdot a$ for all $k \in \mathbb{Z}_n$ and $a \in R$ [since $ka = k(e \cdot a) = (ke) \cdot a$, and we are identifying k with ke]. We see that $\mathbb{Z} \subset R$ in case ch $R = 0$.

The results of the preceding paragraph are stated below for convenient reference.

3.20 Theorem. If R is a ring with unity and ch $R = n$, then $\mathbb{Z}_n$ is a subring of R. In particular, if ch $R = 0$ then $\mathbb{Z}$ is a subring of R.

Exercises

1. Find the characteristics of the elements of $\mathbb{Z}_8$; of $\mathbb{Z}_{14}$.

2. If R is a C-ring with unity 1, prove that ch $x =$ ch 1 for every unit $x \in R$. Illustrate this result with $\mathbb{Z}_n$ for some n.

3. If R is a finite ring with n elements, prove that ch $R \mid n$. Give examples to show that ch R might be less than n.

4. How are ch $(a + b)$ and ch (ab) related to ch a and ch b in a C-ring R? Give examples.

5. If R is a C-ring and $n \in \mathbb{Z}^+$, then define $nR = \{nx \mid x \in R\}$. Prove that nR is an ideal of R. What can be said about ch (R/nR)? Give examples.

6. If R is a C-ring and $n \in \mathbb{Z}^+$, then prove that $A_n = \{x \in R \mid nx = 0\}$ and $B_n = \{y \in R \mid n^k y = 0$ for some $k \in \mathbb{Z}^+\}$ are ideals of R. What can be said about ch (R/A_n)? about ch (R/B_n)? Give examples.

7. If $k,m,n \in \mathbb{Z}^+$ and $n = km$, prove that $\mathbb{Z}_n/k\mathbb{Z}_n$ and $A_k = \{x \in \mathbb{Z}_n \mid kx = 0\}$ are isomorphic to $\mathbb{Z}_k$.

*8. Let R be a C-ring of characteristic $n > 0$, where $n = k \cdot m$ and $(k,m) = 1$. If A_r is defined as in Exercise 6, prove that R is isomorphic to $A_k \times A_m$. [*Hint:* See Exercise 3, p. 61.] If $n = p_1^{j_1} \cdot \ldots \cdot p_t^{j_t}$, where the p_i are distinct prime numbers and each $j_i > 0$, then R is isomorphic to a Cartesian product of t ideals of R. Explain.

9. Prove that each ring $\mathbb{Z}_n$, $n > 1$, is isomorphic to a Cartesian product

$$\mathbb{Z}_{p_1}^{j_1} \times \ldots \times \mathbb{Z}_{p_t}^{j_t}, \qquad p_1, \ldots, p_t \text{ distinct primes.}$$

[*Hint:* Use Exercise 8.]

*10. Find a C-ring R with eight elements such that R is not a zero ring although $x^2 = 0$ for every $x \in R$.

*11. Give an example of a ring R such that ch $R = 0$ and ch $x > 0$ for every $x \in R$.

*12. Prove that the only way the Abelian group $\{\mathbb{Q}/\mathbb{Z} ;+\}$ can be made into a C-ring is by making it the zero ring.

THEORETICAL PROJECT 1

Every C-ring R of characteristic $n \geq 0$ which does not have a unity can be imbedded in a ring S with unity such that ch $S = n$. That is, there exists some ring S with unity, ch $S = n$, such that R is (isomorphic to) a subring of S. We choose *set* S to be

$$S = R \times \mathbb{Z}_n.$$

Then the Abelian group $\{S;+\}$ is the usual Cartesian product of the groups $\{R;+\}$ and $\{\mathbb{Z}_n;+\}$. Multiplication is defined in S as follows:

$$(a,k) \cdot (b,m) = (ab + ma + kb, km).$$

Prove that S is a C-ring with unity $(0,1)$. Also prove that R is isomorphic to the ideal $R_0 = \{(r,0) \mid r \in R\}$ of S. [For more details, see N. H. McCoy, *Rings and Ideals* (La Salle, Ill.: Open Court Publishing Co., 1948).]

THEORETICAL PROJECT 2

Let R be a C-ring. The binomial expansion clearly holds for R. That is, for $x,y \in R$, $n \in \mathbb{Z}^+$,

$$(x + y)^n = x^n + \binom{n}{1} x^{n-1}y + \binom{n}{2} x^{n-2}y^2 + \ldots + \binom{n}{n} y^n,$$

where

$$\binom{n}{k} = \frac{n!}{k!(n - k)!}$$

is the usual binomial coefficient. An element x of R is said to be *nilpotent* if $x^n = 0$ for some $n \in \mathbb{Z}^+$. Let N be the set of all nilpotent elements of R. For example, if $R = \mathbb{Z}_8$ then $N = \{0,2,4,6\}$.

1. Prove that N is an ideal of R.
2. What is N if $R = \mathbb{Z}_n$ for $n \in \mathbb{Z}^+$?
3. Prove that R/N has no nilpotent element other than zero.

If A is an ideal of R, then the *radical of A* is denoted by "rad A" and is defined by

$$\text{rad } A = \{x \in R \mid x^n \in A \text{ for some } n \in \mathbb{Z}^+\}.$$

4. Prove that rad A is an ideal of R containing A for each ideal A of R.
5. Is $N = $ rad A for some ideal A of R?
6. Prove that rad (rad A) = rad A for each ideal A of R.
7. If A and B are ideals of R such that $A \subset B$, prove that rad $A \subset$ rad B.
8. If A and B are ideals of R, how is rad $(A \cap B)$ related to rad A and rad B?

chapter 4

Integral Domains
and Fields

The systems of integers, rational numbers, and real numbers have more properties than a general commutative ring. Thus, the multiplicative cancellation law holds in $\mathbb{Z}$, and each nonzero element of $\mathbb{Q}$ and $\mathbb{R}$ is a unit. Rings having these additional properties are studied in this chapter.

I. Definitions

A commutative ring R is called an *integral domain* iff $R \neq \{0\}$ and:

4.1 The multiplicative cancellation law holds in R.

That is, if $a \cdot c = b \cdot c$ or $c \cdot a = c \cdot b$ for some $a, b, c \in R$, with $c \neq 0$, then $a = b$.

The first example of an integral domain that comes to mind is $\mathbb{Z}$, the domain of integers. Needless to say, the integral domain derived its name from this example.

If R is a C-ring and $d \in R$, then d is called a *divisor of zero* iff $d \cdot x = 0$ for some nonzero $x \in R$. Trivially, 0 is a divisor of zero.

An example of a ring with nonzero divisors of zero is $\mathbb{Z}_4$. Thus, $2 \cdot 2 = 0$ and 2 is a divisor of zero in $\mathbb{Z}_4$.

As another example, let $f,g \in C(\mathbb{R})$ be defined by:

$$f(x) = \begin{cases} 0 \text{ if } x \le 0, \\ x \text{ if } x > 0, \end{cases} \qquad g(x) = \begin{cases} x \text{ if } x \le 0, \\ 0 \text{ if } x > 0. \end{cases}$$

Since $f(x) \cdot g(x) = 0$ for all $x \in \mathbb{R}$, evidently $f \cdot g = 0$. Hence, f and g are nonzero divisors of zero in $C(\mathbb{R})$.

4.2   Theorem. A C-ring R is an integral domain iff it has no nonzero divisors of zero.

Outline of proof: If R is an integral domain and $d \in R$ is a divisor of zero, say $d \cdot x = 0$ for some $x \in R$, $x \ne 0$, then $d \cdot x = 0 \cdot x$ and $d = 0$ by 4.1. Conversely, if R is a C-ring with no nonzero divisors of zero and $a \cdot c = b \cdot c$ for some $a,b,c \in R$, with $c \ne 0$, then $(a - b) \cdot c = 0$ and $a = b$. ∎

A C-ring R is called a *field* iff R has a unity and:

4.3   Every nonzero element of R has a multiplicative inverse.

That is, a C-ring R with unity is a field iff $R' = \{x \in R \mid x \ne 0\}$ is the set of units of R. Actually, $\{R'; \cdot\}$ is an Abelian group if R is a field. The notation a^{-1} or $1/a$ is used for the multiplicative inverse of each $a \in R'$. Then we define $a^{-n} = (a^{-1})^n$ for every $n \in \mathbb{Z}^+$.

Every real field is an example of a field. Thus, $\mathbb{Q}$, $\mathbb{Q}[\sqrt{2}]$, and $\mathbb{R}$ are fields. Evidently $\mathbb{Z}_2$ also is a field, since the only nonzero element of $\mathbb{Z}_2$ is the unity 1.

Every field F is also an integral domain. For if $d \in F$, $d \ne 0$, and $d \cdot a = 0$ for some $a \in F$, then

$$0 = d^{-1} \cdot 0 = d^{-1} \cdot (d \cdot a) = (d^{-1} \cdot d) \cdot a = 1 \cdot a = a.$$

Hence, F has no nonzero divisors of zero and F is an integral domain by 4.2.

A field F has no proper ideals. For if $I \ne \{0\}$ is an ideal of F and $d \in I$, $d \ne 0$, then $r = (rd^{-1})d$ is in I for all $r \in F$. Hence, $I = F$. Consequently, a field has no homomorphic images other than isomorphic images.

Can anything special be said about the characteristic of an integral domain R? By looking at $\mathbb{Z}$, we see that one possibility is that ch $x = 0$ for every nonzero $x \in \mathbb{Z}$ and hence ch $\mathbb{Z} = 0$ also. If an integral domain R has one element b of characteristic $n > 1$, then ch $x = n$ for all nonzero $x \in R$. For $0 = 0 \cdot x = (nb) \cdot x = b \cdot (nx)$ and $nx = 0$. Furthermore, if $mx = 0$ for some $m > 0$, then $0 = b \cdot (mx) = (mb) \cdot x$ and $mb = 0$. Hence, $m \ge n$. We conclude that ch $x = n$ as stated. It is a simple task to prove that n is a prime. For if $n = n_1 \cdot n_2$ with $1 < n_1 \le n$ and $1 \le n_2 < n$, then

$$0 = 0 \cdot b = (nb) \cdot b = (n_1 b) \cdot (n_2 b)$$

and either $n_1 b = 0$ or $n_2 b = 0$. Therefore, $n_1 b = 0$ and $n_1 = n$. Hence, n s a prime. We have proved the following result:

4.4   Theorem. If R is an integral domain, then either ch $x = 0$ for all nonzero $x \in R$ or ch $x = p$, a prime, for all nonzero $x \in R$. In the former case, ch $R = 0$, whereas in the latter case ch $R = p$.

We can now easily decide which of the rings $\mathbb{Z}_n$, $n = 2,3, \ldots$, might be integral domains. Since ch $\mathbb{Z}_n = n$, $\mathbb{Z}_n$ can't be an integral domain unless n is a prime. This proves part of the following result:

4.5   Theorem. The ring $\mathbb{Z}_n$ is a field iff n is a prime.

Proof: Assume that n is a prime and $1 \le k < n$, $k \in \mathbb{Z}$. Then $(k,n) = 1$ and $ku + nv = 1$ for some $u,v \in \mathbb{Z}$. Hence,

$$(k + n\mathbb{Z})(u + n\mathbb{Z}) = 1 + n\mathbb{Z}$$

in $\mathbb{Z}_n$ and $u + n\mathbb{Z}$ is the inverse of $k + n\mathbb{Z}$. Therefore, $\mathbb{Z}_n$ is a field. ∎

As a consequence of 4.5, we now have many examples of fields—$\mathbb{Z}_2$, $\mathbb{Z}_3$ $\mathbb{Z}_5$, $\mathbb{Z}_7$, and $\mathbb{Z}_{101}$, to mention a few.

If F is a field of characteristic $p > 0$, then F contains $\mathbb{Z}_p$ as a subfield by 3.20. On the other hand, if ch $F = 0$, then $\mathbb{Z}$ is a subring of F by 3.20. Actually, $\mathbb{Q} \subset F$ in this case, since each nonzero integer n has an inverse in F and therefore $m \cdot (1/n)$ or m/n is in F for all $m,n \in \mathbb{Z}$ with $n \ne 0$.

Exercises

1. Is each proper subring of an integral domain also an integral domain? Is each proper subring of a field also a field? Give examples.

2. Is a Cartesian product of C-rings ever an integral domain? Explain.

3. Can a proper subring of a C-ring which is not an integral domain be an integral domain? Explain.

4. If F is a field, prove that $a^m a^n = a^{m+n}$, $(a^m)^n = a^{mn}$, and $(ab)^n = a^n b^n$ for all $m,n \in \mathbb{Z}$ and all nonzero $a,b \in F$.

5. Prove that the set of nondivisors of zero of a C-ring is closed under multiplication.

6. If R is a C-ring with unity and A is a maximal proper ideal of R (i.e., R is the only ideal of R properly containing A), then prove that R/A is a field. What can be said if R does not have a unity?

7. If a C-ring R contains an element e such that (i) $e^2 = e$ and (ii) e is a nondivisor of zero, then prove that e is the unity element of R.

8. Let R be a finite C-ring which contains at least one nondivisor of zero. Prove that R has a unity 1 and that for every nondivisor of zero d, $d^n = 1$ for some $n \in \mathbb{Z}^+$. [*Hint:* $\{d^n \mid n \in \mathbb{Z}^+\}$ is a finite set. Hence $(d^m)^2 = d^m$ for some $m \in \mathbb{Z}^+$. Then use Exercise 7.] Therefore, show that the set of nondivisors of zero of R is simply the group of units of R.

9. Prove that every finite integral domain is a field. [*Hint:* Use Exercise 8.]

10. Describe the group of units in $\mathbb{Z}_n$. [*Hint:* Use Exercise 8.]

11. Prove *Fermat's theorem* which states that

$$x^{p-1} \equiv 1 \bmod p$$

for each prime p and each integer $x \notin p\mathbb{Z}$. [*Hint:* Work with $\mathbb{Z}_p$, and use Exercise 8.]

12. Construct addition and multiplication tables for a field with four elements. [*Hint:* Its characteristic must be 2.]

13. Prove *Wilson's theorem* which states that

$$(p - 2)! \equiv 1 \bmod p$$

for every prime number p. [*Hint:* Work with $\mathbb{Z}_p$; each of the elements of the set $\{2, \ldots, p - 2\}$ has an inverse in this set.]

14. If p is a prime number, prove that there are only two rings having p elements.

15. Prove that $(x + y)^p = x^p + y^p$ for all $x, y \in \mathbb{Z}_p$.

2. Field of Quotients of an Integral Domain

Just as the integral domain $\mathbb{Z}$ is contained in a field $\mathbb{Q}$ of quotients of integers, so is every integral domain R contained in a field F of quotients.

To prove this fact, let R be an integral domain and $R' = \{x \in R \mid x \neq 0\}$. Define the relation $\sim$ in $R \times R'$ as follows:

$$(a,b) \sim (c,d) \text{ iff } ad = bc.$$

The reader may easily verify that $\sim$ is an equivalence relation. As such, it induces a partition F of $R \times R'$. If we let $\dfrac{a}{b}$, or a/b, denote the set in F containing (a,b), i.e.,

$$\frac{a}{b} = \{(c,d) \in R \times R' \mid (a,b) \sim (c,d)\},$$

then

$$F = \left\{ \frac{a}{b} \,\middle|\, (a,b) \in R \times R' \right\}.$$

Operations of addition $(+)$ and multiplication $(\cdot)$ are defined in F as in $\mathbb{Q}$. Thus,

4.6
$$\frac{a}{b} + \frac{c}{d} = \frac{ad + bc}{bd} \text{ for all } \frac{a}{b}, \frac{c}{d} \in F.$$

4.7
$$\frac{a}{b} \cdot \frac{c}{d} = \frac{ac}{bd} \text{ for all } \frac{a}{b}, \frac{c}{d} \in F.$$

Of course, we must show that these operations are well-defined. That is, if $a/b = a'/b'$ and $c/d = c'/d'$, then we must show that

$$\frac{ad + bc}{bd} = \frac{a'd' + b'c'}{b'd'} \quad \text{and} \quad \frac{ac}{bd} = \frac{a'c'}{b'd'},$$

or, equivalently, that

$$(ad + bc)b'd' \stackrel{.}{=} bd(a'd' + b'c') \quad \text{and} \quad acb'd' = bda'c'.$$

By what is given, $ab' = ba'$ and $cd' = dc'$. Hence,

$$adb'd' + bcb'd' = ba'dd' + bb'dc' = bd(a'd' + b'c')$$

and, similarly, $acb'd' = ba'dc'$. Thus, the operations in F are well-defined by 4.6 and 4.7.

Straightforward calculations show that $\{F; +, \cdot\}$ is a C-ring. For example, the associative law of addition is proved as follows:

$$\frac{a}{b} + \left(\frac{c}{d} + \frac{e}{f}\right) = \frac{a}{b} + \frac{cf + de}{df} = \frac{adf + (bcf + bde)}{bdf},$$

$$\left(\frac{a}{b} + \frac{c}{d}\right) + \frac{e}{f} = \frac{ad + bc}{bd} + \frac{e}{f} = \frac{(adf + bcf) + bde}{bdf}.$$

The zero element of F is $0/b$, since

$$\frac{0}{b} + \frac{c}{d} = \frac{bc}{bd} = \frac{c}{d} = \frac{c}{d} + \frac{0}{b}.$$

We shall denote $0/b$ henceforth by 0; thus, $0 = \{(0,b) \mid b \in R'\}$. Evidently the negative of a/b is $(-a)/b$, since

$$\frac{a}{b} + \frac{-a}{b} = \frac{ab - ab}{b^2} = \frac{0}{b^2} = 0.$$

That is,

$$-\frac{a}{b} = \frac{-a}{b} \text{ for all } \frac{a}{b} \in F.$$

We leave for the reader to verify that the rest of the properties of a C-ring hold for F.

Actually, F is a field. In the first place, b/b is the unity of F, since

$$\frac{b}{b} \cdot \frac{c}{d} = \frac{bc}{bd} = \frac{c}{d} = \frac{c}{d} \cdot \frac{b}{b}.$$

Let us denote b/b by 1, so that $1 = \{(b,b) \mid b \in R'\}$. Clearly the set F' of nonzero elements of F is given by $F' = \{a/b \in F \mid a \neq 0\}$. Now

$$\frac{a}{b} \cdot \frac{b}{a} = 1 \text{ for all } \frac{a}{b} \in F'.$$

Hence, each element $a/b \in F'$ has an inverse given by

$$(a/b)^{-1} = b/a,$$

and F is a field.

There is a natural mapping of the original integral domain R into the field F,

$$R \xrightarrow{h} F \text{ defined by } h(x) = \frac{xb}{b} \text{ for all } x \in R,$$

where b is any element of R'. Since

$$h(x + y) = \frac{(x + y)bd}{bd} = \frac{xb}{b} + \frac{yd}{d} = h(x) + h(y),$$

$$h(x \cdot y) = \frac{(x \cdot y)bd}{bd} = \frac{xb}{b} \cdot \frac{yd}{d} = h(x) \cdot h(y),$$

evidently h is a homomorphism. Clearly $\ker h = \{0\}$, for $xb/b = 0$ iff $x = 0$. Hence, h is a monomorphism. For convenience, let us identify R with im h; that is, identify each x in R with $(xb)/b$ in F. In this way,

$$R \subset F.$$

Furthermore, each $c/d \in F$ is now a quotient of two elements of R, since

$$\frac{c}{d} = \frac{cb}{b} \cdot \frac{b}{db} = \left(\frac{cb}{b}\right) \cdot \left(\frac{db}{b}\right)^{-1},$$

i.e.,

$$\frac{c}{d} = c \cdot d^{-1} = c \div d.$$

For this reason, F is called a *field of quotients* of R. We have proved most of the following theorem:

4.8 Theorem. Every integral domain R is contained in a unique field of quotients F in the sense that R is a subring of field F and $F = \{a \cdot b^{-1} \mid a, b \in R, b \neq 0\}$.

We have already proved that R is contained in such a field F. It only remains to prove that F is unique. We do this by showing that if R_1 and R_2 are isomorphic integral domains, say $R_1 \xrightarrow{f} R_2$ is an isomorphism, and F_1 and F_2 are respective fields of quotients of R_1 and R_2, then the isomorphism f can be extended to an isomorphism $F_1 \xrightarrow{f'} F_2$. We define f' in the obvious way:

$$f'(ab^{-1}) = f(a)[f(b)]^{-1} \text{ for all } ab^{-1} \in F_1.$$

If $ab^{-1} = cd^{-1}$ for $a,b,c,d \in R_1$, then $ad = bc$, $f(a)f(d) = f(b)f(c)$, and $f(a)[f(b)]^{-1} = f(c)[f(d)]^{-1}$. Thus, f' is well-defined. We leave it as an exercise to verify that f' is an isomorphism.

Exercises

1. Complete the proof of 4.8.

2. Show that the construction of the field of quotients of an integral domain can be generalized as follows. Let R be a C-ring and S be a non-empty subset of nondivisors of zero of R which is closed under multiplication. Define the relation $\sim$ in $R \times S$ as in the proof of 4.8, and form the related partition F. Prove that F is a C-ring with unity containing R as a subring, and that S is contained in the group of units of F.

3. If n is a square-free positive integer, describe the field of quotients of $\mathbb{Z}[\sqrt{n}] = \{a + b\sqrt{n} \mid a,b \in \mathbb{Z}\}$.

*4. A subring R of a C-ring S is called *large* iff $aR \cap R \neq 0$ for every nonzero $a \in S$, where $aR = \{a \cdot x \mid x \in R\}$. If R is a large subring of a C-ring S and R is an integral domain, is S an integral domain? Prove your answer.

3. Ordered Integral Domains and Fields

If R is an integral domain (or field), we call R *ordered* iff there exists a subset P of R having the following properties:

4.9 P is closed under addition and multiplication.

4.10 $0 \notin P$.

4.11 For every nonzero $r \in R$, either $r \in P$ or $-r \in P$.

The elements of P are called the *positive elements* of R. By 4.9, $a + b$ and $a \cdot b$ are in P for all $a,b \in P$. The set

$$N = \{-r \mid r \in P\}$$

is called the set of *negative elements* of R. Clearly $0 \notin N$ and $P = \{-r \mid r \in N\}$
Evidently

$$P \cap N = \varnothing,$$

for if $r \in P \cap N$, then r and $-r$ are both in P and $r + (-r) \in P$, contrary to 4.10. By 4.10 and 4.11,

$$R = P \cup N \cup \{0\}.$$

Let R be an ordered integral domain and P be its set of positive elements. If $a \in R$, $a \neq 0$, then either a or $-a$ is in P and hence either a^2 or $(-a)^2$ is in P by 4.9. Since $a^2 = (-a)^2$, we conclude that

4.12 $a^2 \in P$ for all nonzero $a \in R$.

In particular, if R has a unity 1 then $1 \in P$ since $1^2 = 1$.

For convenience, we shall henceforth label the set of positive elements of an ordered integral domain R by R^+ and the set of negative elements by R^-. This conforms with our notation of Chapter 1.

If R is an ordered integral domain and $a \in R^+$, then by mathematical induction $na \in R^+$ for all $n \in \mathbb{Z}^+$. For $1a \in R^+$, and if $ka \in R^+$, then $(k + 1)a = ka + a$ is in R^+ by 4.9. Therefore, $na \neq 0$ for all $n \in \mathbb{Z}^+$. This proves the following result.

4.13   Theorem. If R is an ordered integral domain, then ch $R = 0$.

By 3.20, every ordered integral domain R with unity contains $\mathbb{Z}$ as a subring.

We conclude from 4.13 that each finite field $\mathbb{Z}_p$ is unordered.

The proof of the following theorem is left as an exercise.

4.14   Theorem. If R is an integral domain and F is its field of quotients, then R is ordered iff F is ordered.

We only remark that if R is ordered, then F^+ is defined by

$$F^+ = \{a/b \in F \mid a \cdot b \in R^+\}.$$

If F is ordered, then R^+ is simply $F^+ \cap R$.

A relation of *greater than* ($>$) may be defined in an ordered integral domain R as follows: For all $a,b \in R$,

4.15 $a > b$ iff $a - b \in R^+$.

We may easily prove the following properties of this relation in R.

4.16 $>$ is transitive.

4.17 For all $a,b,c \in R$, $a > b$ iff $a + c > b + c$.

4.18 For all $a,b \in R$, $c \in R^+$, $a > b$ iff $ac > bc$.

4.19 For all $a,b \in R$ with $a \neq b$, either $a > b$ or $b > a$.

Proof of 4.18: If $a > b$ and $c \in R^+$, then $(a - b)c \in R^+$, $ac - bc \in R^+$, and $ac > bc$. Conversely, if $ac > bc$ and $c \in R^+$, then $ac - bc \in R^+$. Clearly $a \neq b$, for if $a = b$ then $ac = bc$ and $ac - bc \notin R^+$ by 4.10. Now either $a - b \in R^+$ or $-(a - b) = b - a \in R^+$ by 4.11. If $b - a \in R^+$, then $(b - a)c = bc - ac \in R^+$. This is not possible, since $bc - ac = -(ac - bc)$ and $ac - bc \in R^+$. We conclude that $a - b \in R^+$ and $a > b$. ∎

The proofs of 4.16, 4.17, and 4.19 are left as exercises.

If R is an ordered integral domain, then by the definition of $>$,

$$R^+ = \{a \in R \mid a > 0\}, \qquad R^- = \{a \in R \mid 0 > a\}.$$

The relations $\geq$, $<$, and $\leq$ are defined as usual in R. For example, $a < b$ iff $b > a$, and $a \leq b$ iff $a < b$ or $a = b$.

The *absolute value* of $a \in R$ is denoted by $|a|$ and is defined by:

4.20
$$|a| = \begin{cases} a & \text{if } a \geq 0, \\ -a & \text{if } a < 0. \end{cases}$$

According to 4.20, $|0| = 0$ whereas $|a| > 0$ if $a \neq 0$. Useful properties of the absolute value are:

4.21 $$|ab| = |a|\,|b|, \quad |a + b| \leq |a| + |b|.$$

The proof of 4.21 is left as an exercise.

An ordered integral domain R is said to be *well-ordered* iff R has a unity 1 and every nonempty subset of R^+ has a least element. By 1.21, $\mathbb{Z}$ is an example of a well-ordered integral domain.

If R is a well-ordered integral domain, then R^+ itself has a least element d. We claim that $d = 1$. Since $1 \in R^+$, either $d < 1$ or $d = 1$. If $d < 1$, then $d^2 < d$ by 4.18. However, this is contrary to the choice of d, since $d^2 \in R^+$. Thus, 1 is the least element of R^+.

Is there any well-ordered integral domain other than $\mathbb{Z}$? If R is a well-ordered integral domain, then ch $R = 0$ by 4.13 and $\mathbb{Z} \subset R$ by 3.20. Clearly $R^+ \cap \mathbb{Z} = \mathbb{Z}^+$ by our previous remarks. If $R^+ = \mathbb{Z}^+$, then $R = \mathbb{Z}$. Can R^+ be different from $\mathbb{Z}^+$? If it is, then $S = \{a \in R^+ \mid a \notin \mathbb{Z}^+\}$ has a least element $d > 1$. Now $d - 1 \in R^+$, and since $d - 1 < d$, $d - 1 \in \mathbb{Z}^+$. However, then $d = (d - 1) + 1 \in \mathbb{Z}^+$ contrary to assumption. We conclude that R^+ must equal $\mathbb{Z}^+$ and hence $R = \mathbb{Z}$. This proves the following result.

4.22   Theorem. The domain of integers $\mathbb{Z}$ is the only well-ordered integral domain.

Exercises

1. Prove that every proper subring of an ordered integral domain is ordered.

2. If S is a proper subring of an integral domain R, prove that the field of quotients of S is a subfield of the field of quotients of R. Give examples.

3. Let R be an integral domain which has a relation $>$ with the following properties: (i) $>$ is transitive; (ii) if $a > b$, then $a + c > b + c$ for all $c \in R$; (iii) if $a > b$, then $ac > bc$ for all $c \in R$ such that $c > 0$; (iv) if $a \neq b$, then either $a > b$ or $b > a$. Prove that R is an ordered integral domain.

4. Prove 4.14.

5. Prove 4.16.

6. Prove 4.17.

7. Prove 4.19.

8. Prove 4.21.

*9. Let S be an integral domain and R be a large subring of S (see Exercise 4 p. 71 for definitions). If R is ordered, prove that S is also ordered.

*10. A field F has two Abelian groups associated with it, $\{F; +\}$ and $\{F'; \cdot\}$, where $F' = \{x \in F \mid x \neq 0\}$. Prove that these groups are not isomorphic.

*11. Prove that the convolution ring C (defined on p. 56) is an integral domain without unity. The field of quotients of C has proved useful in solving certain problems of analysis. (See the book of Erdélyi, cited on p. 56, for details.)

*12. If $f \in C(\mathbb{R})$, the ring of continuous functions in $\mathbb{R}$, then let

$$\mathbb{R}_f = \{x \in \mathbb{R} \mid f(x) = 0\}.$$

Prove that $\mathbb{R}_f$ is a closed subset of $\mathbb{R}$ (i.e., if $y \in \mathbb{R}$, $y = \lim_{i \to \infty} x_i$ for some $x_i \in \mathbb{R}_f$, then $y \in \mathbb{R}_f$). Use this fact to describe the set of nondivisors of zero in $C(\mathbb{R})$.

chapter 5

Polynomial Rings

Given a C-ring R with unity, a mapping $R \xrightarrow{f} R$ is called a *polynomial function* iff there exists an integer $n \geq 0$ and $a_0, a_1, \ldots, a_n \in R$ such that

$$f(x) = a_0 + a_1 x + \ldots + a_n x^n \text{ for all } x \in R.$$

Since $f + g$ and fg are polynomial functions whenever f and g are, it is clear that the set $P(R)$ of all polynomial functions of R is a C-ring. In fact, $P(R)$ is a C-ring with unity. In the case of the real field $\mathbb{R}$, $P(\mathbb{R})$ is a subring of the ring $C(\mathbb{R})$ of continuous functions described in 3.6.

In this chapter we shall first study polynomials *per se* and then consider their relationship to polynomial functions.

I. Definitions

Although we shall limit our remarks in this chapter to C-rings with unity, it will be clear that much of what we say holds for any ring whatsoever.

Let R be a C-ring with unity 1 and $R[x]$ denote the set of all expressions of the form

$$f(x) = a_0 x^0 + a_1 x^1 + a_2 x^2 + \ldots + a_n x^n,$$

where n is a nonnegative integer and $a_0, a_1, \ldots, a_n \in R$. We think of x merely as a symbol, not an element of R, and of $f(x)$ as a formal sum of terms $a_0 x^0, a_1 x^1, a_2 x^2, \ldots, a_n x^n$—formal in the sense that the terms cannot actually be combined by addition in R. What we hope to do is to make

76

$R[x]$ into a ring containing R as a subring. It is important to keep in mind that we are not considering f as a function; rather, $f(x)$ is a new entity called a *polynomial in the symbol x with coefficients* $a_0, a_1, \ldots, a_n$ *in R*.

We can eliminate the symbol x from our discussion by considering the above polynomial $f(x)$ to be the ordered set

$$f = (a_0, a_1, a_2, \ldots, a_n)$$

of elements of R. If we do so, then $R[x]$ is the set of all finite ordered sets of elements of R. The reader may, if he wishes, carry through the remainder of this section in this context. However, our aims are attained in a more intuitive manner if we continue to use the symbol x.

It is necessary first of all to define equality in $R[x]$. The polynomials

$$f(x) = a_0 x^0 + a_1 x^1 + \ldots + a_n x^n$$

and

$$g(x) = b_0 x^0 + b_1 x^1 + \ldots + b_m x^m$$

are said to be equal, and we write $f(x) = g(x)$ as usual iff corresponding coefficients of f and g are equal and noncorresponding coefficients are zero. Thus, if $n \leq m$,

$$f(x) = g(x) \text{ iff } a_0 = b_0, \ a_1 = b_1, \ldots, a_n = b_n, \qquad b_i = 0 \text{ for all } i > n.$$

For example,

$$2x^0 + 0x^1 + (-4)x^2 = 2x^0 + 0x^1 + (-4)x^2 + 0x^3 + 0x^4$$

in $\mathbb{Z}[x]$.

The reader may easily verify that $=$ is an equivalence relation in $R[x]$, and as such partitions $R[x]$ into sets of "equal" elements. We shall denote each set by any one of the polynomials in the set—usually by the polynomial having the least number of terms. For example, the set

$$\{1x^0 + 3x^1, \ 1x^0 + 3x^1 + 0x^2, \ 1x^0 + 3x^1 + 0x^2 + 0x^3, \ldots\}$$

is usually denoted by $1x^0 + 3x^1$.

Operations of addition and multiplication are defined in $R[x]$ as if polynomials were sums of elements of R of the form $a_i x^i$. Thus, if

$$f(x) = a_0 x^0 + a_1 x^1 + \ldots + a_n x^n, \qquad g(x) = b_0 x^0 + b_1 x^1 + \ldots + b_m x^m,$$

with $n \leq m$, we define

5.1 $f(x) + g(x) = (a_0 + b_0)x^0 + (a_1 + b_1)x^1 + \ldots$
$$+ (a_n + b_n)x^n + b_{n+1}x^{n+1} + \ldots + b_m x^m.$$

It is clear from the definition that addition is associative and commutative in $R[x]$ and that the polynomial $0x^0$ is the additive identity. Furthermore, the polynomial $-f(x)$ defined by

$$-f(x) = (-a_0)x^0 + (-a_1)x^1 + \ldots + (-a_n)x^n$$

is evidently the additive inverse of $f(x)$. Therefore, $\{R[x]; +\}$ is an Abelian group.

Using the Σ-notation, the polynomial $f(x) = a_0 x^0 + a_1 x^1 + \ldots + a_n x^n$ may be expressed in the form

$$f(x) = \sum_{i=0}^{n} a_i x^i.$$

Multiplication is defined in $R[x]$ as follows:

5.2 $\displaystyle\sum_{i=0}^{n} a_i x^i \cdot \sum_{j=0}^{m} b_j x^j = \sum_{k=0}^{n+m} c_k x^k,$ where $c_k = \displaystyle\sum_{l=0}^{k} a_l b_{k-l}.$

In the above expression for c_k, we take $a_l = 0$ if $l > n$ and $b_{k-l} = 0$ if $k - l > m$. Thus, $c_0 = a_0 b_0$, $c_1 = a_0 b_1 + a_1 b_0$, $c_2 = a_0 b_2 + a_1 b_1 + a_2 b_0$, and so on. If x were an element of R, then 5.2 would give the correct product of the two polynomials.

Since

$$\sum_{i=0}^{k} a_i b_{k-i} = \sum_{j=0}^{k} b_j a_{k-j}$$

for each k, evidently multiplication is commutative in $R[x]$. Multiplication is also associative, since each side of the equation

$$\left(\sum_{i=0}^{n} a_i x^i \cdot \sum_{j=0}^{m} b_j x^j \right) \cdot \sum_{k=0}^{p} c_k x^k = \sum_{i=0}^{n} a_i x^i \cdot \left(\sum_{j=0}^{m} b_j x^j \cdot \sum_{k=0}^{p} c_k x^k \right)$$

equals

$$\sum_{l=0}^{n+m+p} d_l x^l, \quad \text{where} \quad d_l = \sum_{i=0}^{l} \sum_{j=0}^{l-i} a_i b_j c_{l-i-j}.$$

The polynomial $1x^0$ is the multiplicative identity according to 5.2. We leave it as an exercise to prove that multiplication is distributive with respect to addition. Hence, $R[x]$ is a C-ring with unity.

There is a natural mapping

$$R \xrightarrow{f} R[x] \text{ defined by } f(a) = ax^0.$$

Since

$$f(a + b) = (a + b)x^0 = ax^0 + bx^0 = f(a) + f(b),$$
$$f(ab) = (ab)x^0 = (ax^0)(bx^0) = f(a)f(b),$$

and ker $f = \{0\}$, f is a monomorphism. In other words, R is isomorphic to the subring $R_1 = \{ax^0 \mid a \in R\}$ of $R[x]$. Thus, R and R_1 are algebraically the same and we may identify each $a \in R$ with the polynomial ax^0. With this identification, R is a subring of $R[x]$ and each $f(x) \in R[x]$ has the form

$$f(x) = a_0 + a_1 x^1 + \ldots + a_n x^n.$$

We have proved the following result:

5.3   Theorem. If R is a C-ring with unity, then $R[x]$ is a C-ring with unity containing R as a subring.

It is conventional in $R[x]$ to replace $1x^1$ by x and $1x^k$ by x^k, to omit terms with zero coefficients, and to replace $(-a)x^k$ by $-ax^k$. For example, the polynomial $3 + (-2)x^1 + (-4)x^2 + 0x^3 + 1x^4 \in \mathbb{Z}[x]$ is written in the form $3 - 2x - 4x^2 + x^4$. With these conventions, $x^k \in R[x]$ for every $k \in \mathbb{Z}^+$, and x^k is the product of k x's. Furthermore, the polynomial $f(x) = a_0 + a_1 x + \ldots + a_n x^n$ actually is a sum of monomials $a_0, a_1 x, \ldots,$ $a_n x^n$ in $R[x]$, and each monomial $a_k x^k$ is the product of a_k and x^k in $R[x]$.

Each nonzero polynomial $f(x) = a_0 + a_1 x + \ldots + a_n x^n$ in $R[x]$ has a *degree*, defined to be the largest integer k for which the coefficient a_k is nonzero. We denote the degree of $f(x)$ by

$$\deg f(x).$$

In $\mathbb{Z}[x]$, for example,

$$\deg (3 - 5x + x^2) = 2, \qquad \deg 7 = 0, \qquad \deg (x^5 - 7x^6) = 6.$$

We shall not assign a degree to the polynomial 0.

If polynomial $f(x) = a_0 + a_1 x + \ldots + a_n x^n$ has degree n, then a_n is called the *leading coefficient* of $f(x)$. A polynomial with leading coefficient 1 is called *monic*. For example, $3 - 5x + x^2$, 1, and x^7 are monic polynomials in $\mathbb{Z}[x]$.

If $f(x) = a_0 + a_1 x + \ldots + a_n x^n$ and $g(x) = b_0 + b_1 x + \ldots + b_m x^m$, then

$$f(x) \cdot g(x) = a_0 b_0 + (a_0 b_1 + a_1 b_0)x + \ldots + a_n b_m x^{n+m}.$$

Therefore, if $\deg f(x) = n$ and $\deg g(x) = m$, then $\deg f(x) \cdot g(x) = n + m$ provided $a_n b_m \neq 0$. It might happen that $a_n b_m = 0$, in which case either $\deg f(x) \cdot g(x) < n + m$ or $f(x) \cdot g(x) = 0$. However, if R is an integral domain, then $a_n b_m \neq 0$. We state this result as follows:

5.4   Theorem. If R is an integral domain with unity, then $\deg f(x) \cdot g(x) = \deg f(x) + \deg g(x)$ for all nonzero $f(x), g(x) \in R[x]$.

With the aid of 5.4, we may easily prove the following result.

5.5   Theorem. Let R be a C-ring with unity. The polynomial ring $R[x]$ is an integral domain iff R is an integral domain.

The proof of 5.5 is left as an exercise.

A simple example of a polynomial ring which is not an integral domain is $\mathbb{Z}_4[x]$. Since

$$(2 + 2x) \cdot (2 + 2x + 2x^2) = 0$$

in $\mathbb{Z}_4[x]$, clearly $\mathbb{Z}_4[x]$ is not an integral domain.

The polynomial domains of the form $\mathbb{Z}_n[x]$ are easy to work with since they have only a finite number of polynomials of each degree. For example, in $\mathbb{Z}_2[x]$,

$$1, \quad x, \quad 1 + x, \quad x^2, \quad 1 + x^2, \quad x + x^2, \quad 1 + x + x^2$$

are all the nonzero polynomials of degree less than 3. In $\mathbb{Z}_n[x]$, there are n choices for each coefficient a_i, $0 \le i < k$, of the kth-degree polynomial

$$a_0 + a_1 x + \ldots + a_{k-1} x^{k-1} + a_k x^k$$

and $n - 1$ choices for a_k. Hence, there are $n^k \cdot (n - 1)$ polynomials in $\mathbb{Z}_n[x]$ of degree k. By allowing a_k also to be zero, we see that there are n^{k+1} polynomials of degree $\le k$ or of no degree.

Exercises

1. If R is a C-ring, prove the distributive law for $R[x]$.

2. Prove 5.5.

3. Describe the set of nondivisors of zero in $\mathbb{Z}_4[x]$.

4. If R is an ordered integral domain with unity, prove that $R[x]$ is also ordered. [*Hint:* Call a polynomial *positive* iff its leading coefficient is positive.]

5. If R is an integral domain with unity, prove that the group of units of $R[x]$ is simply the group of units of R. In particular, if F is a field, then the group of units of $F[x]$ is F', the set of nonzero elements of F.

6. Describe the group of units of $\mathbb{Z}_4[x]$. Generalize.

2. Polynomial Functions

If R is a commutative ring with unity, then there are associated with R the rings $R[x]$ of polynomials in x over R and $P(R)$ of polynomial functions of

R. There is a natural mapping

$$R[x] \xrightarrow{h} P(R)$$

defined as follows: $h(f(x)) = f$ for all $f(x) \in R[x]$ where, if $f(x) = a_0 + a_1 x + \ldots + a_n x^n$, then the mapping $R \xrightarrow{f} R$ is defined by

$$f(t) = a_0 + a_1 t + \ldots + a_n t^n \text{ for all } t \in R.$$

Thus, $f(x)$ is a polynomial in x over R whereas f is a polynomial function mapping R into R.

For example, consider the rings $\mathbb{Z}_3[x]$ and $P(\mathbb{Z}_3)$ and the mapping $\mathbb{Z}_3[x] \xrightarrow{h} P(\mathbb{Z}_3)$ described above. If $f(x) = 1 + x \in \mathbb{Z}_3[x]$, then $h(f(x)) = f \in P(\mathbb{Z}_3)$ is defined by:

$$f: \quad f(0) = 1 + 0 = 1, \quad f(1) = 1 + 1 = 2, \quad f(2) = 1 + 2 = 0.$$

If $g(x) = 2 + 2x + x^2 + x^3$, then $g \in P(\mathbb{Z}_3)$ is defined by

$$g: \quad g(0) = 2, \quad g(1) = 2 + 2 + 1 + 1 = 0,$$
$$g(2) = 2 + 2 \cdot 2 + 2^2 + 2^3 = 0.$$

The ring $\mathbb{Z}_3[x]$ has an infinite number of elements whereas the ring $P(\mathbb{Z}_3)$ has at most 27 elements.

To return to the subject of the first paragraph, the mapping h is a homomorphism by the very nature of the operations in $R[x]$ and $P(R)$. Thus, if

$$f(x) = \sum_{i=0}^{n} a_i x^i, \qquad g(x) = \sum_{j=0}^{m} b_j x^j,$$

then (assuming $n \leq m$ and $a_i = 0$ if $i > n$)

$$f(x) + g(x) = \sum_{i=0}^{m} (a_i + b_i) x^i.$$

On the other hand, the mapping $f + g$ is defined by

$$(f + g)(t) = f(t) + g(t) = \sum_{i=0}^{n} a_i t^i + \sum_{i=0}^{m} b_i t^i = \sum_{i=0}^{m} (a_i + b_i) t^i$$

for all $t \in R$. Hence, $h(f(x) + g(x)) = f + g$. It may be shown similarly that $h(f(x) \cdot g(x)) = f \cdot g$. Therefore, h is a homomorphism. Since $P(R)$ is the set of all polynomial functions of R, evidently h is an epimorphism.

Clearly the mapping $R[x] \xrightarrow{h} P(R)$ is not always an isomorphism; for in the example $\mathbb{Z}_3[x] \xrightarrow{h} P(\mathbb{Z}_3)$, h maps an infinite set into a finite set and hence is not a bijection. Therefore, $\ker h$ must be a proper ideal in this example. We easily verify that $f(x) = x^3 + 2x$ is in ker h, since

$$f(0) = 0, \qquad f(1) = 1^3 + 2 \cdot 1 = 0, \qquad f(2) = 2^3 + 2 \cdot 2 = 0.$$

Thus, f maps every element of $\mathbb{Z}_3$ into 0 and is therefore the zero mapping.

The mapping $\mathbb{Z}[x] \xrightarrow{h} P(\mathbb{Z})$ is an isomorphism, for if $f(x)$ is a nonzero polynomial then $f(t) \neq 0$ for some $t \in \mathbb{Z}$. We shall prove this fact in Section 4. Hence, f is not the zero mapping of $\mathbb{Z}$. We conclude that ker $h = \{0\}$.

Exercises

1. Prove that $P(\mathbb{Z}_3)$ has exactly 27 elements (i.e., every mapping of $\mathbb{Z}_3$ into $\mathbb{Z}_3$ is a polynomial function). Generalize.

2. Describe the kernel of the epimorphism $\mathbb{Z}_2[x] \xrightarrow{h} P(\mathbb{Z}_2)$.

3. If R is the ring $\mathbb{Z}_2 \times \mathbb{Z}_2$ with four elements, describe the kernel of the epimorphism $R[x] \xrightarrow{h} P(R)$.

4. Describe the kernel of the epimorphism $\mathbb{Z}_4[x] \xrightarrow{h} P(\mathbb{Z}_4)$.

3. Polynomial Domain of a Field

We are all familiar with the division process as applied to polynomials with real coefficients. For example, we divide

$$f(x) = 2x^3 - 3x^2 + 2x - 5 \quad \text{by} \quad g(x) = x^2 - 7x + 3$$

as follows:

$$
\begin{array}{r}
2x + 11 \\
x^2 - 7x + 3 \overline{\smash{\big)}\, 2x^3 - 3x^2 + 2x - 5} \\
\underline{2x^3 - 14x^2 + 6x} \\
11x^2 - 4x - 5 \\
\underline{11x^2 - 77x + 33} \\
73x - 38
\end{array}
$$

Hence

$$\frac{2x^3 - 3x^2 + 2x - 5}{x^2 - 7x + 3} = 2x + 11 + \frac{73x - 38}{x^2 - 7x + 3}.$$

We say that $2x + 11$ is the quotient and $73x - 38$ is the remainder on dividing $f(x)$ by $g(x)$. Another form of the result, which avoids fractions, is given below.

$$2x^3 - 3x^2 + 2x - 5 = (2x + 11)(x^2 - 7x + 3) + (73x - 38).$$

Let us prove that this division process holds in any polynomial domain over a field.

5.6 Division process. Let $F[x]$ be the polynomial domain of a field F. For any nonzero $f(x), g(x) \in F[x]$ there exist unique polynomials $q(x)$ and $r(x)$ in $F[x]$ such that

$$f(x) = q(x)g(x) + r(x) \text{ and either } r(x) = 0 \text{ or } \deg r(x) < \deg g(x).$$

Outline of proof: Let

$$S = \{f(x) - h(x)g(x) \mid h(x) \in F[x]\}.$$

If $0 \in S$, then $f(x) = q(x)g(x)$ for some $q(x) \in F[x]$ and the theorem is proved with $r(x) = 0$. If $0 \notin S$, then select an element $r(x) \in S$ of least degree. Now $r(x) = f(x) - q(x)g(x)$ for some $q(x) \in F[x]$. We claim that $\deg r(x) < \deg g(x)$. For if $\deg r(x) = m \geq \deg g(x) = n$, say $r(x) = cx^m +$ terms of lower degree and $g(x) = dx^n +$ terms of lower degree, then $r(x) - cd^{-1}x^{m-n}g(x) = r'(x)$, a polynomial of lower degree than $r(x)$. However,

$$r'(x) = f(x) - [q(x) + cd^{-1}x^{m-n}]g(x) \in S,$$

contrary to the choice of $r(x)$. Hence, $\deg r(x) < \deg g(x)$.

We leave the proof of the uniqueness of $q(x)$ and $r(x)$ as an exercise. ∎

The polynomial $q(x)$ is called the *quotient* and $r(x)$ the *remainder* on dividing $f(x)$ by $g(x)$.

The concepts of factor and multiple have the same meaning for $F[x]$ as they do for $\mathbb{Z}$. Thus, $f(x)$ is a *factor* (or, *divisor*) of $g(x)$, and we write

$$f(x) \mid g(x)$$

iff $g(x) = f(x)q(x)$ for some $q(x) \in F[x]$. If $f(x) \mid g(x)$, then $g(x)$ is called a *multiple* of $f(x)$. The gcd and lcm of two polynomials are defined as for two integers.

A polynomial $p(x)$ of $F[x]$ is called *prime* (or, *irreducible*) iff $\deg p(x) > 0$ and whenever $f(x) \mid p(x)$, either $f(x)$ is a unit or $f(x) = cp(x)$ for some unit $c \in F[x]$. In words, a polynomial is prime iff it has positive degree and only trivial factors.

If $f(x) \in F[x]$, $\deg f(x) > 0$, then $f(x)$ has a factor $p_1(x)$ of minimum positive degree. Since any factor of $p_1(x)$ is also a factor of $f(x)$, clearly $p_1(x)$ is a prime. Thus,

$$f(x) = p_1(x)f_1(x)$$

for some $f_1(x) \in F[x]$. If $f_1(x) \in F$, then $f(x)$ is a prime. Otherwise, if $\deg f_1(x) > 0$, then $f_1(x)$ has a factor $p_2(x)$ of minimum positive degree.

Clearly $p_2(x)$ is a prime and

$$f(x) = p_1(x)p_2(x)f_2(x)$$

for some $f_2(x) \in F[x]$. Continuing this process, we eventually obtain (in at most $\deg f(x)$ steps) a factorization of $f(x)$ into primes.

$$f(x) = p_1(x)p_2(x) \ldots p_k(x).$$

This proves part of the following:

5.7   Theorem. If F is a field, then every polynomial in $F[x]$ of positive degree has a unique factorization into primes.

By uniqueness, we mean that if

$$f(x) = p_1(x)p_2(x) \ldots p_k(x) \quad \text{and} \quad f(x) = q_1(x)q_1(x) \ldots q_m(x)$$

are factorizations of $f(x)$ into primes, then $k = m$ and after reordering the q_i's, $q_i(x) = c_i p_i(x)$, $i = 1, \ldots, k$, for some units $c_i \in F$.

The proof of the uniqueness in 5.7 will be given in Chapter 7.

Each $f(x) \in F[x]$ generates a principal ideal

$$f(x)F[x] = \{f(x)g(x) \mid g(x) \in F[x]\}.$$

Clearly $cf(x)$ and $f(x)$ generate the same ideal if c is a unit of F, i.e., if $c \in F'$. Conversely, if

$$f(x)F[x] = g(x)F[x] \neq \{0\},$$

then

$$f(x) = g(x)h(x) \quad \text{and} \quad g(x) = f(x)q(x) \text{ for some } h(x), q(x) \in F[x].$$

Hence,

$$f(x) = f(x)q(x)h(x) \quad \text{and} \quad 1 = q(x)h(x),$$

i.e., $q(x)$ and $h(x)$ are units of $F[x]$. Thus, $q(x) = c \in F'$ and $g(x) = cf(x)$. We conclude that among all the generators of the proper ideal $f(x)F[x]$, there is a unique monic polynomial $c^{-1}f(x)$ where c is the leading coefficient of $f(x)$.

If $f(x), g(x) \in F[x]$, then

$$f(x) \mid g(x) \quad \text{iff} \quad f(x)F[x] \supset g(x)F[x].$$

We leave the proof of this as an exercise.

Are there any ideals of $F[x]$ other than the principal ideals? If A is a proper ideal of $F[x]$, then if it is principal it clearly is generated by an element of least degree. Whether or not A is principal, it does have an element $f(x)$ of minimum degree by the well-ordering of $\mathbb{Z}$. If $g(x) \in A$ also, then we can divide $g(x)$ by $f(x)$ to obtain $g(x) = f(x)q(x) + r(x)$, where either $r(x) = 0$ or $\deg r(x) < \deg f(x)$. Since $r(x) = g(x) - f(x)q(x) \in A$ and

$f(x)$ is an element of A of minimum degree, evidently $r(x) = 0$. Thus, $g(x) = f(x)q(x) \in f(x) F[x]$. We conclude that $A = f(x)F[x]$. This proves the following result:

5.8 Theorem. Every ideal of the polynomial domain of a field is principal.

This theorem points up an important common property of $\mathbb{Z}$ and $F[x]$: they are both *principal ideal domains*. As we shall see, this will mean that they have similar factorization properties.

If F is a field and $f(x), g(x)$ are nonzero elements of $F[x]$, then

$$A = f(x)F[x], \qquad B = g(x)F[x]$$

are nonzero ideals of $F[x]$. The ideal $A \cap B$ is also nonzero, since $f(x)g(x) \in A \cap B$. Hence,

5.9
$$f(x)F[x] \cap g(x) F[x] = m(x)F[x]$$

for some monic $m(x) \in F[x]$. Since $m(x) \in A \cap B$, $m(x) = f(x)a(x)$ and $m(x) = g(x)b(x)$ for some $a(x), b(x) \in F[x]$. That is, $m(x)$ is a common multiple of $f(x)$ and $g(x)$. Actually, $m(x)$ is a least common multiple; for if $h(x)$ is a multiple of both $f(x)$ and of $g(x)$, then $h(x) \in A \cap B$ and therefore $h(x) = m(x)q(x)$ for some $q(x) \in F[x]$. Thus, $m(x)$ defined by 5.9 is the unique monic *least common multiple* (lcm) of $f(x)$ and $g(x)$. The notation commonly used for the monic lcm is

$$m(x) = [f(x), g(x)].$$

The sum $A + B = \{a(x) + b(x) \mid a(x) \in A, b(x) \in B\}$ of ideals A and B is also an ideal of $F[x]$. Hence,

5.10
$$f(x)F[x] + g(x)F[x] = d(x)F[x]$$

for some monic $d(x) \in F[x]$. Since $d(x) \in f(x)F[x] + g(x)F[x]$,

5.11
$$d(x) = f(x)a(x) + g(x)b(x)$$

for some $a(x), b(x) \in F[x]$. If $h(x) \mid f(x)$ and $h(x) \mid g(x)$, then $h(x) \mid d(x)$ by 5.11. On the other hand, $f(x)F[x] \subset d(x)F[x]$ and $g(x)F[x] \subset d(x)F[x]$, so that that $d(x) \mid f(x)$ and $d(x) \mid g(x)$. We conclude that $d(x)$ is the unique monic *greatest common divisor* (gcd) of $f(x)$ and $g(x)$. The notation commonly used for the monic gcd is

$$d(x) = (f(x), g(x)).$$

A polynomial $p(x)$ in $F[x]$ of positive degree is prime iff

$$\text{either } (p(x), f(x)) = p(x) \quad \text{or} \quad (p(x), f(x)) = 1$$

for all nonzero $f(x) \in F[x]$. In the language of ideals, $p(x)$ is prime iff

$$\text{either } f(x)F[x] \subset p(x)F[x] \quad \text{or} \quad f(x)F[x] + p(x)F[x] = F[x]$$

for every $f(x) \in F[x]$.

An ideal A of a C-ring R is said to be *maximal* iff $A \neq R$ and R is the only ideal of R properly containing A. If A is a maximal ideal and B is any ideal of R, then $A + B$ is also an ideal of R. Since $A + B \supset A$, either $B \subset A$ and $A + B = A$ or $B \not\subset A$ and $A + B = R$. Conversely, if an ideal A of R has the property that

$$\text{either } B \subset A \text{ or } A + B = R \text{ for every ideal } B \text{ of } R,$$

then A is a maximal ideal of R. For if A is not maximal, then $A \subset B \subset R$ for some B different from A and R, and $B \not\subset A$, $A + B = B \neq R$.

An example of a maximal ideal is $p(x)F[x]$, where $p(x)$ is a prime in $F[x]$, the polynomial domain of a field F. This fact follows from our discussion above. It is also clear that if $f(x)F[x]$ is a maximal ideal, then $f(x)$ is a prime. Thus, we have the following result.

5.12   Theorem. If F is a field, then $p(x)F[x]$ is a maximal ideal of $F[x]$ iff $p(x)$ is a prime polynomial.

The same line of reasoning proves that $p\mathbb{Z}$ is a maximal ideal of $\mathbb{Z}$ iff p is a prime number. We recall that $\mathbb{Z}/p\mathbb{Z}$ is a field iff p is prime. A similar result for $F[x]$ is as follows:

5.13   Theorem. If F is a field, then $F[x]/p(x)F[x]$ is a field iff $p(x)$ is a prime polynomial.

Outline of proof: If $p(x)$ is prime and $f(x) \notin p(x)F[x]$, then $p(x)g(x) + f(x)h(x) = 1$ for some $g(x), h(x) \in F[x]$ and

$$(f(x) + p(x)F[x]) \cdot (h(x) + p(x)F[x]) = 1 + p(x)F[x].$$

Thus, $h(x) + p(x)F[x]$ is the multiplicative inverse of $f(x) + p(x)F[x]$ in $F[x]/p(x)F[x]$. Hence, $F[x]/p(x)F[x]$ is a field. The converse is proved similarly. ∎

For example, $p(x) = x^2 + x + 1$ is a prime in $\mathbb{Z}_2[x]$, since neither x nor $x + 1$ is a factor of $p(x)$. Therefore, $R = \mathbb{Z}_2[x]/p(x)\mathbb{Z}_2[x]$ is a field. It will be shown presently that R has precisely four elements—namely, $p(x)\mathbb{Z}_2[x]$, $1 + p(x)\mathbb{Z}_2[x]$, $x + p(x)\mathbb{Z}_2[x]$, and $x + 1 + p(x)\mathbb{Z}_2[x]$. Thus, there exists a field with four elements, although 4 is not a prime. Clearly R is not isomorphic to $\mathbb{Z}_4$ since $\mathbb{Z}_4$ is not a field.

Exercises

1. Complete the proof of 5.6.

2. Prove that if $f(x), g(x) \in F[x]$, then $f(x) \,|\, g(x)$ iff $f(x)F[x] \supset g(x)F[x]$.

3. Complete the proof of 5.13.

4. If every ideal of a C-ring R is principal and A is a proper ideal of R, prove that every ideal of R/A is principal. Give examples.

5. Euclid's algorithm (Exercise 12, p. 19) may be used to find the gcd of two polynomials. Use it to find the gcd of the following pairs of polynomials in $\mathbb{Q}[x]$:

    (a) $3x^3 - x^2 - x - 1,\ 2x^2 + x - 3$;

    (b) $x^4 + x^3 + 4x^2 + x + 3,\ 2x^3 + 3x^2 + 7x + 3$.

6. Find the gcd of the following pairs of polynomials in $\mathbb{Z}_3[x]$:

    (a) $x^4 + x^3 + 2x^2 + x + 2,\ 2x^4 + x^2 + x + 1$;

    (b) $2x^5 + 1,\ x^3 + 2$.

4. Zeros of a Polynomial

If $R[x]$ is the polynomial domain of a commutative ring with unity R and $f(x) \in R[x]$, then an element t of R is called *zero* of $f(x)$ iff $f(t) = 0$.

For example, if $f(x) = x^2 + 1 \in \mathbb{Z}_2[x]$, then 1 is a zero of $f(x)$ since $f(1) = 1^2 + 1 = 0$. As another example $f(x) = x^3 - 4x \in \mathbb{Q}[x]$ has zeros 0, 2, and -2, since $f(0) = 0$, $f(2) = 0$, and $f(-2) = (-2)^3 - 4 \cdot (-2) = 0$.

5.14   *Remainder theorem.* If $F[x]$ is the polynomial domain of a field F and $f(x) \in F[x]$, $t \in F$, then the remainder on dividing $f(x)$ by $x - t$ is $f(t)$.

Proof: By 5.6, $f(x) = q(x)(x - t) + r(x)$, where $r(x) = 0$ or deg $r(x)$ $<$ deg $(x - t)$, for some $q(x), r(x) \in F[x]$. Clearly $r(x) = k \in F$ in either case. Hence, $f(t) = q(t)(t - t) + k$ and $k = f(t)$.   ■

5.15   *Factor theorem.* If $F[x]$ is the polynomial domain of a field F and $f(x) \in F[x]$, $t \in F$, then $(x - t) \,|\, f(x)$ iff $f(t) = 0$.

The proof of 5.15 is left as an exercise.

Consider, for example, the polynomial $f(x) = x^4 + 3x^2 + 2 \in \mathbb{Z}_5[x]$. Since the field $\mathbb{Z}_5$ has only five elements, it is an easy matter to find the zeros of $f(x)$ by computing $f(0),\ f(1), \dots, f(4)$. Thus, $f(0) = 2, f(1) = 1$,

$f(2) = 0$, $f(3) = 0$, and $f(4) = 1$. We conclude that 2 and 3 are the zeros of $f(x)$. By the factor theorem, $x - 2(= x + 3)$ and $x - 3(= x + 2)$ are first-degree factors of $f(x)$. We may readily show that

$$x^4 + 3x^2 + 2 = (x + 2)(x + 3)(x^2 + 2).$$

It is convenient to call a polynomial in $\mathbb{Z}[x]$ an *integral polynomial*, one in $\mathbb{Q}[x]$ a *rational polynomial*, and one in $\mathbb{R}[x]$ a *real polynomial*. Evidently

$$\mathbb{Z}[x] \subset \mathbb{Q}[x] \subset \mathbb{R}[x].$$

Each rational polynomial is a rational number times an integral polynomial. For example,

$$\tfrac{1}{3}x^3 - \tfrac{5}{2}x^2 + x - \tfrac{13}{6} = \tfrac{1}{6}(2x^3 - 15x^2 + 6x - 13).$$

Since $f(x)$ and $cf(x)$, $c \neq 0$, have the same zeros, we see that the zeros of a rational polynomial may be found by finding the zeros of an associated integral polynomial. The rational zeros of an integral polynomial may be found as follows.

5.16 Rational zero theorem. Let $f(x) = a_0 + a_1 x + \ldots + a_n x^n \in \mathbb{Z}[x]$ have degree $n > 0$ and $c,d \in \mathbb{Z}$ with $(c,d) = 1$. If c/d is a zero of $f(x)$, then necessarily $c \mid a_0$ and $d \mid a_n$.

Outline of proof: If $f(c/d) = 0$, then $d^n f(c/d) = 0$ or

$$a_0 d^n + a_1 c d^{n-1} + \ldots + a_{n-1}c^{n-1}d + a_n c^n = 0.$$

It is easily seen from this equation that $c \mid a_0 d^n$ and $d \mid a_n c^n$. Since $(c,d) = 1$, we have $c \mid a_0$ and $d \mid a_n$. ∎

For example, if
$$f(x) = 2x^3 - 5x^2 - 2x + 15,$$

then a rational zero r of $f(x)$, if one exists, must have the form

$$r = \frac{c}{d}, \qquad (c,d) = 1, \qquad \text{where} \quad c \mid 15 \text{ and } d \mid 2.$$

Since ± 1 and ± 2 are the only factors of 2 and ± 1, ± 3, ± 5, and ± 15 are the only factors of 15, the only possible rational zeros of $f(x)$ are

$$1, \quad 3, \quad 5, \quad 15, \quad \tfrac{1}{2}, \quad \tfrac{3}{2}, \quad \tfrac{5}{2}, \quad \tfrac{15}{2}$$

and their negatives. By computing $f(r)$ for each of these rational numbers, we can determine which are actually zeros of $f(x)$. Since $|2t^3|$ is much larger than $|-5t^2 - 2t + 15|$ if $|t| \geq 5$, clearly none of ± 5, ± 15, and $\pm \tfrac{15}{2}$ is a zero. We easily compute $f(1) = 10$, $f(-1) = 10$, $f(3) = 18$, and

$f(-3) = -78$. Hence, $f(x)$ has no integral zeros. It may be shown that $-\frac{3}{2}$ is a rational zero of $f(x)$—in fact, that it is the only rational zero. Hence, $x + \frac{3}{2}$, or on multiplying by $\frac{2}{3}$, $2x + 3$ is a first-degree factor of $f(x)$, and we have

$$2x^3 - 5x^2 - 2x + 15 = (2x + 3)(x^2 - 4x + 5).$$

As the above example indicates, all the rational zeros of an integral polynomial can be found by a straightforward, if sometimes tedious, process. Consequently, all the first-degree factors of a rational polynomial can be obtained.

The rational zero theorem may be used to prove that certain real numbers involving roots of rational numbers are irrational. For example, if $n \in \mathbb{Z}^+$ is not a perfect square of an integer, then $\sqrt{n}$ is irrational. For $\sqrt{n}$ is a zero of the integral polynomial

$$x^2 - n$$

whose rational zeros, if any, must be integers by 5.16; but if k is an integral zero of $x^2 - n$, then $k^2 = n$, contrary to our assumption that n is not a perfect square.

A polynomial in $F[x]$, F a field, cannot have an unlimited number of zeros, according to the following theorem.

5.17   Theorem. If F is a field, then every nonzero $f(x) \in F[x]$ has at most deg $f(x)$ zeros.

Outline of proof: If deg $f(x) = 0$, then $f(x) = a \neq 0$ and $f(x)$ has no zeros. If deg $f(x) = 1$, say $f(x) = a + bx$, then $f(x)$ has one zero, namely $-a/b$. Assume that every polynomial of degree n has at most n zeros and let $f(x)$ be a polynomial of degree $n + 1$. If r is a zero of $f(x)$, then $f(x) = (x - r)\,q(x)$ for some $q(x) \in F[x]$ of degree n. Since $q(x)$ has at most n zeros, $f(x)$ has at most n + 1 zeros.   ∎

We may now answer the question as to when the mapping

$$F[x] \xrightarrow{\ h\ } P(F) \text{ defined by } h(f(x)) = f \text{ for all } f(x) \in F[x],$$

F a field, is an isomorphism. Evidently a nonzero polynomial $f(x)$ is in ker h iff $f(t) = 0$ for all $t \in F$. If $\#(F) = \infty$, then no such polynomial $f(x)$ exists by 5.17. However, if F is a finite field with n elements $a_1, a_2, \ldots, a_n$, then

$$f(x) = (x - a_1) \cdot (x - a_2) \cdot \ldots \cdot (x - a_n)$$

is in ker h since $f(t) = 0$ for all $t \in F$. Thus, we have the following result:

5.18   Theorem. If F is a field, then the mapping $F[x] \xrightarrow{\ h\ } P(F)$ of $F[x]$ into the ring of polynomial functions of F is an isomorphism iff $\#(F) = \infty$.

In view of this theorem, the domains of polynomials and polynomial functions over a field F are not algebraically distinguishable if F is an infinite field—for example, if ch $F = 0$.

Theorems 5.17 and 5.18 are not in general valid for every commutative ring R with unity. For example, the first-degree polynomial $2x$ has two zeros in $\mathbb{Z}_4$, namely 0 and 2. It is possible to give an example of a ring R with unity such that some polynomials in $R[x]$ have an infinite number of zeros. Thus, for example, every element of a Boolean ring (3.7) is a zero of the polynomial $x^2 + x$.

Exercises

1. Find the zeros of each of the following polynomials in $\mathbb{Z}_2[x]$:

(a) $x^2 + 1$,
(b) $x^3 + x^2 + x + 1$,
(c) $x^{19} + x^{13} + x^7 + x^3$.

2. Find the zeros of each of the following polynomials in $\mathbb{Z}_3[x]$:

(a) $x^2 + x + 1$,   (b) $2x + 2$,
(c) $x^5 + 2x$,   (d) $x^6 + x^4 + x + 1$.

3. Find the zeros of each of the following polynomials in $\mathbb{Z}_{11}[x]$:

(a) $5x + 3$,
(b) $2x^2 + 3x + 8$,
(c) $x^6 + 2$.

4. Find the zeros of each of the following polynomials in $\mathbb{Q}[x]$:

(a) $2x^2 + x - 1$,
(b) $x^3 - x^2 - x - 2$,
(c) $x^5 - 1$,
(d) $x^{17} + 1$,
(e) $3x^3 + 5x^2 + 4x - 2$,
(f) $6x^3 - 11x^2 + 7x - 6$,
(g) $8x^4 + 20x^3 + 10x^2 - 5x - 3$,
(h) $18x^4 + 27x^3 - 20x^2 - 20x + 16$.

5. Do Theorems 5.17 and 5.18 hold if F is an integral domain with unity? Explain your answer.

6. If $n \in \mathbb{Z}^+$ is not the cube of an integer, prove that $\sqrt[3]{n}$ is an irrational number.

7. Prove 5.15.

8. If $kx - 1$ is a factor of $a_0 + a_1x + \ldots + a_nx^n$ in $\mathbb{Z}[x]$, prove that k is a zero of $a_n + a_{n-1}x + \ldots + a_0x^n$, and conversely.

9. Show that the zeros of the quadratic polynomial $ax^2 + bx + c \in \mathbb{R}[x]$ are given by the usual *quadratic formula*

$$\frac{-b \pm \sqrt{b^2 - 4ac}}{2a}$$

if the *discriminant* $b^2 - 4ac$ is nonnegative. What can be said about the polynomial $ax^2 + bx + c$ if $b^2 - 4ac < 0$?

10. If $ax^2 + bx + c \in \mathbb{Z}[x]$, give conditions on $b^2 - 4ac$ in order that $ax^2 + bx + c$ be prime in $\mathbb{Q}[x]$.

11. If F is a field and $f(x) \in F[x]$, $\deg f(x) = 2$ or 3, prove that $f(x)$ is prime iff $f(x)$ has no zeros.

12. Find all prime polynomials of degree 2 and 3 in $\mathbb{Z}_2[x]$, in $\mathbb{Z}_3[x]$.

13. Prove that $\sin 10°$ is irrational by showing that it is a zero of the integral polynomial $8x^3 - 6x + 1$. Since this polynomial is prime in $\mathbb{Q}[x]$ and is of the third degree, its real zeros may be shown to be nonconstructible numbers. That is, $\sin 10°$ is nonconstructible. Using this fact, prove that a 30°-angle cannot be trisected by use of a compass and straight edge. [*Hint:* $\sin 3A = 3 \sin A - 4 \sin^3 A$ for every angle A.]

THEORETICAL PROJECT 1

For each nonzero rational polynomial $g(x)$, there exists a positive rational number r such that
$$g(x) = rf(x)$$
for some integral polynomial $f(x)$. Furthermore, r can be selected so that the coefficients of $f(x)$ are relatively prime; i.e.,
$$f(x) = a_0 + a_1 x + \ldots + a_n x^n, \qquad (a_0, a_1, \ldots, a_n) = 1.$$
Clearly $g(x)$ is prime in $\mathbb{Q}[x]$ iff $f(x)$ is. Complete the proof of the famous

5.19 *Lemma of Gauss.* Let $f(x)$ be an integral polynomial of positive degree having relatively prime coefficients. If $f(x)$ is nonprime in $\mathbb{Q}[x]$, then $f(x)$ can be factored in a nontrivial way in $\mathbb{Z}[x]$.

Outline of proof: By assumption, $f(x) = g_1(x)h_1(x)$ for some $g_1(x), h_1(x) \in \mathbb{Q}[x]$ of positive degrees. By our remarks above,
$$g_1(x) = rg(x), \qquad h_1(x) = sh(x)$$

for some $r,s \in \mathbb{Q}^+$ and some $g(x),h(x) \in \mathbb{Z}[x]$ having relatively prime coefficients. Thus,

$$f(x) = rsg(x)h(x).$$

We wish to prove that $rs = 1$, which may be accomplished by showing that the polynomial $g(x)h(x)$ has relatively prime coefficients. Do you see why? If

$$g(x) = \sum_{i=0}^{m} a_i x^i, \qquad h(x) = \sum_{i=0}^{n} b_i x^i,$$

then

$$g(x)h(x) = \sum_{i=0}^{m+n} c_i x^i, \qquad \text{where} \quad c_i = \sum_{j=0}^{i} a_j b_{i-j}.$$

For each prime number p, there exists some least integer $k \geq 0$ such that $p \nmid a_k$, and some least integer $t \geq 0$ such that $p \nmid b_t$. (Why?) Then $p \nmid c_{k+t}$, since it is a factor of each term of $\sum a_j b_{k+t-j}$ with one exception. Therefore, no prime number is a factor of all the c_i, and so on.

Exercise. Prove that $x^4 - 2x^2 + 9$ is prime in $\mathbb{Q}[x]$.

THEORETICAL PROJECT 2

Another famous result on integral polynomials is the following:

5.20 Eisenstein's theorem. If

$$f(x) = c_0 + c_1 x + \ldots + c_n x^n$$

is an integral polynomial of degree $n > 0$ and p is a prime number such that

$$p \mid c_i, \quad i = 0,1, \ldots, n-1, \quad p \nmid c_n, \quad p^2 \nmid c_0$$

then $f(x)$ is prime in $\mathbb{Q}[x]$.

Outline of proof: By 5.19, we need only show that $f(x)$ is not a product of two integral polynomials of positive degree. Assume that $f(x) = g(x)h(x)$, where $g(x),h(x) \in \mathbb{Z}[x]$ and

$$f(x) = \sum_{i=0}^{n} c_i x^i, \qquad g(x) = \sum_{i=0}^{k} a_i x^i, \qquad h(x) = \sum_{i=0}^{m} b_i x^i.$$

Then $k + m = n$ and

$$c_i = \sum_{j=0}^{i} a_j b_{i-j}, \qquad i = 0,1, \ldots, n.$$

Now $c_0 = a_0 b_0$, so that $p \mid a_0$ and $p \nmid b_0$ (or, vice versa). Also, $c_n = a_k b_m$, so that $p \nmid a_k$. Let j be the least integer such that $p \nmid a_j$. Since p is a factor of each term of $c_j = a_0 b_j + a_1 b_{j-1} + \ldots + a_j b_0$ except the last, $p \nmid c_j$. Therefore, $j = n$, and $\deg g(x) = n$.

Using 5.20, it is an easy matter to give examples of prime polynomials in $\mathbb{Q}[x]$ of every degree. For example,

$$x^n + 2 \text{ is prime in } \mathbb{Q}[x] \text{ for every } n \in \mathbb{Z}^+.$$

Thus, 2 is a factor of every coefficient of $x^n + 2$ except the leading coefficient, and 2^2 is not a factor of the constant term. You construct several more examples.

5. Field of Quotients of a Polynomial Domain

If D is an integral domain with unity, then $D[x]$ is also an integral domain with unity and, as such, has a field of quotients according to Section 2 of Chapter 4. We denote the field of quotients of $D[x]$ by $D(x)$:

$$D(x) = \left\{ \frac{f(x)}{g(x)} \;\middle|\; f(x), g(x) \in D[x], g(x) \neq 0 \right\}.$$

The elements $f(x)/g(x)$ of $D(x)$ are called *rational expressions* in x. By definition,

$$\frac{f(x)}{g(x)} = \frac{a(x)}{b(x)} \quad \text{iff} \quad f(x)b(x) = g(x)a(x).$$

The integral domain D also has a field of quotients $F = \{a/b \mid a,b \in D, b \neq 0\}$. Since $D \subset D[x]$, it is clear that we can consider F as a subfield of $D(x)$. If we do so, then it is evident that

$$D(x) = F(x).$$

For, in the first place, $D(x) \subset F(x)$ since $D \subset F$. On the other hand, if $f(x), g(x) \in F[x]$, then $cf(x), dg(x) \in D[x]$ for some nonzero $c, d \in D$ and

$$\frac{f(x)}{g(x)} = \frac{d[cf(x)]}{c[dg(x)]} \in D(x).$$

Hence, $F(x) \subset D(x)$.

In particular, we have

$$\mathbb{Q}(x) = \mathbb{Z}(x)$$

by our remarks above. Thus, for example,

$$\frac{\frac{1}{2}x^2 - \frac{2}{3}x + 4}{\frac{1}{6}x - \frac{2}{5}} = \frac{15x^2 - 20x + 120}{5x - 12}.$$

If F is a field and $f(x)/g(x) \in F(x)$, with $f(x)$, $g(x) \in F[x]$ and deg $f(x) \geq$ deg $g(x)$, then we can divide $f(x)$ by $g(x)$ obtaining

$$f(x) = q(x)g(x) + r(x), \quad \text{where} \quad r(x) = 0 \text{ or deg } r(x) < \text{deg } g(x),$$

for some $q(x), r(x) \in F[x]$. Hence,

5.21
$$\frac{f(x)}{g(x)} = q(x) + \frac{r(x)}{g(x)}.$$

It is evident that if $f(x)$ and $g(x)$ are relatively prime, i.e., $(f(x), g(x)) = 1$, and deg $g(x) > 0$, then $r(x) \neq 0$ and $(r(x), g(x)) = 1$. In this case, $r(x)/g(x)$ is called a *proper rational expression*. By 5.21, every rational expression is either a polynomial or a sum of a polynomial and a proper rational expression.

Every rational expression of the form

$$\frac{f(x)}{g(x)h(x)}, \quad (g(x), h(x)) = 1,$$

can be resolved into a sum of *partial fractions*

5.22
$$\frac{f(x)}{g(x)h(x)} = \frac{f_1(x)}{g(x)} + \frac{f_2(x)}{h(x)}$$

for some $f_1(x), f_2(x) \in F[x]$.

The proof of 5.22 is quite simple. Since $(g(x), h(x)) = 1$,

$$g(x)u(x) + h(x)v(x) = 1$$

for some $u(x), v(x) \in F[x]$. Hence,

$$f(x)g(x)u(x) + f(x)h(x)v(x) = f(x).$$

On dividing each member of this equation by $g(x)h(x)$, we obtain 5.22. ∎

A proper rational expression of the form $f(x)/[g(x)]^n$ can be resolved into a sum of partial fractions as follows:

5.23
$$\frac{f(x)}{[g(x)]^n} = \frac{f_1(x)}{g(x)} + \frac{f_2(x)}{[g(x)]^2} + \ldots + \frac{f_n(x)}{[g(x)]^n},$$

where each $f_i(x)$ is either 0 or a degree less than that of $g(x)$.

The proof of 5.23 is by induction. We may divide $f(x)$ by $g(x)$, obtaining

$$f(x) = q(x)g(x) + f_n(x), \quad \text{deg } f_n(x) < \text{deg } g(x).$$

Hence

$$\frac{f(x)}{[g(x)]^n} = \frac{q(x)}{[g(x)]^{n-1}} + \frac{f_n(x)}{[g(x)]^n},$$

and so on, to get 5.23. ∎

For example, $x^3/(x + 2)^4$ may be resolved as follows:

$$x^3 = (x^2 - 2x + 4)(x + 2) - 8.$$

Hence,

$$\frac{x^3}{(x + 2)^4} = \frac{x^2 - 2x + 4}{(x + 2)^3} - \frac{8}{(x + 2)^4}.$$

In turn,

$$x^2 - 2x + 4 = (x - 4)(x + 2) + 12.$$

Hence,

$$\frac{x^2 - 2x + 4}{(x + 2)^3} = \frac{x - 4}{(x + 2)^2} + \frac{12}{(x + 2)^3}.$$

Continuing,

$$x - 4 = 1(x + 2) - 6.$$

Therefore,

$$\frac{x - 4}{(x + 2)^2} = \frac{1}{x + 2} - \frac{6}{(x + 2)^2}.$$

Putting the above expressions together, we obtain

$$\frac{x^3}{(x + 2)^4} = \frac{1}{x + 2} - \frac{6}{(x + 2)^2} + \frac{12}{(x + 2)^3} - \frac{8}{(x + 2)^4}.$$

This is in the form of 5.23.

By a combination of 5.22 and 5.23, we see that every proper rational expression is a sum of *partial fractions*

$$\frac{h(x)}{[p(x)]^n},$$

where $n \in \mathbb{Z}^+$, $p(x)$ is a prime, and deg $h(x) <$ deg $p(x)$.

For example, let us express

$$A = \frac{x^3 + 3}{(x^2 + 1)^2(x^2 - 1)} \in \mathbb{Q}(x)$$

as a sum of partial fractions. Clearly $((x^2 + 1)^2, (x^2 - 1)) = 1$, and

$$(x^2 + 1)^2 - (x^2 + 3)(x^2 - 1) = 4.$$

Hence,

$$A = \frac{1}{4}\left[\frac{x^3 + 3}{x^2 - 1} - \frac{x^5 + 3x^3 + 3x^2 + 9}{(x^2 + 1)^2}\right].$$

On dividing,

$$A = \frac{1}{4}\left[\frac{x + 3}{x^2 - 1} - \frac{x^3 + 3x^2 - x + 9}{(x^2 + 1)^2}\right]$$

and on further dividing,

$$A = \frac{1}{4}\left[\frac{1}{x + 1} + \frac{4}{(x + 1)(x - 1)} - \frac{x + 3}{x^2 + 1} + \frac{2(x - 3)}{(x^2 + 1)^2}\right].$$

Since $(x + 1) - (x - 1) = 2$, we finally obtain

$$A = \frac{1}{4}\left[\frac{2}{x - 1} - \frac{1}{x + 1} - \frac{x + 3}{x^2 + 1} + \frac{2(x - 3)}{(x^2 + 1)^2}\right]$$

as a sum of partial fractions.

Exercises

Express each of the following rational expressions in $\mathbb{Q}(x)$ as a sum of polynomials and partial fractions.

1. $\dfrac{1}{x^2 - 2x - 3}$.

2. $\dfrac{x^3 + 1}{x^2 - x}$.

3. $\dfrac{x^5 - x^3 + 1}{x^3(x^2 + 2)}$.

4. $\dfrac{3}{(x^2 - 1)^2}$.

5. $\dfrac{x^3 - 3x^2}{(x^2 + x + 1)^2}$.

Express each of the following rational expressions in $\mathbb{Z}_2(x)$ as a sum of polynomials and partial fractions.

6. $\dfrac{x}{x^3 + x^2 + x + 1}$.

7. $\dfrac{x^2 + x + 1}{x^2 + x}$.

8. $\dfrac{x^5 + 1}{x^4 + x^2 + 1}$.

9. $\dfrac{x^8}{(x + 1)^8}$.

10. $\dfrac{x^4}{x^6 + x^2 + 1}$.

THEORETICAL PROJECT 3

If R is a C-ring with unity, then an expression of the form

$$f(x) = a_0 + a_1 x + a_2 x^2 + \ldots + a_n x^n + \ldots,$$

where all $a_i \in R$, is called a *formal power series* in x over R. If

$$g(x) = b_0 + b_1 x + b_2 x^2 + \ldots + b_n x^n + \ldots$$

is also a formal power series, then $f(x) + g(x)$ and $f(x) \cdot g(x)$ are defined in the obvious way:

$$f(x) + g(x) = (a_0 + b_0) + (a_1 + b_1)x + (a_2 + b_2)x^2 + \ldots +$$
$$(a_n + b_n)x^n + \ldots,$$

$$f(x) \cdot g(x) = c_0 + c_1 x + c_2 x^2 + \ldots + c_n x^n + \ldots,$$

where

$$c_n = \sum_{i=0}^{n} a_i b_{n-i}, \qquad n = 0,1,\ldots.$$

The set of all power series in x over R is denoted by

$$R[[x]].$$

5.24   Theorem. The algebraic system $\{R[[x]]; +, \cdot\}$ is a C-ring with unity. If R is an integral domain, then $R[[x]]$ is also an integral domain.

The proof of 5.24 is similar to that for $R[x]$. Incidentally, $R[x]$ is a subring of $R[[x]]$ if we consider the polynomial

$$a_0 + a_1 x + \ldots + a_n x^n$$

to equal the powers series

$$a_0 + a_1 x + \ldots + a_n x^n + 0 x^{n+1} + 0 x^{n+2} + \ldots.$$

That is,

$$R \subset R[x] \subset R[[x]].$$

5.25   Theorem. If F is a field, then the set G of all power series with nonzero constant term is the group of units of $F[[x]]$. The only proper ideals of $F[[x]]$ are the principal ideals

$$x^n F[[x]], \qquad n = 1,2,\ldots.$$

Outline of proof: If $f(x) = a_0 + a_1 x + \ldots + a_n x^n + \ldots$, with $a_0 \neq 0$, then you can select the coefficients of $g(x) = b_0 + b_1 x + \ldots + b_n x^n + \ldots$ so that $f(x)g(x) = 1$. If A is a proper ideal of $F[[x]]$, then let k be the minimum integer such that some $f(x) \in A$, $f(x) = a_0 + a_1 x + \ldots + a_n x^n$ $+ \ldots$ has kth coefficient $a_k \neq 0$. Then, as above, $f(x)h(x) = x^k$ for some $h(x) \in F[[x]]$.

Describe the field of quotients of $F[[x]]$. *Hint:* It must contain x^{-n} for every $n \in \mathbb{Z}^+$.

6. Polynomial Domains in n Symbols

Starting with a C-ring with unity R, we can form the polynomial ring $R[x]$ in the symbol x and, in turn, the polynomial ring

$$R[x,y] = (R[x])[y].$$

Thus, each element of $R[x,y]$ has the form

$$f_0(x) + f_1(x)y + \ldots + f_n(x)y^n, \qquad f_i(x) \in R[x].$$

If we use the distributive law in each term above and then collect like powers of $x^i y^j$, each element of $R[x,y]$ may be expressed in the form

5.26
$$\sum_{i=0}^{m} \sum_{j=0}^{n} a_{ij} x^i y^j, \qquad a_{ij} \in R.$$

We call such an element a *polynomial in x and y over R*. If R is an integral domain, then $R[x]$ and $R[x,y]$ are also integral domains.

In turn, we can form

$$R[x,y,z] = (R[x,y])[z],$$

a polynomial domain in x, y, and z over R. A typical element of $R[x,y,z]$ has the form

$$\sum_{i=0}^{m} \sum_{j=0}^{n} \sum_{k=0}^{p} a_{ijk} x^i y^j z^k, \qquad a_{ijk} \in R.$$

Continuing, we can form polynomial domains in four or more symbols.

A polynomial domain in two or more symbols over a field F is algebraically more complicated than $F[x]$. A fundamental difference is that the ideals are no longer all principal. For example, the set S of all polynomials in $F[x,y]$ having zero constant term is an ideal of $F[x,y]$. However, S is not principal; in fact,

$$S = xF[x,y] + yF[x,y],$$

a sum of two principal ideals. If S were principal, say $S = f(x,y)F[x,y]$, then we would have

$$x = f(x,y)g(x,y), \qquad y = f(x,y)h(x,y)$$

for some $g(x,y), h(x,y) \in F[x,y]$. Since $f(x,y)$ has no constant term, the degree of $f(x,y)$ in either x or y is at least 1. But if deg $f(x,y) \geq 1$ in x, then deg $f(x,y)h(x,y) \geq 1$ in x also, contrary to assumption.

The concepts of *factor*, *multiple*, and *primeness* still apply to a polynomial domain in two or more symbols. For example, we may define the degree of a monomial

$$ax^k y^m, \qquad a \in F',$$

in $F[x,y]$ as $k + m$, and the degree of a polynomial as the maximum degree of any of its monomials (assuming the polynomial in form 5.26). Then the same argument with respect to degrees as in the case of polynomials in one symbol will show that every nonconstant polynomial in $F[x,y]$ may be factored into prime polynomials. Again, it may be shown that the factorization is unique.

The ring

$$T = \mathbb{R}[x,y,z]$$

is important in the branch of mathematics called *algebraic geometry*. Each $f(x,y,z) \in T$ defines a function $\mathbb{R}^3 \xrightarrow{f} \mathbb{R}$ in a natural way. For example, if

$$f(x,y,z) = x^2 + y^2 + z^2 - 1,$$

then

$$f(a,b,c) = a^2 + b^2 + c^2 - 1 \text{ for all } (a,b,c) \in \mathbb{R}^3.$$

The *graph* of $f(x,y,z)$ is defined to be

$$\{(a,b,c) \in \mathbb{R}^3 \mid f(a,b,c) = 0\}.$$

Thus, for example, we recognize the graph of $x^2 + y^2 + z^2 - 1$ to be the sphere with center at $(0,0,0)$ and radius 1.

A set V of points in $\mathbb{R}^3$ is called an *algebraic variety* if

$$V = \bigcap_{i=1}^{m} A_i,$$

where each A_i is the graph of some polynomial in T.

If U is any subset of $\mathbb{R}^3$, then let

$$I = \{f(x,y,z) \in T \mid f(a,b,c) = 0 \text{ for all } (a,b,c) \in U\}.$$

Thus, I contains every polynomial whose graph includes the set U. It is easily shown that I is an ideal of T. On the other hand, we can define the graph of *I* to be

$$\{(a,b,c) \in \mathbb{R}^3 \mid f(a,b,c) = 0 \text{ for every } f(x,y,z) \in I\}.$$

It is an important theorem of algebraic geometry that

U is an algebraic variety iff U is the graph of an ideal of T.

For example, the circle of radius 1 in the *xy*-plane is an algebraic variety, since it is the intersection of the graphs of the polynomials

$$x^2 + y^2 + z^2 - 1 \quad \text{and} \quad x^2 + y^2 - 1$$

(i.e., it is the intersection of a sphere and a cylinder). In the language of ideals, this circle is the graph of an ideal

$$I = (x^2 + y^2 + z^2 - 1)T + (x^2 + y^2 - 1)T.$$

It is also the graph of the ideal $(x^2 + y^2 - 1)T + zT$.

As another example, the set

$$V = \{(a^3,a,a^2) \in \mathbb{R}^3 \mid a \in \mathbb{R}\}$$

is an algebraic variety, since it is the graph of the ideal

$$I = (x - y^3)T + (y^2 - z)T.$$

Exercises

Tell which of the following polynomials in $\mathbb{Q}[x,y]$ are prime. Give reasons for your answers.

1. $x - y + 1$.

2. $x^2 - 3xy + 2y^2$.

3. $x^2 + x - y$.

4. $x^3 + y^3$.

5. $x^2 - xy - 2y^2 + 4x + y + 3$.

6. $x^4 + x^2y^2 + y^4$.

7. $x^4 - y^4$.

8. $x^2 - y^2 + 2x + 1$.

9. $x^3 - 3y^3$.

10. $x^n + 2y^n$, $n > 0$.

Tell which of the following subsets of $\mathbb{R}^3$ are algebraic varieties. Give reasons for your answers.

11. The parabola in the *yz*-plane with equation $y^2 = z$.

12. $\{(a,2a,0) \mid a \in \mathbb{R}\}$.

13. $\{(\sin a, \cos a, a) \mid a \in \mathbb{R}\}$.

14. $\{(a + 1, a^2 + a, a^3) \mid a \in \mathbb{R}\}$.

15. $\{(a + b, a - b, a^2 + b^2) \mid a,b \in \mathbb{R}\}$.

THEORETICAL PROJECT 4

Let F be a field and $R = F[x,y]$, a polynomial domain in two symbols. A polynomial $f(x,y)$ is said to be *homogeneous of degree* $n \geq 0$ iff each monomial in $f(x,y)$ has degree n. Thus,

$$5, \qquad 3x - 2y, \qquad 6x^2 - 4xy + 3y^2, \qquad x^4 + y^4$$

are homogeneous polynomials in $\mathbb{Q}[x,y]$ of degrees 0, 1, 2, and 4, respectively. Let

$$H_n = \{f(x,y) \in R \mid f(x,y) = 0 \quad \text{or} \quad f(x,y) \text{ homogeneous of degree } n\}$$

for $n = 0,1,2,\ldots$. For example,

$$H_0 = F,$$
$$H_1 = \{ax + by \mid a,b \in F\},$$
$$H_2 = \{ax^2 + bxy + cy^2 \mid a,b,c \in F\},$$

and so on.

1. Prove that $\{H_n; +\}$ is an Abelian group for each n, and that

$$H_n \cdot H_m \subseteq H_{n+m}$$

(where $A \cdot B = \{a \cdot b \mid a \in A, b \in B\}$).

2. Prove that $R = H_1 + H_2 + H_3 + \ldots$. That is, prove that each $f(x,y) \in R$ is a sum of homogeneous polynomials.

3. If $f(x,y), g(x,y)$ are nonzero polynomials in R, then prove that deg $[f(x,y)g(x,y)] = \deg f(x,y) + \deg g(x,y)$.

4. Can a homogeneous polynomial be a product of nonhomogeneous polynomials? Justify your answer.

There is a natural mapping

$$R \xrightarrow{\;h\;} R \text{ defined by } h[f(x,y)] = f(y,x).$$

For example,

$$h(x) = y, \qquad h(x^2 - 3x + 5xy^3) = y^2 - 3y + 5x^3y.$$

5. Prove that h is an isomorphism and that $h \circ h$ is the identity mapping of R. Also prove that $h(H_n) = H_n$ for each n.

Let

$$S = \{r \in R \mid h(r) = r\}.$$

For example,

$$x + y, \qquad xy, \qquad x^2 + y^2, \qquad x^3 + x^2 y + xy^2 + y^3$$

are all in S. The elements of S are called *symmetric polynomials*.

6. Prove that S is a subring of R.

7. The polynomials $p = x + y$ and $q = xy$ are called the *elementary symmetric polynomials*. Prove that every symmetric polynomial is a polynomial in p and q; i.e.,

$$S = F[p,q].$$

8. Indicate how the work above carries through if $R = F[x,y,z]$. [*Hint:* There are now three elementary symmetric polynomials, $p = x + y$, $q = xy + xz + yz$, and $r = xyz$.]

chapter 6

Algebraic Extensions
of a Field

Starting with any field F, it is possible to find many fields which contain F as a subfield. One such field is

$$F(x),$$

the field of quotients of the polynomial domain $F[x]$ in the symbol x over F. Clearly F is a proper subfield of $F(x)$. The field $F(x)$ is called a *transcendental extension* of F.

Another type of extension of F, called an *algebraic extension*, will be studied in this chapter. The quadratic field $\mathbb{Q}[\sqrt{2}]$ considered in Chapter 1 is an example of an algebraic extension of the rational field $\mathbb{Q}$.

I. Extensions of $\mathbb{Q}$

We already know of one extension of the rational field $\mathbb{Q}$—namely, the real field $\mathbb{R}$. An element t of $\mathbb{R}$ is called *algebraic* over $\mathbb{Q}$ iff t is a zero of some nonzero $f(x) \in \mathbb{Q}[x]$. For example, $\sqrt{2}$ is algebraic over $\mathbb{Q}$ since $\sqrt{2}$ is a zero of $x^2 - 2 \in \mathbb{Q}[x]$. Also, $1 - \sqrt[3]{5}$ is algebraic over $\mathbb{Q}$ since it is a zero of the polynomial

$$(x - 1)^3 + 5, \quad \text{or} \quad x^3 - 3x^2 + 3x + 4$$

in $\mathbb{Q}[x]$. On the other hand, π and e are *transcendental* over $\mathbb{Q}$ in the sense that neither is a zero of a rational polynomial.† Of course, every rational number r is algebraic over $\mathbb{Q}$, being the zero of the polynomial $x - r \in \mathbb{Q}[x]$.

For every $t \in \mathbb{R}$, let

$$\mathbb{Q}[t] = \{f(t) \mid f(x) \in \mathbb{Q}[x]\}.$$

Thus, $\mathbb{Q}[t]$ is a subring of $\mathbb{R}$ of all elements of the form

$$a_0 + a_1 t + \ldots + a_n t^n, \qquad \text{each} \quad a_i \in \mathbb{Q}.$$

Clearly $\mathbb{Q} \subset \mathbb{Q}[t] \subset \mathbb{R}$, with $\mathbb{Q} = \mathbb{Q}[t]$ iff $t \in \mathbb{Q}$.

From the definition of $\mathbb{Q}[t]$, it is evident that the mapping of the polynomial domain $\mathbb{Q}[x]$ into the subring $\mathbb{Q}[t]$ of $\mathbb{R}$ defined by

6.1 $$\mathbb{Q}[x] \xrightarrow{\varphi} \mathbb{Q}[t], \; \varphi[f(x)] = f(t),$$

is an epimorphism. Clearly φ is an isomorphism iff $f(t) \neq 0$ for every nonzero $f(x) \in \mathbb{Q}[x]$—i.e., iff t is transcendental over $\mathbb{Q}$.

If the epimorphism φ defined in 6.1 is not an isomorphism, then ker φ is a nonzero ideal of $\mathbb{Q}[x]$. By 5.8, $\mathbb{Q}[x]$ is a principal ideal domain and therefore

$$\ker \varphi = h(x)\mathbb{Q}[x]$$

for some unique monic $h(x) \in \mathbb{Q}[x]$. Clearly $h(x)$ is a polynomial of minimal degree having t as a zero, i.e., $h(t) = 0$. The polynomial $h(x)$ is prime; for if $h(x) = f(x) \cdot g(x)$, then $h(t) = f(t) \cdot g(t) = 0$ and either $f(t) = 0$ or $g(t) = 0$. If $f(t) = 0$, then $f(x) \in \ker \varphi$ and deg $f(x) = $ deg $h(x)$, deg $g(x) = 0$. Thus, $g(x)$ is a unit and hence $h(x)$ is a prime. We call the monic prime polynomial $h(x)$ the *minimal polynomial* of t over $\mathbb{Q}$.

If $t \in \mathbb{R}$ is algebraic over $\mathbb{Q}$ and $h(x) \in \mathbb{Q}[x]$ is the minimal polynomial of t, then $\mathbb{Q}[t]$ is isomorphic to $\mathbb{Q}[x]/h(x)\mathbb{Q}[x]$ by the isomorphism theorem (3.18). Hence, by 5.13, $\mathbb{Q}[t]$ is a field. We have proved the following:

6.2   Theorem. If the real number t is algebraic over $\mathbb{Q}$ with minimal polynomial $h(x)$, then $\mathbb{Q}[t]$ is a real field isomorphic to $\mathbb{Q}[x]/h(x)\mathbb{Q}[x]$.

The field $\mathbb{Q}[t]$ of 6.2 is called an *algebraic extension* of field $\mathbb{Q}$.

For example, $\mathbb{Q}[\sqrt{2}]$ is a quadratic extension of $\mathbb{Q}$. It consists of all polynomials in $\sqrt{2}$ with rational coefficients. Actually, it is only necessary to consider first-degree polynomials in $\sqrt{2}$, i.e., $\mathbb{Q}[\sqrt{2}] = \{a + b\sqrt{2} \mid a,b \in \mathbb{Q}\}$, since every power of $\sqrt{2}$ is either a rational number or a rational number times $\sqrt{2}$.

---

† For a proof, see I. Niven, *Irrational Numbers*, (New York: John Wiley & Sons, Inc., 1956), p. 131.

More generally, if $t \in \mathbb{R}$ is algebraic over $\mathbb{Q}$ with minimal polynomial

$$h(x) = x^n + a_{n-1}x^{n-1} + \ldots + a_1 x + a_0,$$

then

6.3 $\mathbb{Q}[t] = \{c_0 + c_1 t + \ldots + c_{n-1}t^{n-1} \mid c_i \in \mathbb{Q}\}.$

To prove that $\mathbb{Q}[t]$ is given by 6.3, let $f(x)$ be any element of $\mathbb{Q}[x]$. Then

$$f(x) = q(x)h(x) + r(x), \quad r(x) = 0 \quad \text{or} \quad \deg r(x) < n,$$

for some $q(x), r(x) \in \mathbb{Q}[x]$ by the division process. Hence,

$$f(t) = q(t)h(t) + r(t) = r(t).$$

If $r(x) = c_0 + c_1 x + \ldots + c_{n-1}x^{n-1}$, then

$$f(t) = c_0 + c_1 t + \ldots + c_{n-1}t^{n-1},$$

as we desired to show.

The representation of an element of $\mathbb{Q}[t]$ in the form $c_0 + c_1 t + \ldots + c_{n-1}t^{n-1}$, each $c_i \in \mathbb{Q}$, is unique. For if

$$c_0 + c_1 t + \ldots + c_{n-1}t^{n-1} = d_0 + d_1 t + \ldots + d_{n-1}t^{n-1},$$

then $(c_0 - d_0) + (c_1 - d_1)t + \ldots + (c_{n-1} - d_{n-1})t^{n-1} = 0$, i.e., t is a zero of the polynomial

$$g(x) = (c_0 - d_0) + (c_1 - d_1)x + \ldots + (c_{n-1} - d_{n-1})x^{n-1} \in \mathbb{Q}[x].$$

However, the minimal polynomial of t, $h(x)$, has degree n and therefore $g(x) = 0$ and $c_0 = d_0, c_1 = d_1, \ldots, c_{n-1} = d_{n-1}$.

As another example,

$$t = \sqrt{2} + \sqrt{3}$$

is algebraic over $\mathbb{Q}$. For $t^2 = 5 + 2\sqrt{6}$, $(t^2 - 5)^2 = 24$, and hence

$$h(x) = x^4 - 10x^2 + 1$$

has t as a zero. We claim that $h(x)$ is prime in $\mathbb{Q}[x]$, and therefore $h(x)$ is the minimal polynomial of t. Clearly $h(x)$ has no rational zero and hence no first-degree factor. If $h(x)$ has a quadratic factor in $\mathbb{Q}[x]$, then

$$h(x) = (x^2 + ax + b)(x^2 + cx + d)$$

in $\mathbb{Z}[x]$ by the lemma of Gauss (5.19). Thus,

$$x^4 - 10x^2 + 1 = x^4 + (a + c)x^3 + (d + ac + b)x^2 + (ad + bc)x + bd$$

for some $a, b, c, d \in \mathbb{Z}$. You can easily show that no such integers a, b, c and d exist. Thus, $h(x)$ is prime. This also proves, incidentally, that $\sqrt{2} + \sqrt{3}$

is irrational. By 6.3,

$$\mathbb{Q}[t] = \{c_0 + c_1 t + c_2 t^2 + c_3 t^3 \mid c_i \in \mathbb{Q}\}.$$

Elements of $\mathbb{Q}[t]$ are added in the obvious way. To multiply two elements, we multiply them as usual and then use the fact that

$$t^4 = 10t^2 - 1$$

to reduce the resulting polynomial to a cubic in t. For example,

$$(1 - 2t + t^3) \cdot (2 + 3t^2) = 2 - 4t + 3t^2 - 4t^3 + 3t^5$$
$$= 2 - 4t + 3t^2 - 4t^3 + 3t(10t^2 - 1)$$
$$= 2 - 7t + 3t^2 + 26t^3.$$

Actually, since $t^2 = 5 + 2\sqrt{6}$ and $t^3 = 11\sqrt{2} + 9\sqrt{3}$, evidently

$$\mathbb{Q}[\sqrt{2} + \sqrt{3}] = \{a + b\sqrt{2} + c\sqrt{3} + d\sqrt{6} \mid a,b,c,d \in \mathbb{Q}\}.$$

Then the sum and product of elements in $\mathbb{Q}[\sqrt{2} + \sqrt{3}]$ are found in the obvious way.

Exercises

Show that each of the following real numbers is algebraic over $\mathbb{Q}$, find its minimal polynomial, and describe the real field over $\mathbb{Q}$ its generates.

1. $\sqrt{5}$ **2.** $\sqrt[3]{7}$.

3. $1 + \sqrt{2}$.   **4.** $\sqrt{5} + \sqrt{7}$.

5. $2 - \sqrt[3]{11}$.   **6.** $\sqrt{1 + \sqrt{2}}$.

7. $\sqrt[3]{2 + \sqrt{3}}$.   **8.** $\sqrt{1 + \sqrt{1 + \sqrt{2}}}$.

2. Extensions of Any Field

In discussing algebraic extensions of $\mathbb{Q}$, we had at hand the field of real numbers $\mathbb{R}$ from which to select algebraic numbers. When we start with any field F, however, we may not have at hand a larger field containing F from which to choose algebraic elements. Hence, our approach to the problem of finding algebraic extensions of F must be different from that of $\mathbb{Q}$. Nevertheless, the work of Section 1 does suggest a method of extending F.

Starting with a field F, we can form the polynomial domain $F[x]$ which contains F as a subfield. If $p(x)$ is a monic prime polynomial of $F[x]$ of degree

$n \geq 1$, then
$$I = p(x)F[x]$$
is a maximal ideal of $F[x]$ and
$$K = F[x]/I$$
is a field by 6.13. Upon identifying each $a \in F$ with $a + I \in K$, we see that
$$F \subset K.$$

Each $f(x) \in F[x]$ can be divided by $p(x)$, obtaining
$$f(x) = q(x)p(x) + r(x), \qquad r(x) = 0 \quad \text{or} \quad \deg r(x) < n,$$
for some $q(x), r(x) \in F[x]$. Then $f(x) - r(x) \in I$ and
$$f(x) + I = r(x) + I$$
in K. We conclude that
$$K = \{(a_0 + a_1 x + \ldots + a_{n-1} x^{n-1}) + I \mid a_i \in F\}.$$
For convenience, let
$$t = x + I.$$
$t \in K$. Then
$$t^k = (x + I)^k = x^k + I \quad \text{and} \quad at^k = (a + I)(x + I)^k = ax^k + I$$
for all $k \in \mathbb{Z}^+$ and all $a \in F$. Hence,
$$(a_0 + a_1 x + \ldots + a_{n-1} x^{n-1}) + I = a_0 + a_1 t + \ldots + a_{n-1} t^{n-1}.$$
If
$$p(x) = b_0 + b_1 x + \ldots + b_{n-1} x^{n-1} + x^n,$$
then $p(x) + I = I = 0$, the zero element of K and F, and
$$b_0 + b_1 t + \ldots + b_{n-1} t^{n-1} + t^n = 0$$
by our remarks directly above. That is, t *is a zero of polynomial* $p(x) \in F[x]$. So $p(x)$, which is prime in $F[x]$, is not prime in $K[x]$ if $n > 1$. Note that
$$t^n = -(b_0 + b_1 t + \ldots + b_{n-1} t^{n-1}),$$
and
$$K = \{a_0 + a_1 t + \ldots + a_{n-1} t^{n-1} \mid a_i \in F\}.$$

If $\deg p(x) = n = 1$, then $K = F$ and nothing has been accomplished. However, if $n > 1$, then K definitely is an enlargement of F. As in Section 1, we call field K an *algebraic extension* of field F. Clearly $K = F[t]$ for some $t \in K$ if K is an algebraic extension of F, and $p(x)$ is the *minimal polynomial* of t over F. We state our results as follows.

6.4   Theorem. If F is a field and $p(x)$ is a monic prime in $F[x]$ of degree $n > 1$, then there exists a field K containing F as a subfield and an element t of K such that $K = F[t]$ and t has minimal polynomial $p(x) \in F[x]$.

Perhaps the simplest example is to take $F = \mathbb{Z}_2$, a field with two elements, and the prime polynomial

$$p(x) = x^2 + x + 1$$

in $\mathbb{Z}_2[x]$. Then

$$K = \mathbb{Z}_2[x]/p(x)\mathbb{Z}_2[x]$$

is a field. By our work above,

$$K = \{a + bt \mid a,b \in \mathbb{Z}_2\},$$

where $t^2 + t + 1 = 0$ in K, i.e.,

$$t^2 = t + 1.$$

Clearly K is a field with four elements,

$$K = \{0,1,t, 1 + t\}$$

Since $\mathbb{Z}_2 \subset K$, evidently ch $K = 2$.

As another example, the polynomial

$$h(x) = x^3 + 2x + 1$$

is prime in $\mathbb{Z}_5[x]$ since $h(x)$ has no zeros in $\mathbb{Z}_5$. Hence,

$$K = \mathbb{Z}_5[x]/h(x)\mathbb{Z}_5[x]$$

is a field. Clearly ch $K = 5$ and

$$K = \{a + bt + ct^2 \mid a,b,c \in \mathbb{Z}_5\},$$

where $t^3 + 2t + 1 = 0$, or

$$t^3 = 3t + 4.$$

This field K contains 5^3, or 125, elements.

In a similar way, for every prime number p and every positive integer n, there exists a prime polynomial $h(x)$ in $\mathbb{Z}_p[x]$ of degree n. We denote the resulting field by $GF(p^n)$,

$$GF(p^n) = \mathbb{Z}_p[x]/h(x)\mathbb{Z}_p[x],$$

and call it a *Galois field*.† The field $GF(p^n)$ has p^n elements in view of our results above. Thus, there is a finite field having p^n elements for every prime number p and every integer $n > 0$. It may be shown that there is only one field having p^n elements. Proofs of these facts will come in a later course in algebra.

---

† Named in honor of the early nineteenth-century French mathematician Evariste Galois, who used such algebraic systems in his work on the unsolvability of polynomial equations of degree higher than four.

Exercises

Describe each of the following Galois fields by finding an appropriate prime polynomial and constructing the associated field.

1. $GF(2^3)$.

2. $GF(2^4)$.

3. $GF(2^5)$.

4. $GF(5^2)$.

5. $GF(7^2)$.

6. $GF(13^2)$.

7. $GF(5^3)$.

8. $GF(3^4)$.

THEORETICAL PROJECT 1

If F is a field and $f(x)$ is any nonzero polynomial in $F[x]$, not necessarily prime, then $f(x)F[x]$ is still an ideal in $F[x]$ and we can form the quotient ring

$$R = F[x]/f(x)F[x].$$

1. Prove that if $\deg f(x) = n$ and $t = x + f(x)F[x]$, then

$$R = \{c_0 + c_1 t + \ldots + c_{n-1} t^{n-1} \mid c_i \in F\}.$$

Thus, $F \subset R$, R has a unity, and ch $F =$ ch R.

2. Illustrate in case $F = \mathbb{Q}$ and $f(x) = x^3$.

3. Illustrate in case $F = \mathbb{Q}$ and $f(x) = x^2 - x$. Prove that R is isomorphic to $\mathbb{Q} \times \mathbb{Q}$ in this case.

4. Describe all C-rings R with unity having four elements. [*Hint:* If ch $R = 2$, then R is an algebraic extension of $\mathbb{Z}_2$.]

THEORETICAL PROJECT 2

Let $R = GF(p^n)$, a Galois field with p^n elements, p a prime number, and $R' = \{x \in R \mid x \neq 0\}$. We know that $\{R'; \cdot\}$ is an Abelian group with $k = p^n - 1$ elements. Prove the following results.

Theorem 1. The group $\{R'; \cdot\}$ is cyclic.

Outline of proof: Each element of R' has order which is a divisor of k by Lagrange's theorem. Therefore $a^k = 1$ for each $a \in R'$. Let m be the lcm of the orders of the k elements of R'. By 2.37, there exists some $b \in R'$ of order m. Also, $a^m = 1$ for each $a \in R'$. Necessarily $m = k$ by 5.17.

Theorem 2. $\{R'; \cdot\}$ is isomorphic to $\{\mathbb{Z}_k; +\}$.

Illustrate these theorems with some examples.

Theorem 3. The mapping $R \xrightarrow{h} R$ defined by $h(x) = x^p$ is an isomorphism. Hence, every element of R has a unique pth root.

3. The Complex Number Field

Undoubtedly every reader of this book is familiar with the complex number field consisting of all numbers of the form $a + bi$, where $a,b \in \mathbb{R}$ and i is a square root of -1, i.e., $i^2 = -1$. This field is simply an algebraic extension of the real number field, as we shall show below.

We know that $x^2 + 1$ is a prime polynomial in $\mathbb{R}[x]$ since it has no real zeros. Thus, $a^2 + 1 > 0$ for every $a \in \mathbb{R}$. Hence,

$$\mathbb{C} = \mathbb{R}[x]/I, \quad \text{where} \quad I = (x^2 + 1)\mathbb{R}[x],$$

is a field. If we let

$$i = x + I,$$

then

$$\mathbb{C} = \{a + bi \mid a,b \in \mathbb{R}\}$$

by the results of Section 2. Clearly

$$i^2 = -1,$$

since i is a zero of the polynomial $x^2 + 1$. We call $\mathbb{C}$ the *complex number field*. It is an algebraic extension of the real field.

$$\mathbb{R} \subset \mathbb{C}.$$

We may work with the field $\mathbb{C}$ in a purely formal way by using the facts that for $a,b,a',b' \in \mathbb{R}$,

$$a + bi = a' + b'i \quad \text{iff} \quad a = a' \quad \text{and} \quad b = b',$$

and

$$i^2 = -1.$$

Thus,

$$(a + bi) + (a' + b'i) = (a + a') + (b + b')i,$$
$$(a + bi) \cdot (a' + b'i) = (aa' - bb') + (ab' + ba')i.$$

The field $\mathbb{C}$ has a truly remarkable property that was first proved by Gauss in about 1800.

6.5   Fundamental theorem of algebra. Every polynomial of positive degree in $\mathbb{C}[x]$ has a zero in $\mathbb{C}$.

Another way of stating 6.5 is that the only prime polynomials in $\mathbb{C}[x]$ are those of degree 1.

We shall not attempt to prove 6.5, but rather refer the interested reader to any book on complex variables. It is clear that a proof must depend on an analysis of the properties of the field $\mathbb{R}$.

Since the primes of $\mathbb{C}[x]$ are all of degree 1, the field $\mathbb{C}$ has no algebraic extension. A field such as $\mathbb{C}$, having no algebraic extensions, is called an *algebraically closed field*. The field $\mathbb{C}$ does have extensions; for example, it has the transcendental extension $\mathbb{C}(x)$.

Each complex number $z = a + bi$, $a,b \in \mathbb{R}$, has a *conjugate* $\bar{z} = a - bi$. For example,

$$\text{if} \quad u = 7 + 3i \quad \text{then} \quad \bar{u} = 7 - 3i;$$
$$\text{if} \quad v = 4 - 5i \quad \text{then} \quad \bar{v} = 4 + 5i.$$

Clearly $\bar{z} = 0$ iff $z = 0$, and $z = \bar{z}$ iff z is a real number. Also, $\bar{\bar{z}} = z$ for every $z \in \mathbb{C}$.

6.6   Theorem. The mapping $\mathbb{C} \xrightarrow{\;h\;} \mathbb{C}$ defined by $h(z) = \bar{z}$ is an isomorphism.

It is clear that h is a bijection. The proof of 6.6 will be complete once we prove

6.7 $\overline{u + v} = \bar{u} + \bar{v}, \overline{u \cdot v} = \bar{u} \cdot \bar{v}$ for all $u,v \in \mathbb{C}$.

Proof: If $u = a + bi$ and $v = c + di$, where $a,b,c,d \in R$, then $\bar{u} = a - bi$ and $\bar{v} = c - di$. Hence,

$$u + v = (a + c) + (b + d)i, \qquad \bar{u} + \bar{v} = (a + c) - (b + d)i,$$

and $\overline{u + v} = \bar{u} + \bar{v}$. Also, $u \cdot v = (ac - bd) + (ad + bc)i$, $\bar{u} \cdot \bar{v} = (ac - bd) - (ad + bc)i$, and therefore $\overline{u \cdot v} = \bar{u} \cdot \bar{v}$. ∎

For each $z \in \mathbb{C}$, $z + \bar{z}$ is called the *trace* of z and is denoted by $T(z)$; $z \cdot \bar{z}$ is called the *norm* of z and is denoted by $N(z)$. Thus, for all $a,b \in \mathbb{R}$,

6.8 $T(a + bi) = (a + bi) + (a - bi) = 2a,$

6.9 $N(a + bi) = (a + bi) \cdot (a - bi) = a^2 + b^2.$

Evidently $T(z)$ and $N(z)$ are real numbers for all $z \in \mathbb{C}$; i.e., T and N are mappings of $\mathbb{C}$ into $\mathbb{R}$. Clearly $N(z) = 0$ iff $z = 0$.

The mappings T and N have the following useful properties:

6.10 $$T(u + v) = T(u) + T(v) \text{ for all } u,v \in \mathbb{C}.$$

6.11 $$N(u \cdot v) = N(u) \cdot N(v) \text{ for all } u,v \in \mathbb{C}.$$

The proofs of 6.10 and 6.11 follow easily from 6.7. Thus,

$$T(u + v) = (u + v) + \overline{(u + v)} = (u + v) + (\bar{u} + \bar{v})$$
$$= (u + \bar{u}) + (v + \bar{v}) = T(u) + T(v),$$

and similarly for 6.11. ∎

We conclude from 6.10 and 6.11 that T and N are group homomorphisms, T of $\{\mathbb{C};+\}$ into $\{\mathbb{R};+\}$ and N of $\{\mathbb{C}';\cdot\}$ into $\{\mathbb{R}';\cdot\}$, where $\mathbb{C}' = \{z \in \mathbb{C} \mid z \neq 0\}$ and $\mathbb{R}' = \{a \in \mathbb{R} \mid a \neq 0\}$.

If z is a complex number, $z \notin \mathbb{R}$, then

$$h(x) = (x - z)(x - \bar{z}) = x^2 - T(z)x + N(z)$$

is a real polynomial having z as a zero. Clearly $h(x)$ is prime in $\mathbb{R}[x]$ and is the minimal polynomial of z.

Every real polynomial

$$f(x) = a_0 + a_1 x + \ldots + a_n x^n, \quad \text{all} \quad a_i \in \mathbb{R},$$

of degree $n > 0$ is also in $\mathbb{C}[x]$ and hence has a complex zero z by 6.5. Since $\overline{f(z)} = f(\bar{z}) = 0$, evidently $\bar{z}$ is also a zero of $f(x)$. If $z \notin \mathbb{R}$, so that $\bar{z} \neq z$, then $(x - z)(x - \bar{z}) \mid f(z)$ by two applications of the factor theorem. Hence, the real polynomial $x^2 - T(z)x + N(z)$ is a factor of $f(x)$ and $f(x)$ is not a prime polynomial unless $n = 2$. If $z = \bar{z}$, then $x - z$ is a real factor of $f(x)$ and $f(x)$ is not prime unless $n = 1$. This proves the following result.

6.12   Theorem. A monic polynomial in $\mathbb{R}[x]$ is prime iff it is either a first-degree polynomial or a second-degree polynomial of the form $x^2 - T(z)x + N(z)$ for some nonreal complex number z.

As a consequence of this theorem, every real polynomial of positive degree can be factored (in theory) into a product of first- and second-degree real prime polynomials.

For example,

$$x^4 + 1 = (x^4 + 2x^2 + 1) - 2x^2$$
$$= (x^2 + 1)^2 - (\sqrt{2}x)^2 = (x^2 + \sqrt{2}x + 1)(x^2 - \sqrt{2}x + 1).$$

We see by the quadratic formula that neither of the quadratic polynomials $x^2 + \sqrt{2}x + 1$ and $x^2 - \sqrt{2}x + 1$ has a real zero. Hence, each is a prime.

Exercises

Factor each of the following polynomials into primes in $\mathbb{R}[x]$.

1. $x^3 + 1$.   **2.** $x^4 + 3x^2 + 1$.

3. $x^4 - 10x^2 + 1$.   **4.** $x^6 - 1$.

5. $x^4 + x^3 + 2x^2 + x + 1$.   **6.** $x^6 + 1$.

7. If F is an ordered field, prove that $x^2 + 1$ is a prime polynomial in $F[x]$. Hence conclude that $\mathbb{C}$ is not an ordered field. [*Hint:* Assume that $x^2 + 1$ is not prime, and that t is a zero of $x^2 + 1$. Is $t > 0$ or $t < 0$?]

8. Find the kernel of each of the group homomorphisms $\mathbb{C} \xrightarrow{\;T\;} \mathbb{R}$ and $\mathbb{C}' \xrightarrow{\;N\;} \mathbb{R}'$.

*9. Prove that no finite field is algebraically closed.

4. The Complex Plane

Part of the usefulness of the complex field $\mathbb{C}$ in applications is due to its geometric representation as $\mathbb{R}^2$, the set of all points in a Cartesian coordinate plane. Each point in the plane with x-coordinate a and y-coordinate b can be assigned the complex-number coordinate $a + bi$, as shown in Figure 6.1. Evidently each real number a is assigned to a point on the x-axis, while each *purely imaginary number* bi is assigned to a point on the y-axis. The mapping $\mathbb{C} \xrightarrow{\;h\;} \mathbb{C}$ defined in 6.6 may be interpreted geometrically as a reflection of the plane through the x-axis, as indicated in Figure 6.1.

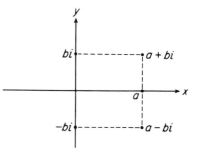

Figure 6.1

Each complex number $a + bi$ may be given in trigonometric form as follows: Let angle θ and the real number $r \geq 0$ be chosen as shown in Figure 6.2. Then by the definition of the sine and cosine functions,

$$\sin \theta = \frac{b}{r}, \quad \cos \theta = \frac{a}{r}.$$

Hence, $a = r \cos \theta$, $b = r \sin \theta$, and

6.13
$$a + bi = r(\cos \theta + i \sin \theta).$$

We call $r(\cos \theta + i \sin \theta)$ a *trigonometric form* of the complex number $a + bi$. Clearly $0 = 0(\cos \theta + i \sin \theta)$ for any θ.

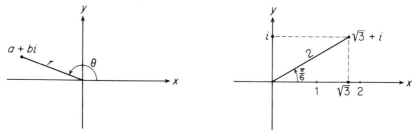

Figure 6.2   **Figure 6.3**

For example, each positive real number r has trigonometric form
$$r = r(\cos 0 + i \sin 0),$$
whereas each negative real number s has trigonometric form
$$s = |s| (\cos \pi + i \sin \pi).$$
A purely imaginary number bi has trigonometric form

$$bi = b\left(\cos \frac{\pi}{2} + i \sin \frac{\pi}{2}\right) \quad \text{if} \quad b > 0,$$

$$bi = |b| \left(\cos \frac{3\pi}{2} + i \sin \frac{3\pi}{2}\right) \quad \text{if} \quad b < 0.$$

The complex number $\sqrt{3} + i$ is plotted in Figure 6.3. It is clear from the figure that
$$\sqrt{3} + i = 2\left(\cos \frac{\pi}{6} + i \sin \frac{\pi}{6}\right).$$

The nonnegative real number r appearing in the trigonometric form 6.13 of $a + bi$ is called the *absolute value* of $a + bi$ and is denoted by $|a + bi|$. By the usual distance formula, $|a + bi| = \sqrt{a^2 + b^2}$; in other words,

6.14
$$|z| = \sqrt{N(z)} = \sqrt{z\bar{z}} \text{ for all } z \in \mathbb{C}.$$

It is clear from 6.11 that

6.15 $$|u \cdot v| = |u| \cdot |v| \text{ for all } u,v \in \mathbb{C}.$$

The angle θ appearing in 6.13 is called an *argument* of $a + bi$ and is denoted by arg $(a + bi)$. To be more precise, θ is the radian measure of an angle having the positive x-axis as initial side and a half-line emanating from the origin and passing through $a + bi$ as terminal side. Clearly θ is not unique; $\theta \pm 2n\pi$ is an argument of $a + bi$ for any $n \in \mathbb{Z}$ if θ is an argument. However, if we restrict θ by $0 \leq \theta < 2\pi$, then θ is unique for any nonzero complex number $a + bi$.

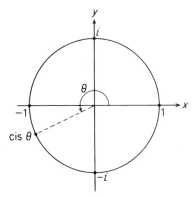

Figure 6.4

Each complex number with absolute value 1 lies on the unit circle with center at the origin (Figure 6.4). Thus

$$G = \{z \in \mathbb{C} \mid |z| = 1\}$$

is the set of all points on this unit circle. The set G is closed under multiplication in view of 6.15. Since $z\bar{z} = 1$ for each $z \in G$, evidently $\bar{z} = z^{-1}$ and $\bar{z} \in G$. Also, $1 \in G$ and therefore $\{G; \cdot\}$ is an Abelian group called the *circle group* for obvious reasons.

There is a natural mapping

$$\mathbb{R} \xrightarrow{\text{cis}} G \text{ defined by cis } \theta = \cos \theta + i \sin \theta \text{ for all } \theta \in \mathbb{R}.$$

Since

$$(\text{cis } \theta)(\text{cis } \varphi) = (\cos \theta \cos \varphi - \sin \theta \sin \varphi) + (\cos \theta \sin \varphi + \sin \theta \cos \varphi)i$$
$$= \cos (\theta + \varphi) + i \sin (\theta + \varphi) = \text{cis } (\theta + \varphi),$$

the following result clearly holds.

6.16 Theorem. The mapping cis is an epimorphism of the Abelian group $\{\mathbb{R}; +\}$ into the circle group $\{G; \cdot\}$.

What is the kernel of the epimorphism cis? By definition, ker (cis) = $\{\theta \in \mathbb{R} \mid \text{cis } \theta = 1\}$. Since cis $\theta = 1$ iff θ is a multiple of 2π, obviously

$$\text{ker (cis)} = 2\pi\mathbb{Z}.$$

A corollary of 6.16, known as *de Moivre's theorem*, is as follows:

6.17 $$(\cos \theta + i \sin \theta)^n = \cos n\theta + i \sin n\theta \text{ for all } n \in \mathbb{Z}.$$

Exercises

1. Express each of the following complex numbers in trigonometric form:
(a) 7,   (b) $3 + 3i$,   (c) $-\sqrt{3} - i$,
(d) $-5i$,   (e) $1 - \sqrt{3}i$,   (f) $-\sqrt{2} + \sqrt{2}i$.

2. Express each of the following complex numbers in the form $a + bi$:
(a) 2 cis 30°,   (b) 4 cis 180°,
(c) 7 cis 315°,   (d) $\sqrt{2}$ cis 90°,
(e) $(3 \text{ cis } 15°)^2$,   (f) $\sqrt{3}$ cis 120°.

3. Prove that the distance between the points in the complex plane with coordinates u and v is $|u - v|$.

4. Expand $(\cos \theta + i \sin \theta)^n$, $n \in \mathbb{Z}^+$, by the binomial theorem and thus obtain formulas for $\cos n\theta$ and $\sin n\theta$. What are the formulas in case $n = 2$, 3, 4, and 5?

5. If $f(x) \in \mathbb{R}[x]$, then $f(x)$ defines a mapping $\mathbb{C} \xrightarrow{f} \mathbb{C}$. Let $A_f = \{u \in \mathbb{C} \mid f(u) \in \mathbb{R}\}$. Describe the graph of A_f in the complex plane in case: (a) deg $f(x) = 1$, (b) deg $f(x) = 2$, (c) deg $f(x) = 3$.

6. Discuss the mapping $\mathbb{C} \xrightarrow{g} \mathbb{C}$ defined by $g(u) = u \cdot i$. Is it a bijection? Is it an isomorphism? What is the geometric significance of g?

7. If $\mathbb{C} \xrightarrow{f} \mathbb{C}$ is an isomorphism such that $f(r) = r$ for every $r \in \mathbb{R}$, then prove that either f is the identity mapping or f is the mapping defined by $f(z) = \bar{z}$.

5. nth Roots of a Complex Number

For each integer $n > 1$, the zeros of the polynomial $x^n - 1$ in C are called the nth *roots of unity*. Thus, $u \in \mathbb{C}$ is an nth root of unity iff $u^n = 1$. Clearly there are at most n nth roots of unity. We can easily find nth roots of unity by de Moivre's theorem:

$$(\text{cis } \theta)^n = 1 \text{ iff } n\theta = 2k\pi \text{ for some } k \in \mathbb{Z}.$$

Therefore, cis $(2k\pi/n)$ is an nth root of unity for every $k \in \mathbb{Z}$. In particular,

$$u = \text{cis } \frac{2\pi}{n} \text{ is an } n\text{th root of unity.}$$

Since $(u^k)^n = (u^n)^k = 1$ for every $k \in \mathbb{Z}$, evidently

$$1, \quad u, \quad u^2, \quad \ldots, \quad u^{n-1}$$

are all nth roots of unity. Since $2k\pi/n < 2\pi$ if $0 < k < n$, the above nth roots of unity are all distinct. Hence they are the only nth roots of unity, and

$$x^n - 1 = (x - 1)(x - u) \cdot \ldots \cdot (x - u^{n-1}).$$

For example, the sixth roots of unity are $1, u, u^2, \ldots, u^5$, where

$$u = \operatorname{cis} \frac{2\pi}{6} = \cos \frac{\pi}{3} + i \sin \frac{\pi}{3}$$

$$= \frac{1}{2}(1 + \sqrt{3}i).$$

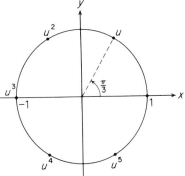

Figure 6.5

Thus, the sixth roots of unity are six equispaced points of the circle group, as shown in Figure 6.5.

The problem of finding the nth roots of any complex number is now easily solved. If $v \in \mathbb{C}$, $v \neq 0$, say v has trigonometric form

$$v = r \operatorname{cis} \theta,$$

then

$$w = \sqrt[n]{r} \operatorname{cis} \frac{\theta}{n}$$

is an nth root of v. Of course, $\sqrt[n]{r}$ indicates the positive real nth root of r. Then

$$\{w, wu, wu^2, \ldots, wu^{n-1}\}$$

is the set of all nth roots of v, where $u = \operatorname{cis}(2\pi/n)$ as above.

For example, we find the cube roots of $-1 + i$ by first representing $-1 + i$ in trigonometric form, $-1 + i = \sqrt{2} \operatorname{cis}(3\pi/4)$. Hence,

$$w = \sqrt[3]{\sqrt{2}} \operatorname{cis} \frac{\pi}{4}$$

is one cube root of $-1 + i$, and w, wu, wu^2 are all the cube roots of $-1 + i$ where $u = \operatorname{cis} 2\pi/3$ is a cube root of unity. Thus,

$$\sqrt[6]{2} \operatorname{cis} \frac{\pi}{4}, \qquad \sqrt[6]{2} \operatorname{cis} \frac{11\pi}{12}, \qquad \sqrt[6]{2} \operatorname{cis} \frac{19\pi}{12}$$

are the cube roots of $-1 + i$.

We can use the results of this section to factor some simple real polynomials into products of primes. For example, to factor

$$f(x) = x^5 + 1,$$

we use the fact that the complex zeros of $f(x)$ are the five fifth roots of -1,

$$-1, -u, -u^2, -u^3, -u^4, \qquad \text{where } u = \text{cis}\, \frac{2\pi}{5}.$$

The zeros $-u$ and $-u^4$ are easily shown to be conjugates, as are $-u^2$ and $-u^3$. Hence

$$f(x) = (x + 1)[(x + u)(x + u^4)][(x + u^2)(x + u^3)]$$

or

$$f(x) = (x + 1)(x^2 + (u + u^4)x + 1)(x^2 + (u^2 + u^3)x + 1)$$

is the factorization of $f(x)$ into primes in $\mathbb{R}[x]$.

Exercises

1. Find the cube roots of 1, the fourth roots of 1, and the fifth roots of 1. Represent the answers geometrically.

2. Find the indicated roots, and represent them geometrically.
   (a) cube roots of $-8 + 8i$.
   (b) seventh roots of -128,
   (c) fifth roots of $-1 - \sqrt{3}i$,
   (d) square roots of i,
   (e) fourth roots of -1,
   (f) cube roots of $27i$.

3. If u is an nth root of 1, u is called a *primitive* nth *root* iff $u^m \neq 1$ for every positive integer $m < n$. Find all the primitive nth roots of 1 for $n = 2, 3, 4, 5,$ and 6.

4. If u is a primitive nth root of 1, prove that u^k is also a primitive nth root of 1 iff $(k,n) = 1$.

5. Prove that the sum of the n distinct nth roots of 1 is zero.

6. Let H be the set of all nth roots of 1, $n = 1,2,3, \ldots$. Prove that $\{H; \cdot\}$ is an Abelian group isomorphic to the group of rationals modulo 1.

7. Show that $x^{10} + x^5 + 1$ is not a prime in $\mathbb{Q}[x]$.

8. If $n \in \mathbb{Z}^+$, factor $x^n - 1$ as a product of primes in $R[x]$.

9. Prove that for any field F, the transcendental extension $F(x)$ of F is not algebraically closed.

10. If S is the field of constructible numbers (Section 6, Chapter 1) and $T = \{a + bi \mid a,b \in S\}$, then each $z \in T$ is constructible in the complex plane. Prove that T is a field and that $\sqrt{z} \in T$ for every $z \in T$.

chapter 7

Factorization in Integral Domains

Factorization can be carried out in such integral domains as $\mathbb{Z}$ and $F[x]$, F a field, and in each case the factorization into primes is unique. These two domains have an important common property—they are principal ideal domains. We shall show in this chapter that unique factorization into primes is a property shared by all principal ideal domains.

I. Unique Factorization Domains

Our only concern in this section is with an integral domain R with unity. We know that the set U of units of R (i.e., elements with multiplicative inverses) is an Abelian group under multiplication. Each $u \in U$ is a factor of every $d \in R$,

$$d = u \cdot (u^{-1}d).$$

We call such a factorization of d a *trivial factorization* and u a *trivial factor* of d. If $R = \mathbb{Z}$, for example, then $U = \{-1,1\}$ and a factorization such as $-8 = (-1) \cdot 8$ is trivial. On the other hand, $-8 = (-2) \cdot 4$ is a nontrivial factorization.

An element p of R is called a *prime* iff $p \neq 0$, $p \notin U$, and p has only trivial factorizations. If $d \in R$ is factored as a product of primes,

$$d = p_1 \cdot p_2 \cdot \ldots \cdot p_k, \qquad \text{each } p_i \text{ prime},$$

119

then the factorization is said to be *unique* if for every other factorization of d into primes,

$$d = q_1 \cdot q_2 \cdot \ldots \cdot q_m, \qquad \text{each } q_i \text{ prime,}$$

necessarily $k = m$ and there exists a permutation $(i_1, i_2, \ldots, i_k)$ of $(1, 2, \ldots, k)$ such that each q_j is a unit times p_{i_j}, $j = 1, \ldots, k$.

An integral domain R is called a *unique factorization domain* (abbreviated "ufd") iff each nonzero, nonunit element of R has a unique factorization into a product of primes. We shall presently show that $\mathbb{Z}$ and $F[x]$ are examples of ufd's.

The relation "is a factor of" in an integral domain R is denoted by $|$ and is defined as usual by

$$a \mid b \text{ iff } b = ac \text{ for some } c \in R.$$

Let U be the group of units of R and $R' = \{x \in R \mid x \neq 0\}$. The reader may easily verify the following properties of the relation $|$.

7.1 $a \mid a$ for all $a \in R'$ (reflexive).

7.2   Whenever $a \mid b$ and $b \mid c$ for $a, b, c \in R'$, then $a \mid c$ (transitive).

7.3 $a \mid b$ and $b \mid a$ for $a, b \in R'$ iff $b = au$ for some $u \in U$.

We shall frequently work with an integral domain R having the following property:

7.4   For every prime $p \in R$ and all $a, b \in R'$,

$$\text{if } p \mid ab \text{ then either } p \mid a \quad \text{or} \quad p \mid b.$$

The domain of integers $\mathbb{Z}$ has this property by 1.24. By the same proof, it may be shown that $F[x]$ also has property 7.4 for every field F.

If R has property 7.4, then it follows by mathematical induction that R also has property 7.5:

7.5   For every prime $p \in R$ and all $a_1, a_2, \ldots, a_n \in R'$,

$$\text{if } p \mid a_1 a_2 \ldots a_n \text{ then } p \mid a_i \text{ for some } i.$$

The importance of property 7.4 is shown by the following:

7.6   Theorem. If R is an integral domain such that every $d \in R'$, $d \notin U$, has a factorization into a product of primes, then R is an ufd iff 7.4 holds.

Proof: Assume that R is an ufd. If $a = p_1 p_2 \ldots p_j$ and $b = p_{j+1} p_{j+2} \cdots p_m$, where each p_i is prime, then ab has the unique factorization $ab = p_1 p_2 \cdots p_m$.

Therefore, if $p \mid ab$ for some prime $p, p = p_i u$ for some i and some $u \in U$, and either $p \mid a$ or $p \mid b$. Hence, 7.4 holds.

Conversely, assume that 7.4 holds. The proof that R is an ufd is by mathematical induction. Let

$$S = \{n \in \mathbb{Z}^+ \mid \text{every } d \in R \text{ which has a factorization into a product}$$
$$\text{of } n \text{ primes has unique factorization into primes}\}.$$

Clearly $1 \in S$, for if d is a prime, d has unique factorization, $d = d$. Assume that $\{1, 2, \ldots, n - 1\} \subset S$ and let d be any element of R such that

$$d = p_1 p_2 \ldots p_n, \qquad \text{each } p_i \text{ prime}.$$

If d also has the factorization

$$d = q_1 q_2 \ldots q_m, \qquad \text{each } q_i \text{ prime},$$

then necessarily $m \geq n$. For otherwise, if $m < n$, then $m \in S$ and d has unique factorization as a product of m primes, contrary to the fact that d is a product of n primes. Since $q_1 \mid d$, evidently $q_1 \mid p_i$ for some i by 7.5. Assume, for simplicity, that $q_1 \mid p_1$, say $q_1 = p_1 u$ for some $u \in U$. Then

$$d = p_1 d' \qquad \text{where} \quad d' = p_2 p_3 \ldots p_n.$$

Note that also

$$d' = q_2' q_3 \ldots q_m \qquad \text{where} \quad q_2' = u q_2.$$

Since d' has a factorization into $n - 1$ primes and $n - 1 \in S$, the factorization of d' is unique. Hence, $n - 1 = m - 1$ and there exists a permutation $(i_2, \ldots, i_n)$ of $(2, \ldots, n)$ such that $q_2' = p_{i_2} u_2$, $q_3 = p_{i_3} u_3, \ldots, q_n = p_{i_n} u_n$ for some $u_i \in U$. Therefore, $m = n$ and

$$q_1 = p_1 u, \quad q_2 = p_{i_2} u_2 u^{-1}, \quad q_3 = p_{i_3} u_3, \quad \ldots, \quad q_n = p_{i_n} u_n.$$

Thus, the factorization of d is unique and $n \in S$. We conclude that $S = \mathbb{Z}^+$ by mathematical induction and hence that R is an ufd. ∎

Since every nonzero, nonunit element of $\mathbb{Z}$ and $F[x]$, F a field, has a factorization into primes and 7.4 holds for both $\mathbb{Z}$ and $F[x]$, clearly both $\mathbb{Z}$ and $F[x]$ are unique factorization domains by 7.6.

Exercises

1. Prove 7.1–7.3.

2. Show that 7.4 holds for $F[x]$, where F is any field.

Find the unique factorization into primes of each of the following elements.

3. 1547 in $\mathbb{Z}$.

4. 10,001 in $\mathbb{Z}$.

5. $x^4 + 1$ in $\mathbb{Z}_2[x]$.

6. $x^4 + 1$ in $\mathbb{Z}_3[x]$.

7. $x^4 + x^3 + x^2 + x + 1$ in $\mathbb{R}[x]$.

8. $x^8 + 1$ in $\mathbb{C}[x]$.

9. 1010101 in $\mathbb{Z}$.

10. $x^{10} + x^5 + 1$ in $\mathbb{Z}_5[x]$.

2. Principal Ideal Domains

An integral domain R is called a *principal ideal domain* (abbreviated "pid") iff R has a unity 1 and every ideal A of R is principal, i.e., $A = aR = \{ax \mid x \in R\}$ for some $a \in R$. Clearly $A = \{0\}$ iff $a = 0$, and $A = R$ iff $a \in U$, the group of units of R. Thus, A is a proper ideal of R iff $a \neq 0$ and $a \notin U$. If $a,b \in R$, then it is easily shown that

7.7 $aR = bR$ iff $a = bu$ for some $u \in U$.

If R is a pid and L is the set of all ideals of R, then there are three useful operations in L—intersection, addition, and multiplication—defined as follows. For all $A,B \in L$,

$$A \cap B = \{x \in R \mid x \in A \quad \text{and} \quad x \in B\},$$
$$A + B = \{x + y \mid x \in A \quad \text{and} \quad y \in B\},$$
$$AB = \{xy \mid x \in A \quad \text{and} \quad y \in B\}.$$

We already know that $A \cap B$ and $A + B$ are ideals of a ring R whenever A and B are ideals. We should keep in mind that

$$A \subset A + B \quad \text{and} \quad B \subset A + B.$$

In fact, $A + B$ is the least ideal of R containing both A and B.

The set AB defined above is not always an ideal of a ring R. However, if R is a pid, then AB is an ideal. For if $A = aR$ and $B = bR$, then each $x \in A$ has the form $x = ac$ and each $y \in B$ the form $y = bd$ for some $c,d \in R$. Hence,

$$xy = (ac)(bd) = (ab)(cd)$$

and $xy \in abR$. On the other hand, each element of abR is in AB since $(ab)r = a(br) \in AB$. Thus,

$$AB = abR,$$

and AB is an ideal of R. Since $ab \in A \cap B$ (why?), evidently

$$AB \subset A \cap B.$$

The ideal AB need not equal $A \cap B$. In $\mathbb{Z}$, for example,

$$(4\mathbb{Z})(6\mathbb{Z}) = 24\mathbb{Z}, \qquad 4\mathbb{Z} \cap 6\mathbb{Z} = 12\mathbb{Z}.$$

7.8 Theorem. Let R be a pid and L be its set of ideals. The operations $\cap$, $+$, and $\cdot$ in L have the following properties:

(1) $\cap$, $+$, and $\cdot$ are commutative.

(2) $\cap$, $+$, and $\cdot$ are associative.

(3) $\cdot$ is distributive with respect to $+$; i.e.,

$$A(B + C) = AB + AC \text{ for all } A,B,C \in L.$$

(4) $\cdot$ is distributive with respect to $\cap$; i.e.,

$$A(B \cap C) = (AB) \cap (AC) \text{ for all } A,B,C \in L.$$

(5) $+$ is distributive with respect to $\cap$; i.e.,

$$A + (B \cap C) = (A + B) \cap (A + C) \text{ for all } A,B,C \in L.$$

(6) $AB = (A + B)(A \cap B)$ for all $A,B,C \in L$.

(7) $AB = A \cap B$ iff $A + B = R$, for all nonzero $A,B \in L$.

Outline of proof: We omit the proofs of (1) and (2) since they are obvious. To prove the others, let

$$A = aR, \qquad B = bR, \qquad C = cR.$$

Then

$$AB = abR, \qquad AC = acR.$$

(3) Clearly $A(B + C) \subset AB + AC$. On the other hand, for all $abx \in AB$ and $acy \in AC$, $abx + acy = a(bx + cy) \in A(B + C)$. Thus, $AB + AC \subset A(B + C)$. Hence, $A(B + C) = AB + AC$.

(4) If A, B, or C is $\{0\}$, then $A(B \cap C) = (AB) \cap (AC) = \{0\}$ and (4) is proved. Next, assume A, B, and C are all nonzero. Since $B \cap C \subset B$ and $B \cap C \subset C$, $A(B \cap C) \subset AB$ and $A(B \cap C) \subset AC$. Thus, $A(B \cap C) \subset (AB) \cap (AC)$. If $x \in (AB) \cap (AC)$, $x \neq 0$, then $x = abr = acs$ for some $r,s \in R$ and $br = cs \in B \cap C$. Hence, $x = a(br) \in A(B \cap C)$. We conclude that $(AB) \cap (AC) \subset A(B \cap C)$. Therefore, $A(B \cap C) = (AB) \cap (AC)$.

(5) A proof is sketched in Theoretical Project 1, p. 125.

(6) We have $AB \subset A^2 + BA$ and $AB \subset AB + B^2$. Hence,

$$AB \subset (A^2 + BA) \cap (AB + B^2) = [(A + B)A] \cap [(A + B)B]$$
$$= (A + B)(A \cap B)$$

by (3) and (4). In turn,

$$(A + B)(A \cap B) = A(A \cap B) + B(A \cap B) \subset AB + BA = AB.$$

Therefore, $AB = (A + B)(A \cap B)$.

(7) If $A + B = R$, then $AB = R(A \cap B) = A \cap B$ by (6). Conversely, if $AB = A \cap B$, then $(A + B)(A \cap B) = A \cap B$ by (6). If $A \cap B = kR$, then $k = x(ky)$ for some $x \in A + B$ and $y \in R$. Since $k \neq 0$ by assumption, $xy = 1$ and x is a unit. Consequently, $A + B = R$. ∎

Factorization of elements is closely related to ideal inclusion in a pid R. If $a,b \in R$, then $a \mid b$ iff $b = ac$ for some $c \in R$. This clearly is equivalent to:

7.9 $a \mid b$ iff $aR \supset bR$.

In $\mathbb{Z}$, for example,

$$6 \mid 24 \quad \text{and} \quad 6\mathbb{Z} \supset 24\mathbb{Z}; \qquad 5\mathbb{Z} \supset 125\mathbb{Z} \quad \text{and} \quad 5 \mid 125.$$

Let R be a pid and $R' = \{x \in R \mid x \neq 0\}$. By definition, a *greatest common divisor* (gcd) of a and b in R' is any element $c \in R'$ such that (1) $c \mid a$ and $c \mid b$ and (2) if $x \mid a$ and $x \mid b$ for some $x \in R'$, then $x \mid c$. Dually, a *least common multiple* (lcm) of a and b in R' is any element $d \in R'$ such that (1) $a \mid d$ and $b \mid d$ and (2) if $a \mid x$ and $b \mid x$ for some $x \in R'$, then $d \mid x$. That such elements exist and are unique is proved below.

7.10   Theorem. If R is a pid, then every pair a, b of elements of R' has unique (up to unit factors) gcd c and lcm d given by

$$aR + bR = cR, \qquad aR \cap bR = dR.$$

Proof: If c is a gcd of a and b, then $cR \supset aR$ and $cR \supset bR$, and hence $cR \supset aR + bR$, by property (1) of a gcd. If $aR + bR = xR$, then $x \mid a$ and $x \mid b$ by 7.9. Therefore, $x \mid c$ and $xR \supset cR$ by property (2) of a *gcd*. Hence, $aR + bR = cR$.

On the other hand, if $a,b \in R'$ and c is any element of R' such that $aR + bR = cR$, then $aR \subset cR$ and $bR \subset cR$ so that $c \mid a$ and $c \mid b$ by 7.9. If $x \mid a$ and $x \mid b$, then $xR \supset aR$ and $xR \supset bR$, so that $xR \supset aR + bR$. Therefore, $xR \supset cR$ and $x \mid c$ by 7.9. Consequently, c is a gcd of a and b. Since the generator of the ideal $aR + bR$ is unique up to a unit factor by 7.7, c is unique up to a unit factor.

The proof for the lcm is almost identical and hence is left as an exercise. ∎

As for $\mathbb{Z}$ and $F[x]$, we shall use the notations

$$(a,b) \quad \text{and} \quad [a,b]$$

for a gcd and lcm, respectively, of the nonzero elements a and b of a pid R. We call a and b *relatively prime* iff

$$(a,b) = 1.$$

That is, a and b (in R') are relatively prime iff

$$aR + bR = R.$$

If $a,b \in R'$, then by 7.8(7),

7.11 $$(a,b) = 1 \text{ iff } [a,b] = ab.$$

Exercises

1. Prove 7.7

2. Prove 7.9.

3. Prove the part of 7.10 for lcm.

4. Interpret 7.8(3), in terms of gcd. Illustrate.

5. Interpret 7.8(4), in terms of lcm. Illustrate.

6. Interpret 7.8(6), in terms of gcd and lcm. Illustrate.

THEORETICAL PROJECT 1

Let R be an integral domain with unity. Call an ideal P of R *prime* iff whenever $AB \subset P$, A and B ideals of R, then either $A \subset P$ or $B \subset P$. Similarly, call an ideal W of R *weakly prime* iff whenever $A \cap B \subset P$, A and B ideals of R, then either $A \subset P$ or $B \subset P$. Finally, call an ideal I of R *irreducible* iff whenever $A \cap B = I$, A and B ideals of R, then either $A = I$ or $B = I$.

1. Show that every prime ideal of R is weakly prime, and every weakly prime ideal of R is irreducible.

2. If R is a pid, show that a proper ideal pR of R is prime iff p is a prime element.

3. Let A be a proper ideal of R. Prove that A is prime iff the quotient ring R/A is an integral domain.

4. If R is a pid, show that a proper ideal A of R is weakly prime iff $A = p^n R$ for some prime element p of R and some $n \in \mathbb{Z}^+$. [*Hint:* If $A = aR$ and a is not prime, then $a = bc$, $(b,c) = 1$ for some $b,c \in R$, b and c nonunits. Now use 7.8(7). Conversely, if $A = p^n R$ and $bR \cap cR \subset A$, then $p^n \mid [b,c]$ and either $p^n \mid b$ or $p^n \mid c$.]

5. If R is a pid, show that every irreducible ideal is weakly prime. [*Hint:* Use 4.]

6. Prove 7.8(5). [*Hint:* Let $A,B,C \in L$. If $D = A + (B \cap C)$, then clearly $D \subset (A + B) \cap (A + C)$. Let E be an irreducible ideal of R containing D. Then $A,B,C \subset E$. Hence, $(A + B) \cap (A + C) \subset E$. Since D is an intersection of irreducible ideals, $(A + B) \cap (A + C) \subset D$.]

7. Let R be a pid and L be its set of ideals. Prove that $\cap$ is distributive with respect to $+$ in L; i.e.,

$$A \cap (B + C) = (A \cap B) + (A \cap C) \quad \text{for all} \quad A,B,C \in L.$$

[*Hint:* Follows directly from 7.8(5).]

8. Let $R = Q[x,y]$ and $A = x^2 R + (x + y)R$. Show that the ideal A of R is irreducible but not weakly prime.

3. Factorization in a Principal Ideal Domain

The pid with which we are familiar, $\mathbb{Z}$ and $F[x]$, F a field, contain prime elements. A natural question to ask is whether or not every pid necessarily contains prime elements. We answer this question below.

Let R be a pid and $p \in R'$, $p \notin U$. The proper ideal pR is called a *maximal ideal* of R iff R and pR are the only ideals of R containing pR. Thus, if pR is a maximal ideal and $xR \supset pR$, then either $xR = R$ and x is a unit or $xR = pR$ and $x = pu$ for some unit. In other words, if $x \mid p$, then either $x \in U$ or $x = pu$ for some $u \in U$. Therefore, if pR is maximal then p is a prime.

7.12   Theorem. If R is a pid and $p \in R'$, $p \notin U$, then pR is a maximal ideal iff p is a prime.

Proof: We need only show that if p is a prime then pR is a maximal ideal. To this end, assume that $xR \supset pR$. Then $x \mid p$ and hence either x is a unit or $x = pu$ for some unit. Therefore, $xR = R$ or $xR = pR$. ∎

That a pid actually contains primes follows from the theorem below.

7.13   Theorem. Every proper ideal of a pid R is contained in at least one maximal ideal.

Proof: If the theorem were false, then there would exist a proper ideal A of R which was contained in no maximal ideal of R. Then there would exist an ideal A_1 of R such that

$$A < A_1 < R.$$

Here we have used "$<$" to mean "$\subset$ but $\neq$." Clearly A_1 is not contained in a maximal ideal, for it it were, then A would be contained in the same maximal ideal, contrary to assumption. By the same reasoning,

$$A_1 < A_2 < R$$

for some ideal A_2.

This process can be carried on endlessly, yielding an infinite ascending chain of ideals,

(1) $$A < A_1 < A_2 < \ldots < A_n < \ldots,$$

of R. Each A_i has the form

$$A_i = a_i R$$

for some $a_i \in R$.

The union of all the sets $A_1, A_2, \ldots,$

(2) $$B = A_1 \cup A_2 \cup \ldots \cup A_n \cup \ldots,$$

is an ideal of R. For if $x, y \in B$, then $x \in A_k$ and $y \in A_m$ for some k and m. Since the A_i's form a chain (1), either $A_k \subset A_m$ or $A_m \subset A_k$. Assuming $A_k \subset A_m$, we see that $x, y \in A_m$ and therefore $x + y$, $-x$, and xr are in A_m, and hence also in B, for every $r \in R$. Thus, B is an ideal of R.

Since B defined by (2) is an ideal,

$$B = bR$$

for some $b \in R$. Now $b \in B$, and hence $b \in A_k$ for some k. Then $br \in A_k$ for every $r \in R$; that is

$$B \subset A_k.$$

However, this is impossible since

$$B \subset A_k < A_{k+1} \subset B.$$

No set is a proper subset of itself!

The assumption that an ideal A exists which is contained in no maximal ideal of R has led us to a contradiction. Hence, no such A exists and 7.13 is proved. ∎

In view of 7.12 and 7.13, every nonzero, nonunit element of a pid R has a prime factor. Actually, we can make the following statement:

7.14   Theorem. If R is a pid, then every nonzero, nonunit element of R can be factored into primes.

Proof: If $a \in R$, $a \notin U$, then $p_1 \mid a$ for some prime p_1 and

$$a = p_1 a_1$$

for some $a_1 \in R'$. If $a_1 \notin U$, then $p_2 \mid a_1$ for some prime p_2 and

$$a_1 = p_2 a_2$$

for some $a_2 \in R'$. Continuing, we obtain elements $a_1, a_2, \ldots, a_n, \ldots$ in R' such that for each n,

$$a_{n-1} = p_n a_n \text{ for some prime } p_n.$$

This process goes on as long as a_n is not a unit. Can it go on indefinitely? It if does, then

$$aR < a_1 R < a_2 R < \ldots < a_n R < \ldots$$

is an infinite ascending chain of ideals. However, as we saw in the proof of 7.13, no such infinite chain can exist in R. Therefore, a_n is a unit for some n and

$$a = p_1 p_2 \cdots p_{n-1} p_n'$$

where $p_n' = p_n a_n$ is also a prime. We have factored a into primes as desired. ∎

We are now in a position to prove the principal result of this section.

7.15 Theorem. Each principal ideal domain is also a unique factorization domain.

Proof: Because of 7.6, we need only show that 7.4 holds; i.e., for every prime p in a pid R and all $a,b \in R'$,

(1)   if $p \mid ab$ then either $p \mid a$ or $p \mid b$.

So let $a,b,p \in R'$ such that p is a prime and $p \mid ab$. If $p \nmid a$, then $(a,p) = 1$ and

$$ar + ps = 1 \text{ for some } r,s \in R.$$

Hence, $b = abr + pbs \in pR$ since $abR \subset pR$, and $bR \subset pR$. Thus, $p \mid b$. Consequently, (1) holds for R. ∎

Knowing only that $\mathbb{Z}$ and $F[x]$, F a field, are pid, we have by 7.15 that they are also ufd. Thus, we have an alternate way of proving that $\mathbb{Z}$ and $F[x]$ are ufd.

A different example of a pid is

$$R = F[[x]],$$

the ring of formal power series in x over a field F (see Chapter 5, p. 97). We recall that its set of ideals consists of the chain

$$R \supset xR \supset x^2R \supset \ldots \supset x^nR \supset \ldots \supset \{0\}.$$

Thus, R is a pid. Since R has only one maximal ideal, namely xR, it has only one prime element (up to a unit factor), namely x. Every element $c \in R'$ has unique factorization $c = x^n u$ for some integer $n \geq 0$ and some $u \in U$. While such rings as R might seem bizarre, they are of fundamental importance in mathematics, especially in algebraic geometry. An ufd having one and only one prime element is called a *local ring*.

Exercises

Find all the maximal ideals in which each of the following ideals is contained.

1. $14\mathbb{Z}$ in $\mathbb{Z}$.

2. $(x^2 + 1)\mathbb{Z}_2[x]$ in $\mathbb{Z}_2[x]$.

3. $24\mathbb{Z}$ in $\mathbb{Z}$.

4. $(x^3 + 8)\mathbb{Q}[x]$ in $\mathbb{Q}[x]$.

5. $(x^5 + x^4 + x^3 + x^2 + x + 1)\mathbb{Z}_2[x]$ in $\mathbb{Z}_2[x]$.

6. $36\mathbb{Z}$ in $\mathbb{Z}$.

7. $(x^3 + 2x + 1)\mathbb{Z}_3[x]$ in $\mathbb{Z}_3[x]$.

8. $(x^2 + 1)\mathbb{C}[x]$ in $\mathbb{C}[x]$.

9. $(x^2 + x^3 + \ldots + x^n + \ldots)\mathbb{Q}[[x]]$ in $\mathbb{Q}[[x]]$.

10. $(y^2 + xy + x + y)F$ in $F[y]$, where $F = \mathbb{Q}(x)$.

*11. Let p be a prime number and

$$R = \left\{ \frac{a}{b} \,\middle|\, a \in \mathbb{Z}, b \in \mathbb{Z}^+, (b,p) = 1 \right\}.$$

Prove that R is an integral domain. Is R a pid? What are the primes of R? What is the group of units of R?

*12. Let p and q be distinct prime numbers and

$$R = \left\{ \frac{a}{b} \,\middle|\, a \in \mathbb{Z}, b \in \mathbb{Z}^+, (b,pq) = 1 \right\}.$$

Prove that R is an integral domain. Is R a pid? What are the primes of R? What is the group of units of R?

4. Euclidean Domains

The division process is very useful in working with the domains $\mathbb{Z}$ and $F[x]$, F a field. In $\mathbb{Z}$ and $F[x]$, the division process is essentially of the following form. Each element d has associated with it an integer $\varphi(d)$ such that:

7.16 $\varphi(d) > \varphi(0)$ for every nonzero d.

7.17 For all a and b, with $b \neq 0$, there exist q and r such that

$$a = bq + r \quad \text{and} \quad \varphi(r) < \varphi(b).$$

In $\mathbb{Z}$, we think of

$$\varphi(n) = |n|$$

whereas in $F[x]$ we think of

$$\varphi(f(x)) = \deg f(x) \quad \text{if} \quad f(x) \neq 0, \qquad \varphi(0) = -1.$$

Our choice of -1 for $\varphi(0)$ is arbitrary; any negative value of $\varphi(0)$ would have insured 7.16's holding.

An integral domain R with unity which has an associated mapping

$$R \xrightarrow{\varphi} \mathbb{Z}$$

satisfying 7.16 and 7.17 is called a *Euclidean domain*. It is a domain in which Euclid's algorithm applies (see p. 19). A fundamental property of Euclidean domains is as follows.

7.18 **Theorem.** Every Euclidean domain is a principal ideal domain.

Proof: Let R be a Euclidean domain and $R \xrightarrow{\varphi} \mathbb{Z}$ be a mapping satisfying 7.16 and 7.17. If I is a nonzero ideal and $S = \{\varphi(a) \mid a \in I'\}$, then S has a lower bound by 7.16 and hence S has a least element by the well-ordering of $\mathbb{Z}$. Select $b \in I$ such that $\varphi(b)$ is the least element of S. For every $a \in I$ there exist $q, r \in R$ such that

$$a = bq + r \quad \text{and} \quad \varphi(r) < \varphi(b)$$

by 7.17. Since $r = a - bq \in I$ and $\varphi(r) < \varphi(b)$, evidently $r = 0$ by our choice of b. Hence, $a \in bR$ and we conclude that $I = bR$. ∎

Since each Euclidean domain is a pid, each Euclidean domain is also an ufd by 7.15.

The converse of 7.18 is not true, although it is difficult to find examples of pid's which are not Euclidean.

Exercises

1. If R is a Euclidean domain and $R \xrightarrow{\varphi} \mathbb{Z}$ is a mapping with properties 7.16 and 7.17, then let k be any element of $\mathbb{Z}$ and $R \xrightarrow{\alpha} \mathbb{Z}$ be defined by $\alpha(d) = \varphi(d) + k$. Prove that the mapping α also has properties 7.16 and 7.17.

2. Let R be an integral domain. Prove that if there exists a mapping $R \xrightarrow{\varphi} \mathbb{Z}$ with properties 7.16 and 7.17, then necessarily R has a unity. [*Hint:* The proof of 7.18 does not use the fact that R has a unity. Hence, R is a principal ideal.]

3. If $\varphi(n) = |n|$ for all $n \in \mathbb{Z}$, then clearly $\varphi(a) \leq \varphi(b)$ if $a \mid b$. A similar remark holds in case $\varphi(f(x)) = \deg f(x)$ in $F[x]$. Give examples of Euclidean domains in which this property does not hold. [*Hint:* If p is a prime, we might define $\varphi(n) = n$ for every $n \in \mathbb{Z}_p = \{0, 1, \ldots, p - 1\}$.]

5. Quadratic Domains

Integers such as

$$2, \quad 3, \quad 6, \quad 14, \quad -1, \quad -7, \quad -10$$

which are different from 0 and 1 and have no square factor other than 1 are called *square-free integers*. For each square-free integer n, we can form the *quadratic field*

$$\mathbb{Q}[\sqrt{n}] = \{a + b\sqrt{n} \mid a,b \in \mathbb{Q}\}.$$

Whenever $n < 0$, we take $\sqrt{n} = i\sqrt{-n}$. If $n > 0$, $\mathbb{Q}[\sqrt{n}]$ is a real field; if $n < 0$, $\mathbb{Q}[\sqrt{n}]$ is a complex field.

If n is a square-free integer, then the polynomial $x^2 - n$ is prime in $\mathbb{Q}[x]$. Thus, in terms of field extensions, $\mathbb{Q}[\sqrt{n}]$ is isomorphic to

$$\mathbb{Q}[x]/(x^2 - n)\mathbb{Q}[x].$$

Just as each complex number has a conjugate, so does each quadratic number. If $u = a + b\sqrt{n}$, $a,b \in \mathbb{Q}$, then u has *conjugate* $\bar{u} = a - b\sqrt{n}$ in

$\mathbb{Q}[\sqrt{n}]$. For example,

$$\text{if} \quad u = 7 - 3\sqrt{5} \quad \text{then} \quad \bar{u} = 7 + 3\sqrt{5}.$$

If $n < 0$, then the conjugate in $\mathbb{Q}[\sqrt{n}]$ is the same as the conjugate in $\mathbb{C}$. It is easily shown that:

7.19 $$\overline{u + v} = \bar{u} + \bar{v}, \; \overline{uv} = \bar{u}\bar{v} \text{ for all } u,v \in \mathbb{Q}[\sqrt{n}].$$

Then we have the following result, corresponding to 6.6 for $\mathbb{C}$.

7.20 Theorem. For each square-free integer n, the mapping $\mathbb{Q}[\sqrt{n}] \xrightarrow{h} \mathbb{Q}[\sqrt{n}]$ defined by $h(u) = \bar{u}$ is an isomorphism.

The *trace function* T and the *norm function* N are defined for $\mathbb{Q}[\sqrt{n}]$ just as they were for $\mathbb{C}$. Thus,

$$T(u) = u + \bar{u}, \qquad N(u) = u\bar{u} \quad \text{for all} \quad u \in \mathbb{Q}[\sqrt{n}].$$

In other words, for all $a,b \in \mathbb{Q}$,

7.21 $$T(a + b\sqrt{n}) = 2a, \; N(a + b\sqrt{n}) = a^2 - nb^2.$$

Thus, T and N are mappings of $\mathbb{Q}[\sqrt{n}]$ into $\mathbb{Q}$. It follows easily from 7.19 that for all $u,v \in \mathbb{Q}[\sqrt{n}]$,

7.22 $$T(u + v) = T(u) + T(v), \; N(uv) = N(u)N(v).$$

Contained in each quadratic field $\mathbb{Q}[\sqrt{n}]$ is the integral domain

$$\mathbb{Z}[\sqrt{n}] = \{a + b\sqrt{n} \mid a,b \in \mathbb{Z}\}.$$

We call $\mathbb{Z}[\sqrt{n}]$ a *domain of quadratic integers*. For example,

$$0, \quad 4, \quad 3 - 2\sqrt{5}, \quad 16\sqrt{5}, \quad 7 + \sqrt{5}$$

are quadratic integers in $\mathbb{Z}[\sqrt{5}]$.

The quadratic domain

$$\mathbb{Z}[\sqrt{-1}] = \{a + bi \mid a,b \in \mathbb{Z}\}$$

is called the domain of *Gaussian integers*. Geometrically, it consists of all points in the complex plane having integral coordinates.

It is clear that $\mathbb{Z}[\sqrt{n}]$ is mapped into $\mathbb{Z}$ by the trace and norm functions. For example,

$$T(3 - 2\sqrt{5}) = 6, \qquad T(6\sqrt{5}) = 0, \qquad T(4) = 8$$

and

$$N(3 - 2\sqrt{5}) = -11, \qquad N(6\sqrt{5}) = -180, \qquad N(4) = 16.$$

What are the units of a quadratic domain $\mathbb{Z}[\sqrt{n}]$? If u is a unit, so that $uv = 1$ for some $v \in \mathbb{Z}[\sqrt{n}]$, then

$$N(uv) = N(u)N(v) = N(1) = 1.$$

Hence, $N(u)$ is a unit of $\mathbb{Z}$, i.e., $N(u) = \pm 1$. This proves part of the following result:

7.23 $u \in \mathbb{Z}[\sqrt{n}]$ is a unit iff $N(u) = \pm 1$.

We leave the rest of the proof of 7.23 as an exercise.

It is now an easy matter to see that each domain $\mathbb{Z}[\sqrt{n}]$ has primes. For if $d \in \mathbb{Z}[\sqrt{n}]$, $d \neq 0$ and d not a unit, then $|N(d)| > 1$. Hence,

$$S = \{|N(c)| \mid c \in \mathbb{Z}[\sqrt{n}], \, c \mid d, \, |N(c)| > 1\}$$

has a least element k. If $p \in \mathbb{Z}[\sqrt{n}]$, $p \mid d$, and $|N(p)| = k$, then clearly p is a prime factor of d. If $d = pd_1$, then $1 \leq |N(d_1)| < |N(d)|$. Now either $|N(d_1)| = 1$, in which case d_1 is a unit and d is a prime, or $|N(d_1)| > 1$ and d_1 has a prime factor p_2. In at most $|N(d)|$ such steps, we can factor d into primes,

$$d = p_1 p_2 \ldots p_m.$$

We state this result as follows.

7.24   Theorem. Every nonzero, nonunit element of a quadratic domain $\mathbb{Z}[\sqrt{n}]$ can be factored into primes.

We shall postpone until the next section the question of whether or not the factorization in $\mathbb{Z}[\sqrt{n}]$ is unique.

For example, let us factor $11 + 7i \in \mathbb{Z}[\sqrt{-1}]$ into primes. If

$$11 + 7i = p_1 p_2 \ldots p_n \text{ then } N(11 + 7i) = N(p_1)N(p_2) \ldots N(p_n).$$

Thus, any factorization of $11 + 7i$ leads to a corresponding factorization of $N(11 + 7i)$ in $\mathbb{Z}$. Since

$$N(11 + 7i) = 170 = 2 \cdot 5 \cdot 17,$$

$11 + 7i$ has at most three prime factors, having norms of 2, 5, and 17. The Gaussian integers of norm 2 are $1 + i$ and $1 - i$. We easily discover that $(1 + i) \mid (11 + 7i)$ and that

$$11 + 7i = (1 + i)(9 - 2i).$$

Gaussian integers of norm 5 are $2 \pm i$ and $1 \pm 2i$. By testing each of these, we find that $(2 - i) \mid (9 - 2i)$ and

$$9 - 2i = (2 - i)(4 + i).$$

We note that $N(4 + i) = 17$. Hence,

$$11 + 7i = (1 + i)(2 - i)(4 + i)$$

is a factorization of $11 + 7i$ into primes in $\mathbb{Z}[\sqrt{-1}]$.

As another example, let us factor $4 + 7\sqrt{2} \in \mathbb{Z}[\sqrt{2}]$. First,

$$N(4 + 7\sqrt{2}) = -2 \cdot 41.$$

Thus, a prime factor of $4 + 7\sqrt{2}$ must have norm ± 2, ± 41, or ± 82. We easily verify that $(2 + \sqrt{2}) \mid (4 + 7\sqrt{2})$ and that

$$4 + 7\sqrt{2} = (2 + \sqrt{2})(-3 + 5\sqrt{2}).$$

Each of the factors is a prime, since its norm is a prime in $\mathbb{Z}$. Now $1 + \sqrt{2}$ is a unit in $\mathbb{Z}[\sqrt{2}]$, with inverse $-1 + \sqrt{2}$. Therefore,

$$(2 + \sqrt{2})(1 + \sqrt{2}) \quad \text{and} \quad (-1 + \sqrt{2})(-3 + 5\sqrt{2})$$

are equivalent prime factors, and

$$4 + 7\sqrt{2} = (4 + 3\sqrt{2})(13 - 8\sqrt{2})$$

is an equivalent factorization (i.e., corresponding primes differ only by unit factors).

Exercises

Factor each of the following quadratic integers into primes.

1. $4 + 3\sqrt{3}$ in $\mathbb{Z}[\sqrt{3}]$.
2. $3 + i$ in $\mathbb{Z}[\sqrt{-1}]$.
3. 2 in $\mathbb{Z}[\sqrt{-1}]$.
4. $4 - \sqrt{-3}$ in $\mathbb{Z}[\sqrt{-3}]$.
5. $9 + \sqrt{5}$ in $\mathbb{Z}[\sqrt{5}]$.
6. $2 - \sqrt{-5}$ in $\mathbb{Z}[\sqrt{-5}]$.
7. $2 + \sqrt{10}$ in $\mathbb{Z}[\sqrt{10}]$.
8. $4 - 2\sqrt{10}$ in $\mathbb{Z}[\sqrt{10}]$.
9. $22 + 8\sqrt{7}$ in $\mathbb{Z}[\sqrt{7}]$.
10. 9 in $\mathbb{Z}[\sqrt{-2}]$.
11. Prove 7.19.
12. Prove 7.20.
13. Prove 7.22.
14. Complete the proof of 7.23.

15. Prove that $\{-1,1\}$ is the group of units of $\mathbb{Z}[\sqrt{n}]$ if $n < -1$. What is the group of units of $\mathbb{Z}[\sqrt{-1}]$?

*16. Let G be the group of units of $\mathbb{Z}[\sqrt{2}]$. Show that $1 + \sqrt{2} \in G$ and that $1 + \sqrt{2}$ is the least element of the set $P = \{u \in G \mid u > 1\}$. Prove that $P = \{(1 + \sqrt{2})^n \mid n \in \mathbb{Z}^+\}$. Hence, ·conclude that $G = \{\pm(1 + \sqrt{2})^n \mid n \in \mathbb{Z}\}$. [*Hint:* If $1 \le a + b\sqrt{2} < 1 + \sqrt{2}$ and $|a^2 - 2b^2| = 1$ for some $a,b \in \mathbb{Z}$, show that $a = 1$ and $b = 0$. If $u \in P$, then $(1 + \sqrt{2})^n \le u < (1 + \sqrt{2})^{n+1}$ for some $n \in \mathbb{Z}^+$. Hence, $1 \le u/(1 + \sqrt{2})^n < 1 + \sqrt{2}$. Now apply the first result.]

*17. Find the group of units of $\mathbb{Z}[\sqrt{3}]$. [*Hint:* Follow Exercise 16.]

*18. For each square-free integer n, let $R_n = \{d \in \mathbb{Q}[\sqrt{n}] \mid T(d), N(d) \in \mathbb{Z}\}$. Prove that R_n is an integral domain containing $\mathbb{Z}[\sqrt{n}]$. There are good reasons, which we shall not go into now, for calling R_n the domain of integers of $\mathbb{Q}[\sqrt{n}]$. For what integers n is $R_n = \mathbb{Z}[\sqrt{n}]$? [*Hint:* Show that if $d = a + b\sqrt{n} \in R_n$, then either a and b are both integers or both halves of odd integers. Show that the latter case occurs iff $n \equiv 1 \pmod 4$.]

6. Euclidean Quadratic Domains

Some of the quadratic domains are Euclidean, as we shall now show.

7.25 Theorem. Each of the domains $\mathbb{Z}[\sqrt{-2}]$, $\mathbb{Z}[\sqrt{-1}]$, $\mathbb{Z}[\sqrt{2}]$, and $\mathbb{Z}[\sqrt{3}]$ is Euclidean.

Proof: It is natural to let φ be the absolute value of the norm, i.e.,

$$\mathbb{Z}[\sqrt{n}] \xrightarrow{\;\varphi\;} \mathbb{Z} \quad \text{is defined by} \quad \varphi(x) = |N(x)|.$$

Then $\varphi(x) > \varphi(0) = 0$ if $x \neq 0$, and 7.16 is satisfied by φ.

To prove that φ has property 7.17 if n equals -2, -1, 2, or 3, let $a,b \in \mathbb{Z}[\sqrt{n}]$, $b \neq 0$. Then $ab^{-1} \in \mathbb{Q}[\sqrt{n}]$, i.e.,

$$ab^{-1} = s + t\sqrt{n} \quad \text{for some} \quad s,t \in Q,$$

and we can select integers j and k such that

$$|s - j| \le \tfrac{1}{2}, \qquad |t - k| \le \tfrac{1}{2}.$$

(That is, every rational number is within one-half a unit of an integer.)

A simple computation shows that

$$a = bq + r \quad \text{where} \quad q = j + k\sqrt{n} \quad \text{and} \quad r = [(s - j) + (t - k)\sqrt{n}]b.$$

Since a and bq are in $\mathbb{Z}[\sqrt{n}]$ so is $r \in \mathbb{Z}[\sqrt{n}]$. Now

$$\varphi(r) = |(s - j)^2 - n(t - k)^2| \, \varphi(b)$$

and therefore $\varphi(r) < \varphi(b)$ if $|(s - j)^2 - n(t - k)^2| < 1$. However $(s - j)^2 \leq \frac{1}{4}$, $(t - k)^2 \leq \frac{1}{4}$, and therefore

$$|(s - j)^2 - n(t - k)^2| < 1 \quad \text{if} \quad n = -2, -1, 2, \text{ or } 3.$$

Hence, 7.17 holds if $n = -2, -1, 2,$ or 3.   ∎

Each of the domains of 7.25 is a pid by 7.18, and hence an ufd by 7.15.

The problem of finding all Euclidean quadratic domains has been solved only recently. The interested reader is referred to the book of Hardy and Wright for details.

For example, the Gaussian integer $7 - 3i$ has norm $58 = 2 \cdot 29$. If it is not prime, it has prime factors of norm 2 and 29. We can divide $7 - 3i$ by $1 + i$, an integer with norm 2, by multiplying by $(1 + i)^{-1} = (1 - i)/2$. This yields $2 - 5i$, another Gaussian integer. Hence,

$$7 - 3i = (1 + i)(2 - 5i)$$

is the unique factorization of $7 - 3i$ into primes. Any other factorization of $7 - 3i$ must be as a product of two primes only unit factors different from $1 + i$ and $2 - 5i$.

Finally, let us give an example of a quadratic domain which is not an ufd. We claim that

$$\mathbb{Z}[\sqrt{-5}]$$

is not an ufd. Thus, for example,

$$6 = 2 \cdot 3 \quad \text{and} \quad 6 = (1 + \sqrt{-5})(1 - \sqrt{-5})$$

are two different factorizations of 6 into primes. They clearly differ by more than unit factors, since -1 and 1 are the only units of $\mathbb{Z}[\sqrt{-5}]$. To prove that 2, 3, $1 + \sqrt{-5}$, and $1 - \sqrt{-5}$ are actually primes, we note that their norms are 4, 9, 6, and 6, respectively. If they are not all primes, then there must exist primes of norm 2 or 3. However,

$$N(a + b\sqrt{-5}) = a^2 + 5b^2 \neq 2 \quad \text{or} \quad 3$$

for any integers a and b, as we easily show. Therefore, 2, 3, $1 + \sqrt{-5}$, and $1 - \sqrt{-5}$ are all primes.

Exercises

Factor each of the following quadratic integers into primes, and tell whether or not the factorization is unique.

1. $11 + i$ in $\mathbb{Z}[\sqrt{-1}]$.

2. $4 + 7i$ in $\mathbb{Z}[\sqrt{-1}]$.

3. 17 in $\mathbb{Z}[\sqrt{-2}]$.

4. 8 in $\mathbb{Z}[\sqrt{-5}]$.

5. $4 - 5\sqrt{2}$ in $\mathbb{Z}[\sqrt{2}]$.

6. $19 + 5\sqrt{3}$ in $\mathbb{Z}[\sqrt{3}]$.

7. 9 in $\mathbb{Z}[\sqrt{-5}]$.

8. 6 in $\mathbb{Z}[\sqrt{10}]$.

9. $15 + \sqrt{-13}$ in $\mathbb{Z}[\sqrt{-13}]$.

10. $11 - \sqrt{-5}$ in $\mathbb{Z}[\sqrt{-5}]$.

THEORETICAL PROJECT 2

A natural question to ask is whether the polynomial domain $\mathbb{Z}[x]$ is an ufd; another is whether $F[x,y]$ is an ufd for every field F. These questions are both answered in the affirmative below.

First, you should have no trouble provihg the following result.

7.26   Theorem. If R is an ufd, then every nonzero, nonunit element of $R[x]$ can be factored into primes.

[*Hint:* Select a factor of $f(x)$ of minimum positive degree; then factor out the gcd of its coefficients.]

Then, complete the proof of the following important theorem.

7.27   Theorem. If R is an ufd, then the polynomial domain $R[x]$ is also an ufd.

[*Outline of proof* as given by C. H. Giffin in the *Proceedings of the American Mathematical Society*, **14** (1963), 366]:

Assume that $R[x]$ is not an ufd. From the set S of all nonzero, nonunit polynomials in $R[x]$ which do not have a unique factorization into primes, select one of minimum degree, say $f(x)$. Then

$$f(x) = p_1(x)p_2(x) \ldots p_r(x), \qquad f(x) = q_1(x)q_2(x) \ldots q_s(x)$$

for some primes $p_i(x), q_j(x)$. No $p_i(x) = uq_j(x)$ for a unit u (why?). Assume that $m = \deg p_1(x) > 0$, $n = \deg q_1(x) > 0$, and $m \geq n$. (Why can we assume this?) Let a be the leading coefficient of $p_1(x)$ and b of $q_1(x)$. Define $g(x) = aq_1(x)x^{m-n}p_2(x) \ldots p_r(x) - bf(x)$. Then

$$g(x) = [aq_1(x)x^{m-n} - bp_1(x)]p_2(x) \ldots p_r(x)$$
$$= q_1(x)[ax^{m-n}p_2(x) \ldots p_r(x) - bq_2(x) \ldots q_s(x)].$$

Either $g(x) = 0$, and $aq_1(x)x^{m-n} = bp_1(x)$, or $\deg g(x) < \deg f(x)$. In the latter case, $g(x)$ has a unique factorization, and therefore

$$q_1(x) \mid [aq_1(x)x^{m-n} - bp_1(x)] \quad \text{and} \quad q_1(x) \mid bp_1(x).$$

Thus, in either case, $q_1(x) \mid bp_1(x)$; i.e., $bp_1(x) = q_1(x)h(x)$ for some $h(x)$. Now use the lemma of Gauss to prove that $b \mid h(x)$, remembering that $q_1(x)$ is prime. Hence, $p_1(x) = q_1(x)h_1(x)$ for some $h_1(x)$. The primeness of $p_1(x)$ means that $h_1(x)$ is a unit. However, this contradicts the choice of $f(x)$.

A corollary of 7.27 is as follows:

7.28   Theorem. If F is a field, then every polynomial domain over F in one or more symbols is an ufd.

chapter 8

Vector Spaces

It is convenient when working with the Abelian group $\{\mathbb{R}^3; +\}$ to consider an operation of scalar multiplication. The scalar product of a "vector" $(a,b,c) \in \mathbb{R}^3$ by a "scalar" $r \in \mathbb{R}$ is defined by

$$r(a,b,c) = (ra,rb,rc).$$

Geometrically speaking, the points (a,b,c), $2(a,b,c)$, $(-1)(a,b,c)$, and, generally, $r(a,b,c)$ lie on a line passing through the origin, as indicated in Figure 8.1. We shall discuss such algebraic systems, called *vector spaces*, in this chapter.

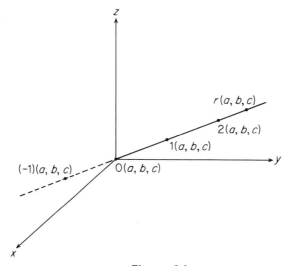

Figure 8.1

I. Definitions

Before giving a formal definition of a vector space, let us describe the prototype of all finite-dimensional vector spaces. Let F be a field, $n \in \mathbb{Z}^+$, and V_n be the Abelian group $\{F^n; +\}$,

$$V_n = \{(a_1, a_2, \ldots, a_n) \mid a_i \in F\}.$$

Although multiplication is also defined in F_n, and $\{F^n; +, \cdot\}$ is a C-ring, we are not interested in the ring structure of F_n at this time. However, we are interested in an operation of *scalar multiplication* in V_n defined as follows: For all $c \in F$, $(a_1, a_2, \ldots, a_n) \in V_n$,

$$c(a_1, a_2, \ldots, a_n) = (ca_1, ca_2, \ldots, ca_n).$$

We easily verify the following properties of scalar multiplication: For all $c, d \in F$, $x, y \in V_n$,

8.1 $$c(x + y) = cx + cy,$$

8.2 $$(c + d)x = cx + dx,$$

8.3 $$(cd)x = c(dx),$$

8.4 $$1x = x.$$

Proof of 8.2: If $x = (a_1, a_2, \ldots, a_n) \in V_n$ and $c, d \in F$, then

$$\begin{aligned}
(c + d)x &= ((c + d)a_1, (c + d)a_2, \ldots, (c + d)a_n) \\
&= (ca_1 + da_1, ca_2 + da_2, \ldots, ca_n + da_n) \\
&= (ca_1, ca_2, \ldots, ca_n) + (da_1, da_2, \ldots, da_n) \\
&= cx + dx. \quad \blacksquare
\end{aligned}$$

We leave the proofs of 8.1, 8.3, and 8.4 as exercises.

The above example of a vector space will be denoted by

$$V_n(F).$$

Thus, $V_n(F)$ is the vector space of all n-tuples over a field F.

Formally, a *vector space* is an algebraic system consisting of an Abelian group V, a field F, and a scalar multiplication of V by F having properties 8.1–8.4. The elements of V are called *vectors* and those of F, *scalars*. We denote this vector space by

$$V(F)$$

when we wish to indicate both the group of vectors V and the field of scalars F. At other times, when the field F is obvious, we shall denote the vector space simply by V.

By scalar multiplication of V by F we understand any mapping $F \times V \longrightarrow V$. Thus, for each pair $(a,x) \in F \times V$ there corresponds a unique element of V designated by ax.

Usually we shall denote scalars by early letters of the alphabet such as $a,b,c, \ldots$ and vectors by later letters such as $u,v,w, \ldots$.

We must realize that in a vector space $V(F)$ operations of addition enter twice, in V and in F, and similarly for multiplication. In 8.2, for example, addition on the left side of the equation is in F whereas addition on the right side is in V. In 8.3, cd is a product in F while $c(dx)$ involves two scalar multiplications. The additive identity elements of V and F are both denoted by 0. The context in which they are used will always clearly indicate which is meant. The unity in F is denoted by 1, as usual. We shall always put the scalar on the left and the vector on the right in scalar multiplication. The additive inverse of $x \in V$ is denoted by $-x$, and similarly for F.

Some useful properties of a vector space $V(F)$ are listed below.

8.5 $\qquad\qquad\qquad cx = 0$ iff either $c = 0$ or $x = 0$.

8.6 $\qquad\qquad -(cx) = (-c)x = c(-x)$ for all $c \in F$, $x \in V$.

Proof of 8.5: If $c = 0$, then $cx = (c + c)x = cx + cx$ and $cx = 0$. (In an Abelian group, $a + a = a$ iff $a = 0$.) A similar proof shows that $cx = 0$ if $x = 0$. Conversely, if $ax = 0$ and $a \neq 0$, then $a^{-1}0 = 0$ and

$$0 = a^{-1}(ax) = (a^{-1}a)x = 1x = x,$$

that is, $x = 0$. ∎

The proof of 8.6 is left as an exercise.

We described above one example of a vector space, namely $V_n(F)$. Another example is as follows: Let R be a C-ring with unity having a field F, whose unity is the unity of R, as a subring. Then we may consider R as a vector space over F, with scalar multiplication simply ordinary multiplication. Then 8.1 and 8.2 hold because of the distributive law in R, 8.3 because of the associative law, and 8.4 because of the fact that the unity of F is the unity of R. Hence, $\{R;+\}$ is an Abelian group and F is a field of scalars of R satisfying 8.1–8.4.

For example,

$$\mathbb{C} \text{ is a vector space over } \mathbb{R};$$
$$\mathbb{R} \text{ is a vector space over } \mathbb{Q};$$
$$\mathbb{Z}_2[x] \text{ is a vector space over } \mathbb{Z}_2;$$
$$\mathbb{Q}[\sqrt{3}] \text{ is a vector space over } \mathbb{Q}.$$

We cannot consider $\mathbb{Z}[\sqrt{3}]$ to be a vector space over $\mathbb{Z}$, since $\mathbb{Z}$ is not a field.

Another example of a somewhat different nature is afforded by a homogeneous linear differential equation such as

8.7
$$\frac{d^2y}{dx^2} - 3\frac{dy}{dx} + 2y = 0.$$

Let V be the set of all twice-differentiable functions in $C(\mathbb{R})$ which are solutions of 8.7. Thus, $f \in V$ iff

$$f''(x) - 3f'(x) + 2f(x) = 0 \text{ for all } x \in \mathbb{R},$$

where f' and f'' denote the first and second derivatives of f, respectively. If $f, g \in V$, then $f + g \in V$ also, since

$$(f + g)''(x) - 3(f + g)'(x) + 2(f + g)(x)$$
$$= [f''(x) + g''(x)] - 3[f'(x) + g'(x)] + 2[f(x) + g(x)]$$
$$= [f''(x) - 3f'(x) + 2f(x)] + [g''(x) - 3g'(x) + 2g(x)] = 0.$$

Clearly, $0 \in V$, and $-f \in V$ whenever $f \in V$. Thus, $\{V; +\}$ is an Abelian group. For each $c \in \mathbb{R}$ and $f \in V$, $cf \in V$ also since

$$(cf)''(x) - 3(cf)'(x) + 2(cf)(x) = cf''(x) - 3cf'(x) + 2cf(x)$$
$$= c[f''(x) - 3f'(x) + 2f(x)] = 0.$$

Evidently 8.1–8.4 hold, and therefore $V(\mathbb{R})$ is a vector space. We point out that two elements of V are the exponential functions f and g defined by

$$f(x) = e^x \quad \text{and} \quad g(x) = e^{2x}.$$

Exercises

1. Prove 8.1, 8.3, and 8.4 for $V_n(F)$.

2. Prove that 8.6 holds for any vector space $V(F)$.

2. Subspaces and Independence

If V is a vector space over a field F and S is a nonempty subset of V, then S is called a *subspace* of V if $\{S; +\}$ is a subgroup of $\{V; +\}$ and S is closed under scalar multiplication; i.e., $cx \in S$ for all $c \in F$ and $x \in S$. Thus, $S(F)$ is a vector space in its own right. A useful criterion for a subspace is given below.

8.8   Theorem. If $V(F)$ is a vector space and $S \subset V$, $S \neq \phi$, then S is a subspace of V iff S is closed under addition and scalar multiplication.

Outline of proof: For every $x \in S$, $-x = (-1)x \in S$ also; and $0 = 0x \in S$. Hence, $\{S;+\}$ is a subgroup of $\{V;+\}$.   ∎

Two trivial subspaces of a vector space $V(F)$ are $\{0\}$ and V. We call any other subspace a *proper subspace*. For each $x \in V$, Fx defined by

$$Fx = \{cx \mid c \in F\}$$

is a subspace of V. For $cx + dx = (c + d)x \in Fx$ and $c(dx) = (cd)x \in Fx$. If $x = 0$, then, of course, $Fx = \{0\}$. On the other hand, if $x \neq 0$, then Fx is a *minimal* nonzero subspace of V. For if S is a nonzero subspace of V and $S \subset Fx$, then some nonzero dx is in S and $(cd^{-1})(dx) = cx \in S$ for all $c \in F$. That is, $Fx \subset S$ and therefore $S = Fx$.

Geometrically, the minimal nonzero subspaces of $\mathbb{R}^3$ are the lines through the origin, as shown in Figure 8.1. For example, $\mathbb{R}(1,0,0)$ is the set of all vectors on the x-axis.

The *intersection* $A \cap B$ and *sum* $A + B$ of two subspaces A and B of $V(F)$ are easily seen to be subspaces also. More generally, if $\{A_1, A_2, \ldots, A_n\}$ is a set of subspaces of V, then their intersection

$$A_1 \cap A_2 \cap \ldots \cap A_n$$

and their sum

$$A_1 + A_2 + \ldots + A_n$$

are also subspaces of V. In fact, $A_1 \cap A_2 \cap \ldots \cap A_n$ is the *largest* subspace contained in all A_i, $i = 1, \ldots, n$, and $A_1 + A_2 + \ldots + A_n$ is the *least* subspace containing all A_i, $i = 1, \ldots, n$.

For example, if u_1, u_2, and u_3 are the vectors

8.9 $$u_1 = (1,0,0), \; u_2 = (0,1,0), \; u_3 = (0,0,1)$$

in $V_3(\mathbb{R})$, then $\mathbb{R}u_1$, $\mathbb{R}u_2$, and $\mathbb{R}u_3$ are the coordinate axes as indicated in Figure 8.2. Now

$$\mathbb{R}u_1 + \mathbb{R}u_2, \quad \mathbb{R}u_1 + \mathbb{R}u_3, \quad \mathbb{R}u_2 + \mathbb{R}u_3$$

are the xy-, xz-, and yz-planes. For example, each vector $(a,b,0)$ in the xy-plane has the form

$$(a,b,0) = au_1 + bu_2.$$

Clearly,

$$\mathbb{R}u_1 + \mathbb{R}u_2 + \mathbb{R}u_3 = V_3$$

since

$$au_1 + bu_2 + cu_3 = (a,b,c) \quad \text{for all} \quad a,b,c \in \mathbb{R}.$$

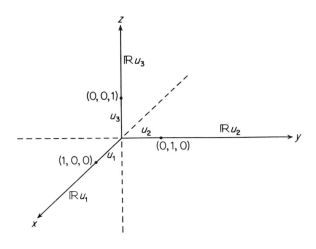

Figure 8.2

The intersection of any two of the subspaces $\mathbb{R}u_1$, $\mathbb{R}u_2$, $\mathbb{R}u_3$ is the zero subspace. For example, $\mathbb{R}u_1 \cap \mathbb{R}u_2 = \{0\}$. Note that also

$$(\mathbb{R}u_1 + \mathbb{R}u_2) \cap \mathbb{R}u_3 = \{0\},$$

and so on.

A set

$$\{A_1, A_2, \ldots, A_n\}$$

of subspaces of a vector space $V(F)$ is called *independent* iff every $A_i \neq \{0\}$ and

8.10 $A_i \cap (A_1 + \ldots + A_{i-1} + A_{i+1} + \ldots + A_n) = \{0\}$, $i = 1, \ldots, n$.

In words, the intersection of any A_i with the sum of the remaining A_j's is the zero subspace. The notation

$$\{A_1 A_2, \ldots, A_n\}^\perp$$

is used to indicate an independent set of subspaces.

For example, if $u_1, u_2, u_3 \in V_3(\mathbb{R})$ are as defined in 8.9, then

$$\{\mathbb{R}u_1, \mathbb{R}u_2, \mathbb{R}u_3\}^\perp.$$

8.11   **Theorem.** A set $\{A_1, A_2, \ldots, A_n\}$ of $n > 1$ nonzero subspaces of a vector space $V(F)$ is independent iff

(1) $A_i \cap (A_{i+1} + \ldots + A_n) = \{0\}$, $i = 1, \ldots, n - 1$.

Proof: If $\{A_1, A_2, \ldots, A_n\}^{\perp}$, then 8.10 holds. Since $A_{i+1} + \ldots + A_n$ is a subset of $A_1 + \ldots + A_{i-1} + A_{i+1} + \ldots + A_n$, evidently (1) also holds. Conversely, assume that (1) holds. If there exists an integer i such that

$$A_i \cap (A_1 + \ldots + A_{i-1} + A_{i+1} + \ldots + A_n) \neq \{0\},$$

then there exist $x_j \in A_j, j = 1, \ldots, n$, with $x_i \neq 0$, such that

$$x_i = x_1 + \ldots + x_{i-1} + x_{i+1} + \ldots + x_n.$$

Let k be the least positive integer for which $x_k \neq 0$. Clearly $k \leq i$. On solving the above equation for x_k, we get

$$\pm x_k = x_{k+1} + \ldots + x_n \neq 0.$$

Hence, $A_k \cap (A_{k+1} + \ldots + A_n) \neq \{0\}$, contradicting (1). We conclude that 8.10 holds; i.e., $\{A_1, A_2, \ldots, A_n\}^{\perp}$. ∎

According to 8.11, in order to prove that a set of nonzero subspaces $\{A_1, A_2, \ldots, A_n\}$ of $V(F)$, arranged in some order, is independent, we need only show that the intersection of each A_i with the sum of the succeeding A_j's is zero.

For example, $\{\mathbb{R}u_1, \mathbb{R}u_2, \mathbb{R}u_3\}$ is independent since

$$\mathbb{R}u_1 \cap (\mathbb{R}u_2 + \mathbb{R}u_3) = \{0\} \quad \text{and} \quad \mathbb{R}u_2 \cap \mathbb{R}u_3 = \{0\}.$$

By 8.10 and 8.11, if $A_1, A_2, \ldots$ are subspaces of a vector space $V(F)$, then

$\{A_1\}^{\perp}$ iff $A_1 \neq \{0\}$,

$\{A_1, A_2\}^{\perp}$ iff each $A_i \neq \{0\}$ and $A_1 \cap A_2 = \{0\}$,

$\{A_1, A_2, A_3\}^{\perp}$ iff each $A_i \neq \{0\}$ and

$$A_1 \cap (A_2 + A_3) = \{0\}, \quad A_2 \cap A_3 = \{0\},$$

and so on.

A set of vectors is said to be *linearly independent*, or simply *independent*, iff the set of subspaces they generate is independent. Again, the notation

$$\{x_1, x_2, \ldots, x_n\}^{\perp}$$

is used to indicate that $\{x_1, x_2, \ldots, x_n\}$ is an independent set of vectors. By definition,

$$\{x_1, x_2, \ldots, x_n\}^{\perp} \quad \text{iff} \quad \{Fx_1, Fx_2, \ldots, Fx_n\}^{\perp}.$$

8.12   Theorem. If $\{x_1, x_2, \ldots, x_n\}$ is a set of vectors in a vector space $V(F)$, then $\{x_1, x_2, \ldots, x_n\}^{\perp}$ iff $c_1 = 0, c_2 = 0, \ldots, c_n = 0$ is the only solution of the equation

(1) $$\sum_{i=1}^{n} c_i x_i = 0, \qquad c_i \in F.$$

Proof: Assume that there exist $c_i \in F$, not all zero, such that (1) holds and let k be the least positive integer for which $c_k \neq 0$. Then

$$c_k x_k = -(c_{k+1} x_{k+1} + \ldots + c_n x_n)$$

and either $x_k = 0$ or $Fx_k \cap (Fx_{k+1} + \ldots + Fx_n) \neq \{0\}$. In either case, $\{Fx_1, \ldots, Fx_n\}^\perp$ and therefore $\{x_1, x_2, \ldots, x_n\}^{\not\perp}$. (Of course, "$\not\perp$" means "is not $\perp$.")

Conversely, if $\{x_1, x_2, \ldots, x_n\}^{\not\perp}$, then $\{Fx_1, \ldots, Fx_n\}^{\not\perp}$ and either some $x_k = 0$, in which case

$$\sum_{i=1}^{n} c_i x_i = 0, \qquad \text{where } c_i = 0 \ \text{ if } \ i \neq k, c_k = 1,$$

or all $x_i \neq 0$ and $Fx_k \cap (Fx_{k+1} + \ldots + Fx_n) \neq \{0\}$ for some k. In the second case,

$$c_k x_k = c_{k+1} x_{k+1} + \ldots + c_n x_n \neq 0$$

for some $c_i \in F$ and

$$\sum_{i=1}^{n} a_i x_i = 0, \qquad \text{where } a_i = 0 \ \text{ if } \ i < k, a_k = -c_k,$$
$$a_i = c_i \ \text{ if } \ i > k.$$

In either case, (1) has a solution other than $c_i = 0$ for all i. ∎

The set $\{f,g\}$ of solutions of the differential equation

$$\frac{d^2 y}{dx^2} - 3\frac{dy}{dx} + 2y = 0$$

defined by

$$f(x) = e^x, \qquad g(x) = e^{2x}$$

is independent. For if, $a,b \in \mathbb{R}$ and

$$ae^x + be^{2x} = 0 \quad \text{for all} \quad x \in \mathbb{R},$$

then $e^x(a + be^x) = 0$ and, since $e^x \neq 0$ for all x,

$$a + be^x = 0 \quad \text{for all } x \in \mathbb{R}.$$

This equation has the unique solution $a = 0$ and $b = 0$. Hence, by 8.12,

$$\{f,g\}^\perp.$$

It is shown in the calculus that $\mathbb{R}f + \mathbb{R}g = V$, the set of all solutions of the differential equation.

We shall often say "the vectors $x_1, x_2, \ldots, x_n$ are independent" in place of "the set of vectors $\{x_1, x_2, \ldots, x_n\}$ is independent." Thus, we can say the functions f and g are independent solutions of the differential equation above.

In the vector space $V_n(F)$ of all n-tuples over a field F, the vectors

$$u_1 = (1,0,0, \ldots ,0,0),$$
$$u_2 = (0,1,0, \ldots ,0,0),$$
$$\ldots \ldots \ldots \ldots \ldots \ldots ,$$
$$u_n = (0,0,0, \ldots ,0,1),$$

are called *unit vectors*. Note that

(1) $$\sum_{i=1}^{n} c_i u_i = (c_1,c_2, \ldots ,c_n) \quad \text{for all } c_i \in F.$$

Therefore,

$$\sum_{i=1}^{n} c_i u_i = 0 \text{ iff } c_i = 0 \quad \text{for all} \quad i.$$

Hence,

$$\{u_1,u_2, \ldots ,u_n\}^{\perp}$$

by 8.12. Furthermore, we see by (1) that every vector $(c_1,c_2, \ldots ,c_n) \in V_n$ is a *linear combination* of the vectors $u_1,u_2, \ldots ,u_n$; i.e.,

$$Fu_1 + Fu_2 + \ldots + Fu_n = V_n.$$

A set of vectors or subspaces which is not independent is called *dependent*. For example, the vectors $(1,0),(0,1),(2,3) \in V_2(R)$ are dependent, since

$$2(1,0) + 3(0,1) - (2,3) = (0,0).$$

Exercises

Tell whether each of the following sets of vectors is independent or dependent in the given vector space.

1. $\{(1,1),(1,-1)\}$ in $V_2(\mathbb{R})$.

2. $\{x^2 + 1, x, x + 2\}$ in $\mathbb{Q}[x]$ over $\mathbb{Q}$.

3. $\{1,\sqrt{2},\sqrt{3}\}$ in $\mathbb{R}$ over $\mathbb{Q}$.

4. $\{(1,0,1),(1,1,0),(0,1,-1)\}$ in $V_3(\mathbb{Q})$.

5. $\{x^3, x^2 + x, x + 1, x^3 + 1\}$ in $\mathbb{Z}_2[x]$ over $\mathbb{Z}_2$.

6. $\{f,g,h\}$ in $C(\mathbb{R})$ over $\mathbb{R}$, where $f(x) = \sin^2 x$, $g(x) = \cos^2 x$, and $h(x) = \cos 2x$.

7. $\{i - 1, 2 + 3i, 1 + 5i\}$ in $\mathbb{C}$ over $\mathbb{R}$.

8. $\{1 + 3\sqrt{2}, 2 - \sqrt{2}\}$ in $\mathbb{Q}[\sqrt{2}]$ over $\mathbb{Q}$.

9. $\{(1,1,0,2),(0,1,0,1),(2,1,1,0),(0,1,1,1)\}$ in $V_4(\mathbb{Z}_3)$.

10. $\{u_1, u_1 + u_2, u_1 + u_2 + u_3, \ldots ,u_1 + u_2 + \ldots + u_n\}$ in $V_n(\mathbb{R})$.

Describe geometrically and sketch each of the following subspaces of $V_3(\mathbb{R})$.

11. $\mathbb{R}(1,1,1)$.

12. $\mathbb{R}(1,0,0) + \mathbb{R}(1,1,0)$.

13. $[\mathbb{R}(1,0,0) + \mathbb{R}(0,1,0)] \cap [\mathbb{R}(0,1,1) + \mathbb{R}(1,0,-1)]$.

14. $[\mathbb{R}(1,0,1) + \mathbb{R}(1,1,0)] \cap [\mathbb{R}(0,1,1) + \mathbb{R}(2,1,0)]$.

15. $\mathbb{R}(1,0,1) + \mathbb{R}(0,-1,1) + \mathbb{R}(1,-1,0)$.

16. Let $A_1, A_2, \ldots, A_n$ be subspaces of a vector space $V(F)$ such that $\{A_1, A_2, \ldots, A_n\}^{\perp}$. Prove that $\{A_1, A_2, \ldots, A_i\}^{\perp}$ for every i, $1 \leq i \leq n$. If B is a nonzero subspace of V and $B \cap (A_1 + \ldots + A_n) = \{0\}$, prove that $\{A_1, A_2, \ldots, A_n, B\}^{\perp}$.

17. List all subspaces of $V_2(\mathbb{Z}_2)$ and of $V_3(\mathbb{Z}_2)$.

18. If $V(F)$ is a vector space, prove that

$$n(cx) = (nc)x = c(nx) \text{ for all } n \in \mathbb{Z}, c \in F, x \in V.$$

19. Prove that if $\{A_1, A_2, \ldots, A_n\}$ is a dependent set of subspaces of a vector space $V(F)$ and B is any subspace of V, then $\{A_1, A_2, \ldots, A_n, B\}$ is dependent.

3. Bases

Let $V(F)$ be a vector space. A set $\{x_1, x_2, \ldots, x_n\}$ of vectors of V is called a *basis* of V iff:

8.13 $\{x_1, x_2, \ldots, x_n\}^{\perp}$ and $Fx_1 + Fx_2 + \ldots + Fx_n = V$.

For example, the set $\{u_1, u_2, \ldots, u_n\}$ of unit vectors of $V_n(F)$ is a basis by our previous remarks.

As another example, the field $\mathbb{C}$ of complex numbers may be considered to be a vector space over $\mathbb{R}$. Since $1\mathbb{R} \cap i\mathbb{R} = \{0\}$ and each $z \in \mathbb{C}$ has the form

$$z = a1 + bi, \qquad a, b \in \mathbb{R},$$

evidently $\{1, i\}$ is a basis of $\mathbb{C}$ over $\mathbb{R}$.

If $\{x_1, x_2, \ldots, x_n\}$ is a basis of $V(F)$, then every $x \in V$ may be expressed *uniquely* in the form

$$x = \sum_{i=1}^{n} c_i x_i$$

for some $c_i \in F$. We call x a *linear combination* of the vectors $x_1, x_2, \ldots, x_n$. To see that the expression for x in terms of the x_i is unique, assume that $x = \sum c_i x_i$ and also $x = \sum d_i x_i$. Then

$$\sum_{i=1}^{n} c_i x_i - \sum_{i=1}^{n} d_i x_i = \sum_{i=1}^{n} (c_i - d_i) x_i = 0$$

and $c_i - d_i = 0$, $i = 1, \ldots, n$, by the independence of the x_i. Thus, $c_i = d_i$ for each i.

Most vector spaces have many bases. For example, each of the sets

$$\{u_1, u_2, u_3\}, \quad \{u_1, u_1 + u_2, u_1 + u_3\}, \quad \{u_1 - u_2, u_1 + u_3, u_2 - u_3\}$$

is easily seen to be a basis of $V_3(\mathbb{R})$.

As another example, $\{z_1, z_2\}$ is a basis of $\mathbb{C}(\mathbb{R})$ as long as $z_1 \neq 0$, $z_2 \neq 0$, and $z_1 \neq c z_2$ for every $c \in \mathbb{R}$, Thus, $\{i + 1, i - 1\}$, $\{3, 1 - 2i\}$, and $\{\sqrt{2}i, \sqrt{3} + 3i\}$ are bases of $\mathbb{C}(\mathbb{R})$.

A vector space need not have a finite basis as defined in 8.13. For example, the vector space $F[x]$ over a field F does not have such a basis. Thus, if $\{f_1(x), \ldots, f_n(x)\}$ is a finite set of polynomials and k is an integer greater than deg $f_i(x)$ for each i, then

$$x^k \neq \sum_{i=1}^{n} c_i f_i(x) \text{ for any } c_i \in F.$$

Hence, the given set does not generate all of $F[x]$. The set $\{1, x, x^2, \ldots, x^n, \ldots\}$ is an infinite basis of $F[x]$ over F, but we shall not discuss such bases in this book.

We shall occasionally be interested in the order in which the elements of a basis are given, in which case we shall speak of an *ordered basis*.

8.14   **Replacement property.** Let $(x_1, x_2, \ldots, x_n)$ be an ordered basis of a vector space $V(F)$ and y be any nonzero vector in V. If k is the least positive integer such that

$$y \in Fx_1 + \ldots + Fx_k, \quad \text{then} \quad (x_1, \ldots, x_{k-1}, y, x_{k+1}, \ldots, x_n)$$

is also an ordered basis of $V(F)$.

Proof: By assumption, $y = c_1 x_1 + \ldots + c_k x_k$ for some $c_i \in F$. Clearly $c_k \neq 0$, for otherwise $y \in Fx_1 + \ldots + Fx_j$ for some $j < k$. Therefore,

$$x_k = -\frac{1}{c_k}(c_1 x_1 + \ldots + c_{k-1} x_{k-1} - y)$$

and

$$Fx_k \subset Fx_1 + \ldots + Fx_{k-1} + Fy.$$

Thus,

$$Fx_1 + Fx_2 + \ldots + Fx_n \subset Fx_1 + \ldots + Fx_{k-1} + Fy + Fx_{k+1} + \ldots + Fx_n$$

and

$$Fx_1 + \ldots + Fx_{k-1} + Fy + Fx_{k+1} + \ldots + Fx_n = V.$$

We still must prove that $\{x_1, \ldots, x_{k-1}, y, x_{k+1}, \ldots, x_n\}^{\perp}$. To this end, assume that

$$a_1 x_1 + \ldots + a_{k-1} x_{k-1} + ay + a_{k+1} x_{k+1} + \ldots + a_n x_n = 0$$

for some a_i, $a \in F$. If $a \neq 0$, then

$$y = -\frac{1}{a}(a_1 x_1 + \ldots + a_{k-1} x_{k-1} + a_{k+1} x_{k+1} + \ldots + a_n x_n),$$

contrary to the fact that $y = c_1 x_1 + \ldots + c_k x_k$ and such a representation of y in terms of a basis is unique. Hence, $a = 0$,

$$a_1 x_1 + \ldots + a_{k-1} x_{k-1} + a_{k+1} x_{k+1} + \ldots + a_n x_n = 0,$$

and each $a_i = 0$ since $\{x_1, x_2, \ldots, x_n\}^{\perp}$. We conclude that

$$\{x_1, \ldots, x_{k-1}, y, x_{k+1}, \ldots, x_n\}^{\perp}. \quad \blacksquare$$

The replacement property (8.14) of bases may be used to prove the following result:

8.15 Theorem. If vector space $V(F)$ has basis $\{x_1, \ldots, x_n\}$ and if $\{y_1, \ldots, y_m\}^{\perp}$, then $m \leq n$ and there exists a basis consisting of $y_1, \ldots, y_m$ and $n - m$ of the x_i's.

Outline of proof: By 8.14, there is a basis of V consisting of one y_i and $n - 1$ x_i's. Assume that $1 \leq k < m$ and that there exists a basis of the form

$$\{y_1, \ldots, y_k, z_{k+1}, \ldots, z_n\}$$

where each z_i is equal to some x_j. Since $y_{k+1} \notin Fy_1 + \ldots + Fy_k$, there also exists a basis of the form

$$\{y_1, \ldots, y_k, y_{k+1}, u_{k+2}, \ldots, u_n\}$$

by 8.14, where each u_r is equal to some z_i and hence also to some x_j. Continuing, we can find a basis with n elements containing all the y_i's and some x_j's, if necessary. Therefore, $m \leq n$. $\quad \blacksquare$

Although a basis of a vector space is not usually unique, the number of elements in a basis is unique according to the theorem below.

8.16 Theorem. If a vector space $V(F)$ has a basis with n elements, then every basis of $V(F)$ contains n elements.

We leave the proof of 8.16 as an exercise, since it follows easily from 8.15.

The number of elements in a basis of $V(F)$, being a property of $V(F)$ and not of any particular basis of $V(F)$, is called an *invariant* of $V(F)$. Assuming that $V(F)$ has a basis with n elements, we call the invariant n the *dimension* of $V(F)$ and denote it by dim V,

$$n = \dim V.$$

If $V = \{0\}$, then the dimension of V is defined to be 0, dim $\{0\} = 0$.

For example, $\mathbb{C}$ is a 2-dimensional vector space over $\mathbb{R}$, since $\{1,i\}$ is a basis.

As another example, $V_n(F)$ has the unit basis $\{u_1, u_2, \ldots, u_n\}$ and is therefore n-dimensional.

$$\dim V_n = n.$$

In particular, $V_3(\mathbb{R})$ is 3-dimensional as we have always claimed!

As a somewhat different example, let F be a field and $p(x)$ be a prime polynomial in $F[x]$ of degree $n > 1$. The field

$$K = F[x]/p(x)F[x]$$

may be considered to be a vector space over its subfield F. In Chapter 6 we saw that every element $a \in K$ has a unique representation

$$a = c_0 + c_1 t + \ldots + c_{n-1} t^{n-1},$$

where $t = x + p(x)F[x]$ and each $c_i \in F$. Therefore,

$$\{1, t, t^2, \ldots, t^{n-1}\}$$

is a basis of K over F, and

$$\dim K = n.$$

In view of 8.15, every set of n independent elements of an n-dimensional vector space is a basis. Hence, to prove that a set $\{y_1, \ldots, y_n\}$ is a basis, we need only prove $\{y_1, \ldots, y_n\}^\perp$.

For example, is

$$\{(1,0,1),(0,1,1),(1,1,0)\}$$

a basis of $V_3(\mathbb{R})$? It is if it is independent. To test its independence, assume that

$$a(1,0,1) + b(0,1,1) + c(1,1,0) = (0,0,0)$$

for some $a,b,c \in F$. Then

$$(a + c, b + c, a + b) = (0,0,0)$$

and

(1)
$$\begin{cases} a + c = 0, \\ b + c = 0, \\ a + b = 0. \end{cases}$$

We easily verify that the only solution of system (1) is $a = b = c = 0$. Therefore, the given set is independent by 8.12. Hence, it is a basis.

Exercises

In each of the following exercises, find a basis of the vector space which contains the given set of vectors.

1. $\{(1,-1)\}$ in $V_2(\mathbb{Q})$.

2. $\{(2,1,-1),(4,0,3)\}$ in $V_3(\mathbb{R})$.

3. $\{(1,0,2,1),(2,1,0,1)\}$ in $V_4(\mathbb{Z}_3)$.

4. $\{(0,i,0,1),(i,1,1,0)\}$ in $V_4(\mathbb{C})$.

5. $\{1 + \sqrt{2}, 2 - \sqrt{3}\}$ in $\mathbb{Q}[\sqrt{2} + \sqrt{3}]$ over $\mathbb{Q}$.

6. $\{1,\sqrt[3]{2}\}$ in $\mathbb{Q}[\sqrt[3]{2}]$ over $\mathbb{Q}$.

7. Prove 8.16.

8. Find all bases of $V_2(\mathbb{Z}_2)$ and $V_2(\mathbb{Z}_3)$.

9. Let $V(F)$ be an n-dimensional vector space and A be a nonzero subspace of V. Prove that dim $A \leq n$, with dim $A = n$ only if $A = V$.

10. Let $V(F)$ be an n-dimensional vector space. For every subspace A of V, prove that there exists a subspace A' such that $A + A' = V$ and $A \cap A' = \{0\}$. (A' is called a *complement* of A.) Is A' ever unique?

11. A set $\{x_1,x_2, \ldots ,x_n\}$ of nonzero elements of a vector space $V(F)$ is called a set of *generators* of a subspace A of V iff $A = Fx_1 + Fx_2 + \ldots + Fx_n$. Prove that if $\{x_1,x_2, \ldots ,x_n\}$ is a set of generators of A, then some subset of $\{x_1,x_2, \ldots ,x_n\}$ is a basis of A.

12. Let $V(F)$ be a vector space and A, B, and C be subspaces of V with $A \supset B$. Prove the *modular law*: $A \cap (B + C) = B + (A \cap C)$.

*13. Let F_1 be a subfield of F_2 and F_2 be a subfield of F_3. If the vector space $F_2(F_1)$ has dimension m and $F_3(F_1)$ dimension n, then what is the dimension of the vector space $F_3(F_2)$? Prove your answer.

4. Homomorphisms

If $V(F)$ and $W(F)$ are vector spaces over the same field F, then a mapping $V \xrightarrow{f} W$ is called a *homomorphism* iff

$$f(x + y) = f(x) + f(y), \quad f(cx) = cf(x) \quad \text{for all } x,y \in V, c \in F.$$

Epimorphisms, monomorphisms, and isomorphisms are defined as before. Isomorphic vector spaces clearly have the same dimension. The converse is also true in the sense of the following theorem:

8.17 Theorem. If $V(F)$ and $W(F)$ are vector spaces having the same dimension n, then V and W are isomorphic.

Outline of proof: The gist of the proof is obvious. We take ordered bases of V and W and map one onto the other with a bijection. Then we extend this mapping to V and W in a natural way. Thus, if V has ordered basis $(x_1, \ldots, x_n)$ and W has ordered basis $(y_1, \ldots, y_n)$, then define $\{x_1, \ldots, x_n\} \xrightarrow{f} \{y_1, \ldots, y_n\}$ by $f(x_i) = y_i$, $i = 1, \ldots, n$, and, more generally, $V \xrightarrow{f} W$ by

$$f\left(\sum_{i=1}^{n} a_i x_i\right) = \sum_{i=1}^{n} a_i y_i.$$

That f is an isomorphism is easily verified. ∎

For every field F and every positive integer n, there exists a vector space over F of dimension n, namely

$$V_n(F).$$

By 8.17, every other n-dimensional vector space over F is isomorphic to $V_n(F)$. Thus, up to an isomorphism, $V_n(F)$ is the only n-dimensional vector space over F. Therefore, in discussing algebraic properties of finite-dimensional vector spaces, we may limit ourselves to the vector spaces $V_n(F)$ if we wish.

Each finite-dimensional vector space V over the finite field $\mathbb{Z}_p$ is isomorphic to $V_n(\mathbb{Z}_p)$ for some $n \in \mathbb{Z}^+$. Clearly the number of n-tuples

$$(a_1, a_2, \ldots, a_n), \qquad a_i \in \mathbb{Z}_p,$$

in V_n is p^n. Thus,

8.18 $\#(V) = p^n$ if V is an n-dimensional vector space over $\mathbb{Z}_p$.

If K is a finite field of characteristic p, then $\mathbb{Z}_p$ is a subfield of K and hence K is a vector space over $\mathbb{Z}_p$. Therefore we have the following corollary of 8.18.

8.19 If K is a finite field and ch $K = p$, then

$$\#(K) = p^n \text{ for some } n \in \mathbb{Z}^+.$$

If $V(F)$ and $W(F)$ are vector spaces and $V \xrightarrow{f} W$ is a homomorphism, then the kernel of f,

$$\ker f = \{x \in V \mid f(x) = 0\},$$

is a subspace of V. We already know ker f is a subgroup of $\{V;+\}$. All we need verify is that ker f is closed under scalar multiplication. This is easily verified as follows: If $x \in$ ker f and $c \in F$, then

$$f(cx) = cf(x) = c0 = 0$$

and therefore $cx \in$ ker f.

Given a vector space $V(F)$ and a subspace A, we can form the quotient group of V by A,

$$V/A = \{x + A \mid x \in V\}.$$

We easily make V/A into a vector space by defining scalar multiplication in the expected way:

8.20 $c(x + A) = cx + A$ for all $c \in F$, $x + A \in V/A$.

This multiplication is easily shown to be well-defined and to make V/A into a vector space over the field F.

Finally, the isomorphism theorem of Abelian groups (2.30) applies equally well to vector spaces. Thus, if $V(F)$ and $W(F)$ are vector spaces and $V \xrightarrow{f} W$ is an epimorphism, then the quotient vector space $V/\text{ker } f$ is isomorphic to W under the mapping

$$V/\text{ker } f \xrightarrow{h} W \text{ defined by } h(x + \text{ker } f) = f(x).$$

Corresponding to Lagrange's theorem (2.26) for Abelian groups, we have the following result for vector spaces:

8.21   Theorem. If $V(F)$ is a finite-dimensional vector space and A is a subspace of V, then V/A is finite-dimensional and

$$\dim V = \dim A + \dim V/A$$

Outline of proof: Complete a basis $\{x_1, \ldots, x_k\}$ of A to a basis $\{x_1, \ldots, x_k, x_{k+1}, \ldots, x_n\}$ of V. Then $\{x_{k+1} + A, \ldots, x_n + A\}$ is easily seen to be a basis for V/A. ∎

Exercises

1. Prove that scalar multiplication is well-defined by 8.20.

2. Fill in the details of the proof of 8.17.

3. Fill in the details of the proof of 8.21.

4. Prove that

$$\dim A + \dim B = \dim (A + B) + \dim (A \cap B)$$

for all subspaces A and B of a finite-dimensional vector space $V(F)$. [*Hint:* Prove that it is true if $A \cap B = \{0\}$. Then note that $(A + B)/(A \cap B) = A/(A \cap B) + B/(A \cap B)$ and $[A/(A \cap B)] \cap [B/(A \cap B)] = \{0\}$.]

5. Inner Products

Some vector spaces $V(F)$ have another operation, called an *inner product* (or *dot product*, or *scalar product*). An inner product is a mapping $V \times V \xrightarrow{\cdot} F$ such that:

8.22 $(x + y) \cdot z = x \cdot z + y \cdot z$ for all $x, y, z \in V$.

8.23 $(cx) \cdot y = c(x \cdot y)$ for all $x, y \in V$, $c \in F$.

In case F is ordered, we shall also insist that:

8.24 $x \cdot x \geq 0$, with $x \cdot x = 0$ iff $x = 0$.

An example of an inner product in the n-dimensional vector space $V_n(F)$ is the mapping $V_n \times V_n \xrightarrow{\cdot} F$ defined by:

8.25 $(a_1, a_2, \ldots, a_n) \cdot (b_1, b_2, \ldots, b_n) = a_1 b_1 + a_2 b_2 + \ldots + a_n b_n.$

It is easily proved that 8.22 and 8.23 hold. Also, if F is ordered and $x = (a_1, a_2, \ldots, a_n)$, then

$$x \cdot x = a_1^2 + a_2^2 + \ldots + a_n^2 \geq 0, \qquad \text{with } x \cdot x = 0 \quad \text{iff} \quad x = 0.$$

In this example,

8.26 $x \cdot y = y \cdot x$ for all $x, y \in V_n$.

The inner product in this example is *bilinear* in the sense that

8.27 $$\left(\sum_{i=1}^{k} c_i x_i \right) \cdot \left(\sum_{j=1}^{m} d_j y_j \right) = \sum_{i=1}^{k} \sum_{j=1}^{m} c_i d_j (x_i \cdot y_j).$$

This is easily proved from 8.22, 8.23, and 8.26. For the unit vectors $u_1, u_2, \ldots, u_n$ of V_n, we have

$$u_i \cdot u_j = \delta_{ij}, \qquad i, j = 1, \ldots, n,$$

where δ_{ij} is the *Kronecker* delta,

$$\delta_{ij} = \begin{cases} 1 & \text{if } i = j, \\ 0 & \text{if } i \neq j. \end{cases}$$

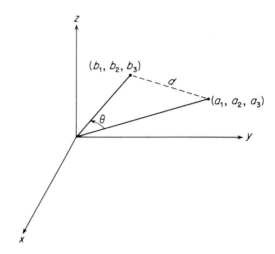

Figure 8.3

The inner product 8.25 has geometrical significance in $V_3(\mathbb{R})$. In the first place, if we consider $x = (a_1, a_2, a_3)$ as the vector shown in Figure 8.3, then $x \cdot x = a_1^2 + a_2^2 + a_3^2$ is the square of the length of x. Thus, if we denote the *length* of vector x by $|x|$, we have

8.28
$$|x| = \sqrt{x \cdot x}.$$

If $x = (a_1, a_2, a_3)$ and $y = (b_1, b_2, b_3)$, then the distance d between these points in $\mathbb{R}^3$ is given by (see Figure 8.3)

$$d^2 = (a_1 - b_1)^2 + (a_2 - b_2)^2 + (a_3 - b_3)^2 = |x|^2 + |y|^2 - 2(x \cdot y).$$

By the law of cosines,

$$d^2 = |x|^2 + |y|^2 - 2\,|x|\,|y| \cos \theta,$$

where θ is the angle of least measure between x and y. On comparing the two equations above, we see that

8.29
$$\cos \theta = \frac{x \cdot y}{|x|\,|y|}.$$

Since $\cos \theta = 0$ iff $\theta = 90°$, evidently the nonzero vectors x and y are perpendicular iff $x \cdot y = 0$,

8.30
$$x \perp y \text{ iff } x \cdot y = 0.$$

For example, the vectors $x = (-1,2,1)$ and $y = (3,-2,7)$ are perpendicular in $V_3(\mathbb{R})$, since

$$x \cdot y = (-1) \cdot 3 + 2 \cdot (-2) + 1 \cdot 7 = 0.$$

Another example of an inner product is afforded by the vector space $V(\mathbb{R})$ of all continuous real functions having the closed interval $[0,1]$ as domain. We define the inner product operation by:

8.31
$$f \cdot g = \int_0^1 f(u)g(u) \, du \text{ for all } f,g \in V.$$

Properties 8.22–8.24, 8.26, and 8.27 are easily shown to hold.

A vector space over $\mathbb{R}$ is called a *Euclidean space* if it has an inner product satisfying 8.22–8.24 and 8.26. For example, $V_n(\mathbb{R})$ with inner product 8.25 is Euclidean, as is the function space $V(\mathbb{R})$ with inner product 8.31. Every vector x in a Euclidean space has *length* $|x|$ defined by 8.28.

An example of a somewhat different nature is shown by the vector space $V_n(\mathbb{C})$. We define the inner product in $V_n(\mathbb{C})$ as follows:

8.32 $(a_1,a_2, \ldots ,a_n) \cdot (b_1,b_2, \ldots ,b_n) = a_1\bar{b}_1 + a_2\bar{b}_2 + \ldots + a_n\bar{b}_n.$

Note the difference between this definition and 8.25.

For example, in $V_2(\mathbb{C})$,

$$(3 - i, 2 - i) \cdot (i, 1 - i) = (3 - i)(-i) + (2 - i)(1 + i) = 2 - 2i.$$

It is easily verified that 8.22 and 8.23 hold for the inner product 8.32 in $V_n(\mathbb{C})$. Although $\mathbb{C}$ is not ordered, it does contain an ordered subfield $\mathbb{R}$. If $x = (a_1,a_2, \ldots ,a_n)$, then $x \cdot x \in \mathbb{R}$ and

$$x \cdot x = a_1\bar{a}_1 + a_2\bar{a}_2 + \ldots + a_n\bar{a}_n = N(a_1) + N(a_2) + \ldots + N(a_n) \geq 0,$$

with $x \cdot x = 0$ iff $N(a_1) = N(a_2) = \ldots = N(a_n) = 0$, i.e., iff $x = 0$. Thus, 8.24 holds for $V_n(\mathbb{C})$. The inner product 8.32 does not have property 8.26, but it does have the following analogous property:

8.33
$$x \cdot y = \overline{y \cdot x} \text{ for all } x,y \in V_n(\mathbb{C}).$$

A vector space $V(\mathbb{C})$ is called a *unitary space* iff it has an inner product satisfying 8.22–8.24 and 8.33. Note that 8.33 implies that $x \cdot x \in \mathbb{R}$ for each $x \in V$. Every vector x in a unitary space has a *length* $|x|$ defined by 8.28 as usual.

If $V(F)$ is an n-dimensional vector space possessing an inner product, then a basis $\{x_1,x_2, \ldots ,x_n\}$ of $V(F)$ is called *normal* iff

8.34
$$x_i \cdot x_i = 1, i = 1,2, \ldots ,n$$

and *orthogonal* iff

8.35 $x_i \cdot x_j = 0, \, i \neq j, \, i,j = 1,2, \ldots ,n.$

Naturally, if both 8.34 and 8.35 are satisfied, then $\{x_1,x_2, \ldots ,x_n\}$ is called a *normal orthogonal basis of V(F)*.

In either $V_n(\mathbb{R})$, with inner product defined by 8.25, or $V_n(\mathbb{C})$, with inner product defined by 8.32, the unit basis $\{u_1,u_2, \ldots ,u_n\}$ is easily shown to be a *normal orthogonal basis*. In particular, this means that in $V_3(\mathbb{R})$ the vectors of the basis $\{u_1,u_2,u_3\}$ are mutually perpendicular and of length 1.

Exercises

1. Prove that 8.22, 8.23, and 8.26 hold for the vector space $V_n(F)$ having the inner product defined by 8.25.

2. Let $V(F)$ be a vector space which has an inner product satisfying 8.22, 8.23, and 8.26. Prove that 8.27 also holds.

3. Prove that 8.22, 8.23, and 8.33 hold for the unitary space $V_n(\mathbb{C})$.

4. Although 8.27 does not hold for a unitary space, a similar property does hold. State and prove this property.

5. Let $V(\mathbb{R})$ be the vector space of all continuous real functions on $[0,1]$ having inner product 8.31. Prove that 8.22–8.24 and 8.26 hold.

Find a normal orthogonal basis for each of the following subspaces of $V_4(\mathbb{R})$.

6. $\mathbb{R}(2,-1,1,2).$

7. $\mathbb{R}(1,1,0,1) + \mathbb{R}(-1,0,1,2).$

8. $\mathbb{R}(1,1,0,0) + \mathbb{R}(1,0,1,0) + \mathbb{R}(0,1,0,1).$

9. $\mathbb{R}(1,2,1,-2) + \mathbb{R}(3,1,-1,3).$

10. $\mathbb{R}(1,0,0,0) + \mathbb{R}(0,1,0,-1) + \mathbb{R}(1,1,0,0).$

THEORETICAL PROJECT 1

Prove that

$$|x \cdot y| \leq |x| \, |y| \qquad \text{(Cauchy's inequality)}$$

for all vectors x and y in a Euclidean or unitary vector space V. Note that $|x \cdot y|$ is simply the absolute value of the real or complex number $x \cdot y$.

Outline of proof: It is clearly true if $x = 0$ or $y = 0$, so let us assume $x \neq 0$ and $y \neq 0$. Let us also assume that V is Euclidean. Then for each $k \in \mathbb{R}$, $(x + ky) \cdot (x + ky) = |x|^2 + 2k(x \cdot y) + k^2 |y|^2 \geq 0$. If a quadratic polynomial $ak^2 + bk + c$ is greater than or equal to 0 for every $k \in \mathbb{R}$, then necessarily its discriminant $b^2 - 4ac$ is less than or equal to zero; and so on.

Interpret Cauchy's inequality in the vector space:

(a) $V_n(\mathbb{R})$ with inner product 8.25,
(b) $V_n(\mathbb{C})$ with inner product 8.32,
(c) of continuous real functions in $[0,1]$ with inner product 8.31.

THEORETICAL PROJECT 2

Let $V(\mathbb{R})$ be a Euclidean vector space. Prove that every finite-dimensional subspace S of $V(\mathbb{R})$ has a normal orthogonal basis (n.o. basis).

Outline of proof: If $\dim S = 1$, then $S = \mathbb{R}y$ for any nonzero $y \in S$. Hence, show that $S = \mathbb{R}x$ for some $x \in S$ such that $x \cdot x = 1$. The proof is by mathematical induction. Assume that every subspace of $V(\mathbb{R})$ of dimension $n > 0$ has a n.o. basis. Let $\dim S = n + 1$. Then $S = T + \mathbb{R}x$, $T \cap \mathbb{R}x = \{0\}$, for some subspace T, $\dim T = n$. By assumption, T has a n.o. basis $\{x_1, x_2, \ldots, x_n\}$. Show that a vector x_{n+1} of the form

$$x_{n+1} = ax + \sum_{i=1}^{n} a_i x_i$$

can be chosen so that $\{x_1, x_2, \ldots, x_n, x_{n+1}\}$ is a n.o. basis of S.

Can the proof above be modified so as to apply to a unitary space $V(\mathbb{C})$ (i.e., a space having an inner product which satisfies 8.22–8.24 and 8.33)?

Next, assume that $V(\mathbb{R})$ is finite-dimensional. For each subspace S of $V(\mathbb{R})$, let $S^{\perp}$ be the set of all vectors of V which are perpendicular to every vector of S, $S^{\perp} = \{x \in V \mid x \cdot y = 0 \text{ for every } y \in S\}$. Prove that $S^{\perp}$ is a subspace of V and that

$$S + S^{\perp} = V, \qquad S \cap S^{\perp} = \{0\}.$$

Illustrate this result in $V_3(\mathbb{R})$.

6. Modules

An Abelian group $\{G; +\}$ is similar to a vector space in that there is defined a "scalar" multiplication of G by integers. Thus, for all $x \in G$ and $c \in \mathbb{Z}$, the multiple cx is in G, and

8.36 $$c(x + y) = cx + cy,$$

8.37 $$(c + d)x = cx + dx,$$

8.38 $$(cd)x = c(dx),$$

8.39 $$1x = x$$

hold for all $c,d \in \mathbb{Z}$ and $x,y \in G$. Note that these are precisely the properties 8.1–8.4 of a vector space. The group G fails to be a vector space in that its set of scalars $\mathbb{Z}$ is not a field.

Let R be a C-ring with unity and M be an Abelian group. A multiplication $R \times M \longrightarrow M$ is called a *scalar multiplication* of M by R. Thus, for each $(a,x) \in R \times M$ there corresponds a unique element of M denoted by ax. We shall call M an *R-module* iff M has a scalar multiplication by R having properties 8.36–8.39 for all $c,d \in R$ and $x,y \in M$.

By our remarks above, every Abelian group G may be considered to be a $\mathbb{Z}$-module. Of course, every vector space V over a field F is an F-module. Each C-ring R with unity is an R-module if we take scalar multiplication ax to be ordinary multiplication $a \cdot x$ for all $a,x \in R$. Finally, if $M_1, M_2, \ldots, M_n$ are R-modules, then so is their Cartesian product $M = M_1 \times M_2 \times \ldots \times M_n$ if we define scalar multiplication of M by R in the obvious way:

$$a(x_1,x_2, \ldots, x_n) = (ax_1, ax_2, \ldots, ax_n).$$

If M is an R-module and $N \subset M$, then N is called a *submodule* of M iff N is a subgroup of M and N is closed under scalar multiplication, i.e., $ax \in N$ for all $a \in R$, $x \in N$. Each $x \in M$ generates a *cyclic submodule* Rx,

$$Rx = \{ax \mid a \in R\}.$$

If $M = Rx$ for some $x \in M$, then M is called *cyclic*.

The *intersection* $K \cap N$ and *sum* $K + N$ of two submodules of an R-module M are again submodules of M. More generally, if $\{N_1, N_2, \ldots, N_m\}$ is a set of submodules of M, then their intersection

$$N_1 \cap N_2 \cap \ldots \cap N_m$$

and their sum

$$N_1 + N_2 + \ldots + N_m$$

are also submodules of M. An R-module M is said to be *finitely generated* iff there exists a finite set $\{x_1, x_2, \ldots, x_n\} \subset M$, called a *set of generators of* M, such that

$$M = Rx_1 + Rx_2 + \ldots + Rx_n.$$

In this case, every $y \in M$ has the form

$$y = b_1 x_1 + b_2 x_2 + \ldots + b_n x_n \text{ for some } b_i \in R.$$

Clearly a vector space is finitely generated iff it is finite-dimensional.

Just as in a vector space, a set $\{A_1, A_2, \ldots, A_n\}$ of submodules of an R-module M is called *independent* iff every $A_i \neq \{0\}$ and

$$A_i \cap (A_1 + \ldots + A_{i-1} + A_{i+1} + \ldots + A_n) = \{0\}, \qquad i = 1, 2, \ldots, n.$$

The notation

$$\{A_1, A_2, \ldots, A_n\}^{\perp}$$

is again used to denote an independent set of submodules of M. It is easily seen that 8.11 holds for modules as well as for vector spaces.

Corresponding to the dimension of a vector space, we shall speak of the rank of a finitely generated R-module M. Of all the possible sets of generators of M, one with the least number of elements is called a *minimal* set of generators of M. If $\{x_1, x_2, \ldots, x_n\}$ is a minimal set of generators of M, then n, the number of elements in this set, is called the *rank* of M. Clearly M has rank 1 iff M is cyclic.

The modules encountered in many applications are over principal ideal domains. So let us restrict our attention in the remainder of this section to an R-module M, where R is a pid. For example, each Abelian group G is a $\mathbb{Z}$-module.

If R is a pid and M is an R-module, then

$$I_x = \{a \in R \mid ax = 0\}$$

is easily seen to be an ideal of R for each $x \in M$. Since R is a pid, $I_x = cR$ for some $c \in R$. Evidently $I_x = R$ and c is a unit iff $x = 0$. We shall call I_x the *order ideal* and c an *order* of x in R.

The fundamental theorem on finitely generated modules is as follows:

8.40   Theorem. Let R be a pid and M be an R-module of rank n. Then there exist $x_1, x_2, \ldots, x_n \in M$ such that

$$M = Rx_1 + Rx_2 + \ldots + Rx_n, \qquad \{Rx_1, Rx_2, \ldots, Rx_n\}^{\perp}.$$

Outline of proof: The theorem is true if $n = 1$. Let us assume that the theorem is true for every module of rank $< n$, and let M be an R-module of rank $n > 1$.

If $\{x_1, x_2, \ldots, x_n\}$ is a minimal set of generators of M for which $\{Rx_1, Rx_2, \ldots, Rx_n\}^{\perp}$, then necessarily

$$(1) \qquad\qquad a_1 x_1 + a_2 x_2 + \ldots + a_n x_n = 0$$

for some $a_i \in R$ such that not all $a_i = 0$ (in fact, not all $a_i x_i = 0$). While some a_i might be 0, no a_i can be a unit. For example, if a_1 were a unit, then we could solve (1) for x_1,

$$x_1 = -a_1^{-1}(a_2x_2 + \ldots + a_nx_n)$$

and we would have $M = Rx_2 + \ldots + Rx_n$ contrary to the fact that $\{x_1, x_2, \ldots, x_n\}$ is a minimal set of generators of M.

As a matter of notation, let $p(c)$ denote the number of factors in a factorization of the nonzero element c of R into primes. Thus, if $c = p_1p_2 \ldots p_k$, where each p_i is a prime, then $p(c) = k$. Clearly $p(c) = 1$ iff c is a prime, and $p(c) = 0$ iff c is a unit. Since R is a unique factorization domain, $p(c)$ is well-defined.

If for some minimal set $\{x_1, x_2, \ldots, x_n\}$ of generators of M, there exists no relation of the form (1) except with all $a_i = 0$ (as will be the case if M is a vector space), then clearly $\{Rx_1, Rx_2, \ldots, Rx_n\}^\perp$ and the theorem is proved. Otherwise, for every minimal set $\{x_1, x_2, \ldots, x_n\}$ of generators there exists a relation (1) with not all $a_i = 0$. Among all such minimal sets and all such relations (1), select a nonzero a_i such that $p(a_i)$ is minimal. By our remarks above, $p(a_i) > 0$. For convenience of notation, assume that $p(a_1)$ is minimal. Let us also assume that $a_1, a_2, \ldots, a_t$ are the only nonzero a_i appearing in (1), so that (1) has the form

(2) $a_1x_1 + a_2x_2 + \ldots + a_tx_t = 0,$ each $a_i \neq 0$.

Case 1. If $t = 1$, then $a_1x_1 = 0$ and evidently a_1 is the order of x_1. Then

(3) $Rx_1 \cap N = \{0\},$ where $N = Rx_2 + \ldots + Rx_n$.

For otherwise, $b_1x_1 = b_2x_2 + \ldots + b_nx_n \neq 0$ for some $b_i \in R$. Then if $c = (a_1, b_1), p(c) < p(a_1)$ and $c = a_1f + b_1g$ for some $f, g \in R$. Hence, $cx_1 = (a_1f + b_1g)x_1 = b_2gx_2 + \ldots + b_ngx_n$ and

$$cx_1 - b_2gx_2 - \ldots - b_ngx_n = 0$$

contrary to the choice of a_1.

Since (3) holds and N has rank $n - 1$,

$$N = Rx_2' + \ldots + Rx_n', \qquad \{Rx_2', \ldots, Rx_n'\}^\perp$$

by the induction assumption. Hence,

$$M = Rx_1 + Rx_2' + \ldots + Rx_n', \qquad \{Rx_1, Rx_2', \ldots, Rx_n'\}^\perp$$

by 8.11, and the theorem is proved.

Case 2. If $t > 1$ in (2), we claim that $a_1 \mid a_i$ for $i = 2, \ldots, t$. For suppose $a_1 \nmid a_i$ for some i, say $a_1 \nmid a_2$. If $b = (a_1, a_2)$, then $b = a_1c_1 + a_2c_2$, $a_1 = bb_1$, and $a_2 = bb_2$ for some $b_i, c_i \in R$. Clearly $b_1c_1 + b_2c_2 = 1$, and if

$$y_1 = c_2x_1 - c_1x_2, \qquad y_2 = b_1x_1 + b_2x_2,$$

then

$$x_1 = b_2 y_1 + c_1 y_2, \qquad x_2 = -b_1 y_1 + c_2 y_2.$$

Hence, $\{y_1, y_2, x_3, \ldots, x_n\}$ is a minimal set of generators of M for which

$$by_2 + a_3 x_3 + \ldots + a_t x_t = 0.$$

Since $p(b) < p(a_1)$, this contradicts the choice of a_1.

Now $a_1 \mid a_i$ for each i, say $a_i = a_1 d_i$. Hence,

$$a_1(x_1 + d_2 x_2 + \ldots + d_t x_t) = 0.$$

If $x = x_1 + d_2 x_2 + \ldots + d_t x_t$, then $x_1 = x - d_2 x_2 - \ldots - d_t x_t$ and therefore $\{x_1, x_2, \ldots, x_n\}$ is a minimal set of generators of M for which

$$a_1 x = 0.$$

We may now revert to Case 1, thereby completing the proof of 8.40. ∎

In view of 2.38, we may also state the fundamental theorem 8.40 as follows:

8.41 Theorem. Each finitely generated module over a pid is isomorphic to a Cartesian product of cyclic modules.

In the special case of a finite Abelian group, which is a $\mathbb{Z}$-module, we have the following result:

8.42 Theorem. Every finite Abelian group is isomorphic to a Cartesian product of finite cyclic groups.

Proof: If $G = \{g_1, g_2, \ldots, g_n\}$, then clearly G is finitely generated, since

$$G = \mathbb{Z} g_1 + \mathbb{Z} g_2 + \ldots + \mathbb{Z} g_n.$$

Hence, 8.42 is a corollary of 8.41. ∎

Since $\{\mathbb{Z}_n \mid n > 1\}$ is the set of all finite cyclic groups, every finite Abelian group is isomorphic to

$$\mathbb{Z}_{n_1} \times \mathbb{Z}_{n_2} \times \ldots \times \mathbb{Z}_{n_k}$$

for some integers $n_i \geq 1$ by 8.42. Each $\mathbb{Z}_{n_i}$ is, in turn, isomorphic to a Cartesian product of cyclic groups of prime power order (Exercise 8, p. 63). Hence, every finite Abelian group is isomorphic to a Cartesian product

8.43 $$\mathbb{Z}_{p_1^{k_1}} \times \mathbb{Z}_{p_2^{k_2}} \times \ldots \times \mathbb{Z}_{p_m^{k_m}}$$

for some primes p_i.

We can now easily find all Abelian groups with a given finite number of elements. For example,

$$\mathbb{Z}_4, \qquad \mathbb{Z}_2 \times \mathbb{Z}_2$$

are the only Abelian groups with four elements;

$$\mathbb{Z}_8, \qquad \mathbb{Z}_4 \times \mathbb{Z}_2, \qquad \mathbb{Z}_2 \times \mathbb{Z}_2 \times \mathbb{Z}_2$$

are the only Abelian groups with eight elements. To find all Abelian groups with 36 elements, we first factor $36 = 2^2 \cdot 3^2$. Then

$$\mathbb{Z}_4 \times \mathbb{Z}_9, \quad \mathbb{Z}_2 \times \mathbb{Z}_2 \times \mathbb{Z}_9, \quad \mathbb{Z}_4 \times \mathbb{Z}_3 \times \mathbb{Z}_3, \quad \mathbb{Z}_2 \times \mathbb{Z}_2 \times \mathbb{Z}_3 \times \mathbb{Z}_3$$

are the only Abelian groups with 36 elements.

Exercises

Describe all Abelian groups of order:

1. 6.   **2.** 12.   **3.** 16.   **4.** 30.

5. 50.   **6.** 200.   **7.** 1,111.   **8.** 140.

*9. How many nonisomorphic Abelian groups are there of order p^m, p a prime? $p^n q^m$, p and q distinct primes? Generalize.

*10. If R is a pid, an R-module M is called *torsion-free* iff $I_x = \{0\}$ for every nonzero $x \in M$. Prove that for every integer $n > 0$, R^n is a torsion-free R-module (with scalar multiplication defined in the usual way). Prove that every finitely generated torsion-free R-module is isomorphic to R^n for some integer $n > 0$.

*11. If R is a C-ring with unity and A is an ideal of R, prove that R/A may be considered to be an R-module. Prove that R/A is a cyclic R-module. Conversely, prove that every cyclic R-module is isomorphic to R/A for some ideal A of R.

*12. If R is a pid and M is an R-module, let

$$T = \{x \in M \mid I_x \neq 0\}.$$

Prove that T is a submodule of M (called the *torsion* submodule). Also prove that M/T is a torsion-free R-module.

*13. Let $G = \{a_1, a_2, \ldots, a_n\}$ be an Abelian group of order $n > 2$. Prove that $a_1 + a_2 + \ldots + a_n = 0$.

chapter 9

Groups

Up to this point, we have considered algebraic systems with commutative operations only. In this chapter, we shall present one of the most useful noncommutative algebraic systems, the group.

I. Basic Properties

An algebraic system $\{G; \cdot\}$ having a binary operation of multiplication ($\cdot$) is called a *group* iff

9.1 Multiplication is associative;

9.2 There exists an identity element e relative to multiplication;

and

9.3 Multiplication is inversive.

By 9.3, each $a \in G$ has an *inverse* a^{-1} such that

$$a \cdot a^{-1} = a^{-1} \cdot a = e.$$

As usual, we shall often denote the product $a \cdot b$ by ab, omitting the multiplication sign.

Every Abelian group is a group, so we have at hand many examples of groups. Thus, for example, $\{\mathbb{Z};+\}$ and $\{\mathbb{Q}^+;\cdot\}$ are groups. Examples of non-Abelian groups will be given in Section 2.

When we speak of a group G, its operation is understood to be multiplication unless otherwise stated.

The *cancellation law* holds in a group G:

9.4   If $ac = bc$ or $ca = cb$ for some $a,b,c \in G$, then $a = b$.

The same proof holds here as in the Abelian case (2.5). From this, it follows that the inverse of an element of G is unique and (2.6)

9.5 $(a^{-1})^{-1} = a$ for all $a \in G$.

Also, by 2.7,

9.6 $(ab)^{-1} = b^{-1}a^{-1}$ for all $a,b \in G$.

Products of three or more elements of a group G are defined as in the Abelian case, and the general associative law (2.11) holds. In particular, the *powers* of each $a \in G$ are defined as usual: $a^0 = e$, $a^1 = a$, and recursively, $a^{n+1} = a^n \cdot a$ for each positive integer n. Since a^{-1} is also defined, we can define $a^{-n} = (a^{-1})^n$ for every $n > 0$. In this way, a^m is defined for every $a \in G$ and every $m \in \mathbb{Z}$. The following laws of exponents clearly hold:

9.7 $a^{m+n} = a^m a^n,\ a^{mn} = (a^m)^n$ for all $a \in G,\ m,n \in \mathbb{Z}$.

A nonempty subset H of a group G is called a *subgroup* of G if H is closed under multiplication, the identity element e of G is in H, and $a^{-1} \in H$ whenever $a \in H$.

For example, if G is a group and $a \in G$, then

$$H = \{a^n \mid n \in \mathbb{Z}\}$$

is a subgroup of G. Thus, H is closed under multiplication by 9.7, $a^0 = e \in H$, and $a^{-n} \in H$ is the inverse of $a^n \in H$. Evidently H is an Abelian subgroup—in fact, a cyclic subgroup of G.

The number of elements in a finite group G is called the *order* of G. For each $a \in G$, the *order* of a is the order of the subgroup $\{a^n \mid n \in \mathbb{Z}\}$ generated by a. As we saw in Chapter 2, the order of $a \in G$ is the least positive integer n such that $a^n = e$.

If H is a subgroup of a finite group G, then the sets

$$aH = \{a \cdot x \mid x \in H\}, \qquad Ha = \{x \cdot a \mid x \in H\}$$

are defined for each $a \in G$. We call aH a *left coset* and Ha a *right coset* of H

in G. By the same proof as for Abelian groups (2.20), it may be shown that

$$\{aH \mid a \in G\} \quad \text{and} \quad \{Ha \mid a \in G\}$$

are partitions of G. This does not imply that we can define a quotient group G/H for each subgroup H of G. We shall consider this question in Section 5. It does imply, however, the following form of 2.26.

9.8   Lagrange's theorem. If G is a finite group of order n and H is a subgroup of order k, then necessarily $k \mid n$.

It is readily verified that if $G_1, G_2, \ldots, G_n$ are groups, then their *Cartesian product*

$$G = G_1 \times G_2 \times \ldots \times G_n$$

is also a group. If e_i is the identity element of G_i, then $e = (e_1, e_2, \ldots, e_n)$ is the identity element of G. For each $a = (a_1, a_2, \ldots, a_n) \in G$, we have $a^{-1} = (a_1^{-1}, a_2^{-1}, \ldots, a_n^{-1})$.

Homomorphisms are defined as expected for groups. Thus, if G and K are groups, a mapping $G \xrightarrow{f} K$ is called a *homomorphism* iff

$$f(ab) = f(a)f(b) \text{ for all } a, b \in G.$$

Epimorphisms, monomorphisms, and isomorphisms are defined in the usual way.

Exercises

1. Let G be a group and $a \in G$ have order mn, where $(m,n) = 1$. Prove that a may be uniquely expressed in the form $a = b \cdot c$ where b and c have orders m and n, respectively, and $b \cdot c = c \cdot b$.

2. For any group G, the *center* of G, $C(G)$, is defined by:

$$C(G) = \{a \in G \mid ax = xa \text{ for all } x \in G\}.$$

Prove that $C(G)$ is an Abelian subgroup of G.

3. Let G be a group and $b \in G$. The *normalizer* of b in G, $N(b)$, is defined by: $N(b) = \{x \in G \mid xb = bx\}$. Prove that $N(b)$ is a subgroup of G containing b and $C(G)$.

4. If G is a finite group and $x, y \in G$, prove that the elements xy and yx have the same order.

5. Under what conditions on a group G is the mapping $G \xrightarrow{f} G$ defined by $f(x) = x^{-1}$ an isomorphism?

6. Prove that a nonempty subset H of a finite group G is a subgroup provided H is closed under multiplication.

*7. If every element of a finite group G is of order 1 or 2, prove that G is isomorphic to the Abelian group $(\mathbb{Z}_2)^n$ for some positive integer n.

*8. Prove that every finite group of even order contains an odd number of elements of order 2. [*Hint:* If $S = \{x \mid \text{order } x > 2\}$, then $\{x, x^{-1}\} \subset S$ whenever $x \in S$. Is $\#(S)$ even or odd?]

2. Permutation Groups

A bijection $A \longrightarrow A$ is commonly called a *permutation* of set A. If a and b are permutations of A, then so is their composite $a \circ b$ defined by

$$a \circ b(x) = a(b(x)) \text{ for all } x \in A.$$

The identity mapping $A \overset{e}{\longrightarrow} A$ defined by $e(x) = x$ clearly is a permutation, and for each permutation a its inverse a^{-1} as defined in Chapter 0 is also a permutation. Since the composite operation $\circ$ is associative and

$$e \circ a = a \circ e = a, \qquad a \circ a^{-1} = a^{-1} \circ a = e$$

for every permutation a, evidently the set S_A of all permutations of A with operation $\circ$ is a group. We call S_A the *symmetric group* on set A. The subgroups of S_A for each set A are called *permutation groups*.

If A is a finite set with n elements, then the symmetric group on A is denoted by

$$S_n$$

and is called the *symmetric group on n letters*. It is evident that S_n is independent of the nature of the elements of A.

For example, if $A = \{1,2\}$ then S_2 has two elements e and a defined by:

$$e: \quad e(1) = 1, \, e(2) = 2; \qquad a: \quad a(1) = 2, \, a(2) = 1.$$

Before giving other examples, let us give a notation for permutations of the set $A = \{1,2, \ldots ,n\}$. If $a \in S_n$ is defined by

$$a(k) = i_k, \qquad k = 1,2, \ldots ,n,$$

then we may indicate a by the array

$$a = \begin{pmatrix} 1 & 2 & \cdots & n \\ i_1 & i_2 & \cdots & i_n \end{pmatrix}.$$

Thus, a maps each element of the first row into the element of the second row directly below it.

If, for example, $a \in S_4$ is defined by

$$a(1) = 2, \quad a(2) = 3, \quad a(3) = 1, \quad a(4) = 4,$$

then we may indicate a by the array

$$a = \begin{pmatrix} 1 & 2 & 3 & 4 \\ 2 & 3 & 1 & 4 \end{pmatrix}.$$

With this notation, the elements of S_2 are

$$\begin{pmatrix} 1 & 2 \\ 1 & 2 \end{pmatrix}, \quad \begin{pmatrix} 1 & 2 \\ 2 & 1 \end{pmatrix}$$

and of S_3 are

$$\begin{pmatrix} 1 & 2 & 3 \\ 1 & 2 & 3 \end{pmatrix}, \quad \begin{pmatrix} 1 & 2 & 3 \\ 1 & 3 & 2 \end{pmatrix}, \quad \begin{pmatrix} 1 & 2 & 3 \\ 3 & 2 & 1 \end{pmatrix},$$

$$\begin{pmatrix} 1 & 2 & 3 \\ 2 & 1 & 3 \end{pmatrix}, \quad \begin{pmatrix} 1 & 2 & 3 \\ 2 & 3 & 1 \end{pmatrix}, \quad \begin{pmatrix} 1 & 2 & 3 \\ 3 & 1 & 2 \end{pmatrix}.$$

The group S_4 has 24 elements, and in general S_n consists of $n!$ elements.

It is easy to multiply elements of S_n expressed in the form above. Schematically,

$$\begin{pmatrix} \cdots & k & \cdots \\ \cdots & m & \cdots \end{pmatrix} \circ \begin{pmatrix} \cdots & j & \cdots \\ \cdots & k & \cdots \end{pmatrix} = \begin{pmatrix} \cdots & j & \cdots \\ \cdots & m & \cdots \end{pmatrix}.$$

That is, if $a(k) = m$ and $b(j) = k$, then $(a \circ b)(j) = m$.

For example,

$$\begin{pmatrix} 1 & 2 & 3 \\ 2 & 3 & 1 \end{pmatrix} \circ \begin{pmatrix} 1 & 2 & 3 \\ 2 & 1 & 3 \end{pmatrix} = \begin{pmatrix} 1 & 2 & 3 \\ 3 & 2 & 1 \end{pmatrix},$$

$$\begin{pmatrix} 1 & 2 & 3 \\ 2 & 1 & 3 \end{pmatrix} \circ \begin{pmatrix} 1 & 2 & 3 \\ 2 & 3 & 1 \end{pmatrix} = \begin{pmatrix} 1 & 2 & 3 \\ 1 & 3 & 2 \end{pmatrix}.$$

This shows, incidentally, that S_3 is not an Abelian group.

If $\{G; \cdot\}$ is a group, then each element a of G induces a mapping a^* of *set* G into G defined by

$$a^*(x) = a \cdot x \quad \text{for all} \quad x \in G.$$

That is, a^* is the *left multiplication* of G by a. Since $a \cdot x = a \cdot y$ iff $x = y$, evidently a^* is an injection. In fact, a^* is a permutation of G since $a^*(a^{-1}x) = x$ for every $x \in G$. Thus,

$$G^* = \{a^* \mid a \in G\}$$

is a set of permutations of G. We easily verify that

$$a^* \circ b^*(x) = (ab)^*(x) = (ab) \cdot x \quad \text{for all} \quad x \in G,$$

$$e^*(x) = e \cdot x = x \quad \text{for all} \quad x \in G,$$

and

$$(a^{-1})^*(x) = (a^*)^{-1}(x) \quad \text{for all} \quad x \in G.$$

Hence, G^* is a permutation group. Finally, the mapping

$$G \xrightarrow{f} G^* \quad \text{defined by} \quad f(a) = a^*$$

is readily shown to be an isomorphism. This proves the following famous theorem of group theory.

9.9 Cayley's theorem. † Every group G is isomorphic to some permutation group.

Often, the symmetries of a geometric figure can be conveniently described by a group of permutations. This fact is useful to the crystallographer studying the structure of a crystal and to the physicist or chemist studying the symmetries of a molecule.

To illustrate, let us consider the symmetries of the equilateral triangle T of Figure 9.1. There are two types of symmetries of T: rotations in the plane of T about its center O through angles $2\pi/3$ and $4\pi/3$, namely,

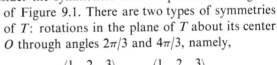

and rotations in space about the medians of T through angles of π, namely

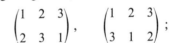

Figure 9.1

Each of these rotations keeps a vertex fixed. Of course, there is also the identity symmetry

$$\begin{pmatrix} 1 & 2 & 3 \\ 1 & 2 & 3 \end{pmatrix}.$$

Clearly the set of symmetries of T is S_3, the symmetric group on three letters.

By the product of two symmetries, we understand the successive application of the symmetries. Clearly the product is again a symmetry. Also,

---

† Cayley was a nineteenth-century English mathematician, whose accomplishment included the discovery of matrix algebras.

the inverse of a symmetry is a symmetry. If the geometric figure is a polygon or polyhedron, then each symmetry can be represented as a permutation of the vertices and the product of two symmetries is simply the product of the corresponding permutations. Hence, the set of all symmetries of such a figure can be represented as a permutation group, as was illustrated above. If the figure has n vertices, then its group of symmetries is a subgroup of S_n.

Every regular polygon P_n with n vertices has two types of symmetries, as illustrated above with P_3, rotations in its plane about its center and rotations in space about axes of symmetry. There are n rotations of each type (counting the identity as a rotation in its plane), and therefore the group of symmetries of P_n has $2n$ elements. This group is called the *dihedral group* and is denotéd by D_n.

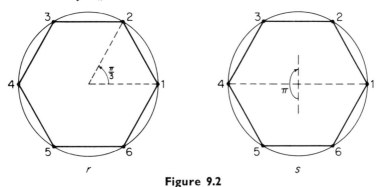

r s

Figure 9.2

For example, the two kinds of rotations of P_6 are shown in Figure 9.2. Thus, r is a rotation about its center through an angle of $\pi/3$ in the plane of P_6, and s is a rotation in space through an angle of π about the axis of symmetry 14. As permutations in S_6,

$$r = \begin{pmatrix} 1 & 2 & 3 & 4 & 5 & 6 \\ 2 & 3 & 4 & 5 & 6 & 1 \end{pmatrix}, \qquad s = \begin{pmatrix} 1 & 2 & 3 & 4 & 5 & 6 \\ 1 & 6 & 5 & 4 & 3 & 2 \end{pmatrix}.$$

It is easily seen that the rotations of P_6 in its plane are

$$e, \quad r, \quad r^2 \quad r^3, \quad r^4, \quad r^5,$$

and the rotations in space about axes of symmetry are

$$s, \quad r \circ s, \quad r^2 \circ s, \quad r^3 \circ s, \quad r^4 \circ s, \quad r^5 \circ s.$$

These consist of rotations about diagonals, such as s, and rotations about lines joining midpoints of opposite sides, such as $r \circ s$ shown in Figure 9.3. Thus, by multiplication,

$$r \circ s = \begin{pmatrix} 1 & 2 & 3 & 4 & 5 & 6 \\ 2 & 1 & 6 & 5 & 4 & 3 \end{pmatrix}.$$

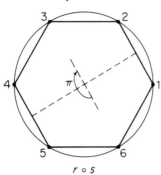

r ∘ s

Figure 9.3

Clearly $s^2 = (r \circ s)^2 = e$ and therefore

$$s \circ r = r^{-1} \circ s = r^5 \circ s.$$

Hence,

$$D_6 = \{e, r, r^2, r^3, r^4, r^5, s, r \circ s,$$

$$r^2 \circ s, r^3 \circ s, r^4 \circ s, r^5 \circ s\},$$

with multiplication easily carried out by means of the equations

$$s^2 = e, \qquad r^6 = e, \qquad s \circ r^k = r^{6-k} \circ s.$$

We note that D_6 is far from being all of S_6, since S_6 has 6!, or 720, elements whereas D_6 has only 12 elements. Thus, most of the permutations of the vertices of P_6 are not symmetries.

Exercises

1. Construct a multiplication table for the symmetric group S_3.

2. Give a geometric and algebraic description of the dihedral group D_4.

3. Give a geometric and algebraic description of the dihedral group D_5.

4. Prove that every group of order 5 or less is Abelian.

5. List all the subgroups of S_3.

6. List all the subgroups of D_4.

7. If A is a finite set and B a subset of A, then let

$$G = \{a \in S_A \mid a(x) \in B \quad \text{for all} \quad x \in B\}.$$

Prove that G is a subgroup of S_A.

8. Verify that for every positive integer n the dihedral group D_n contains elements r and s of orders n and 2, respectively, such that $(r \circ s)^2 = e$ and

$$D_n = \{r^i \circ s^j \mid i = 0,1, \ldots, n-1, j = 0,1\}.$$

9. Describe the group of symmetries of a rectangle.

10. Give examples of nonregular polygons with more than four vertices which possess nontrivial groups of symmetries.

3. Cycles

A permutation $c \in S_n$ is called a *cycle* iff there exists an ordered subset $(k_1, k_2, \ldots, k_m)$ of $\{1, 2, \ldots, n\}$ such that

$$c(k_1) = k_2, \; c(k_2) = k_3, \ldots, \; c(k_{m-1}) = k_m, \; c(k_m) = k_1,$$

and

$$c(j) = j \text{ for all other } j \in \{1, 2, \ldots, n\}.$$

The shorthand notation

$$c = (k_1 k_2 \ldots k_m)$$

is used for this cycle.

For example,

$$c = \begin{pmatrix} 1 & 2 & 3 & 4 \\ 3 & 2 & 4 & 1 \end{pmatrix}$$

is a cycle in S_4, since

$$c(1) = 3, \quad c(3) = 4, \quad c(4) = 1, \quad \text{while} \quad c(2) = 2.$$

This cycle is denoted by

$$c = (134).$$

On the other hand,

$$d = \begin{pmatrix} 1 & 2 & 3 & 4 \\ 4 & 3 & 2 & 1 \end{pmatrix}$$

is not a cycle. Thus,

$$d(1) = 4, \quad d(4) = 1, \qquad \text{but} \qquad d(2) \neq 2, \quad d(3) \neq 3.$$

The cycle (14) is the permutation

$$\begin{pmatrix} 1 & 2 & 3 & 4 \\ 4 & 2 & 3 & 1 \end{pmatrix}.$$

A cycle can be indicated in several ways. Thus, the cycle

$$\begin{pmatrix} 1 & 2 & 3 & 4 \\ 3 & 4 & 2 & 1 \end{pmatrix}$$

can be indicated in any one of the following ways.

$$(1324), \qquad (3241), \qquad (2413), \qquad (4132).$$

If we equispace the numbers 1, 3, 2, and 4 on a circle (Figure 9.4), then a cycle can be thought of as a clockwise rotation of the circle which carries each number into the following one.

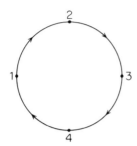

Figure 9.4

The cycle $c = (k_1 k_2 \ldots k_m) \in S_n$ is said to have *length* m. The powers of c are easily described: thus
$$c^j(k_i) = k_{i+j}$$
for each i, with addition modulo m in the subscript $i + j$. Hence, m is the least integer such that $c^m(k_i) = k_i$ for each i. We conclude that $c^m = e$ and that the *order of a cycle is its length*.

For example, if $c = (134) \in S_4$, then
$$c^2(1) = 4, \quad c^2(3) = 1, \quad c^2(4) = 3, \quad c^2(2) = 2$$
$$c^3(1) = 1, \quad c^3(3) = 3, \quad c^3(4) = 4, \quad c^3(2) = 2$$

and $c^3 = e$. Incidentally, the power of a cycle need not be a cycle.

Every element of S_3 is a cycle. Thus,

$$S_3 = \{(1),(12),(13),(23),(123),(132)\}.$$

We use (1) to indicate the identity permutation.

The cycles of length 2 in S_n are of particular importance; they are called *transpositions*. Thus, a transposition is a cycle of the form (ij) which interchanges the distinct elements i and j of $A = \{1,2,\ldots,n\}$ and maps every other element of A into itself.

Two cycles $(j_1 j_2 \ldots j_r)$ and $(k_1 k_2 \ldots k_s)$ of S_n are said to be *disjoint* iff $\{j_1, j_2, \ldots, j_r\} \cap \{k_1, k_2, \ldots, k_s\} = \varnothing$. Similarly, a set of cycles of S_n is called disjoint if the cycles in the set are pairwise disjoint. The cycles (124), (37), (85) of S_8 are disjoint, for example, whereas the cycles (124), (2857) are not disjoint, having the element 2 in common.

If a and b are disjoint cycles of S_n, then a and b commute, i.e.,

$$a \circ b = b \circ a.$$

For if i appears in cycle a but not in b, then

$$a \circ b(i) = a(b(i)) = a(i) = b(a(i)) = b \circ a(i)$$

and similarly if i appears in b but not a. If i appears in neither a nor b, then $a \circ b(i) = b \circ a(i)$. Hence, $a \circ b(i) = b \circ a(i)$ for all $i \in \{1,2,\ldots,n\}$, and $a \circ b = b \circ a$.

9.10   Theorem. Every element of S_n has a unique representation as a product of disjoint cycles.

Outline of proof: Evidently $e = (1)(2)\ldots(n)$. Let $b \in S_n$, $b \neq e$, and let m be the least positive integer such that $b^m(1) = 1$. If $b_1 = (1 \ b(1) \ldots b^{m-1}(1))$ then b_1 is a cycle of length m such that $b_1(i) = b(i)$ for each i appearing in b_1. If $b(j) = j$ for all j not appearing in b_1, then $b = b_1$ and the theorem is proved. Otherwise, if $b(j) \neq j$ for some j not appearing in b_1, and if r is the least positive integer such that $b^r(j) = j$, then define $b_2 = (j\ b(j) \ldots b^{r-1}(j))$. Clearly b_1 and b_2 are disjoint cycles, and $b_1 \circ b_2(k) = b(k)$ for all k appearing in either b_1 or b_2. If $b(k) = k$ for all other k, then $b = b_1 \circ b_2$ and the theorem is proved. Continuing, the theorem is proved in at most n such steps. The uniqueness is evident. ∎

For example, let $b \in S_8$ be defined by

$$b = \begin{pmatrix} 1 & 2 & 3 & 4 & 5 & 6 & 7 & 8 \\ 3 & 7 & 2 & 6 & 5 & 8 & 1 & 4 \end{pmatrix}.$$

Then

$$b(1) = 3, \quad b^2(1) = b(3) = 2, \quad b^3(1) = b(2) = 7, \quad b^4(1) = b(7) = 1,$$
$$b(4) = 6, \quad b^2(4) = b(6) = 8, \quad b^3(4) = b(8) = 4,$$

and $b(5) = 5$, so that

$$b = (1327) \circ (468).$$

We shall not usually include the operation symbol $\circ$ between cycles, writing instead $b = (1327)(468)$.

If $b \in S_n$ is given as a product of nondisjoint cycles, then b can easily be expressed as a product of disjoint cycles. For example, if $b \in S_8$ is given by

$$b = (1462)(2547)(36)(413578),$$

then cycle (413578) maps 1 into 3, cycle (36) maps 3 into 6, cycle (2547) maps 6 into 6, and cycle (1462) maps 6 into 2. Hence,

$$b(1) = 2.$$

In turn,

$$b^2(1) = b(2) = 5 \quad \text{and} \quad b^3(1) = b(5) = 1.$$

Therefore (125) is one of the disjoint cycles of b. Continuing, $b(3) = 6$ and $b^2(3) = b(6) = 3$. Hence, (36) is another disjoint cycle of b. Next, $b(4) = 4$, $b(7) = 8$, $b^2(7) = b(8) = 7$, and (78) is the final disjoint cycle of b,

$$b = (125)(36)(78).$$

The dihedral group D_6 is generated by

$$r = (123456) \quad \text{and} \quad s = (26)(35).$$

We note that $r \circ s = (12)(36)(45)$.

Exercises

Express each element of each of the following groups as a product of disjoint cycles.

1. D_4.   **2.** D_5.   **3.** D_6

4. Under what conditions on a cycle are all its powers also cycles?

5. If $c \in S_n$ is expressed as a product of disjoint cycles, $c = a_1 \cdot a_2 \cdot \ldots \cdot a_k$, how is the order of c related to the orders of the a_i?

6. Find a maximal cyclic subgroup of S_4; of S_5; of S_6.

7. If a and b are disjoint cycles of S_n, find a transposition c such that $c\, a\, b$ is a cycle.

*8. Let $c \in S_n$ be expressed as a product of disjoint cycles, $c = a_1 \cdot a_2 \cdot \ldots \cdot a_k$. Call c *regular* if all a_i have the same order. Prove that every power of a regular permutation is regular.

4. Even and Odd Permutations

Each cycle $(123 \ldots m)$ may be expressed as a product of transpositions as follows:

9.11 $(123 \ldots m) = (12)(23) \ldots (m - 1\ \ m).$

Thus, if b is the permutation on the right side of 9.11,

$$b(i) = (12)(23) \ldots (i\ \ i + 1)(i) = i + 1 \text{ if } i < m$$

and

$$b(m) = (12)(23) \ldots (m - 2\ \ m - 1)(m - 1) = \ldots = (12)(2) = 1,$$

from which we conclude that $b = (123 \ldots m)$.

Since each permutation is a product of cycles, we have by 9.11 that each permutation may be expressed as a product of transpositions. For example, if $b \in S_8$ is given by

$$b = (1327)(2563), \qquad \text{then } b = (13)(32)(27)(25)(56)(63).$$

This is by no means the only way to express b as a product of transpositions. First, note that as a product of disjoint cycles, $b = (137)(256)$. Hence, also

$$b = (13)(37)(25)(56).$$

Since $(ij)^2 = e$ for every transposition (ij), we can insert transpositions $(ij)(ij)$ at will. For example,

$$b = (13)(28)(28)(37)(25)(35)(35)(56)(18)(18).$$

As we see from the example above, the representation of a permutation as a product of transpositions is not unique. However, there is a uniqueness modulo 2 in the number of transpositions in a representation according to the result below.

9.12 Theorem. If $b \in S_n$ can be represented both as a product of k and of m transpositions, then $k \equiv m$ modulo 2.

Outline of proof: Let $f \in \mathbb{Z}[x_1, x_2, \ldots, x_n]$ be defined by

$$f = \prod_{i>j} (x_i - x_j) = (x_2 - x_1)(x_3 - x_1)(x_3 - x_2) \ldots (x_n - x_{n-1}).$$

Then define

$$b(f) = \prod_{i>j} (x_{b(i)} - x_{b(j)}) \text{ for every } b \in S_n.$$

For example, if $n = 3$ and $b = (132)$, then

$$f = (x_2 - x_1)(x_3 - x_1)(x_3 - x_2), \qquad b(f) = (x_1 - x_3)(x_2 - x_3)(x_2 - x_1).$$

Note that $b(f) = f$ in this example.

To return to the general case, what is $b(f)$ in case $b = (rs)$, a transposition? Assuming $r < s$, b maps $x_s - x_r$ into $x_r - x_s = -(x_s - x_r)$. All other factors of f having r or s as subscripts can be paired as follows:

$$(x_i - x_s)(x_i - x_r) \text{ if } i > s; \qquad (x_s - x_i)(x_i - x_r) \text{ if } r < i < s;$$

$$(x_s - x_i)(x_r - x_i) \text{ if } i < r.$$

Clearly b maps each of these quadratic factors into itself. All other factors of f are unchanged by b. Hence,

(1) $\qquad\qquad b(f) = -f$ for every transposition $b \in S_n$.

If $b \in S_n$ is expressed as a product of k transpositions, then $b(f) = (-1)^k f$ by (1) above. If b is also a product of m transpositions, then $b(f) = (-1)^m f$. Therefore, $(-1)^k = (-1)^m$ and $k \equiv m$ modulo 2. ∎

We may now define $b \in S_n$ to be an *even permutation* if b can be expressed as a product of an even number of transpositions, and an *odd permutation* otherwise. Thus, the identity element e is an even permutation, each transposition is odd, each 3-cycle $(ijk) = (ij)(jk)$ is even, and so on.

If $G \subseteq S_n$ is a permutation group and

$$H = \{a \in G \mid a \text{ even}\}$$

then H is a subgroup of G. Thus, $e \in H$ and $ab \in H$ whenever $a, b \in H$. Furthermore, if $a \in H$, say $a = b_1 b_2 \ldots b_k$ where each b_i is a transposition, then $a^{-1} = b_k b_{k-1} \ldots b_1$ and hence $a^{-1} \in H$. Is the set of all odd permutations in G a subgroup?

The subgroup

$$A_n = \{a \in S_n \mid a \text{ even}\}$$

of S_n is called the *alternating group* on n letters. For example,

$$A_3 = \{e,(123),(132)\}.$$

The reader may easily convince himself that the order of A_n is $(n!)/2$.

The alternating group A_4 has an interesting geometric interpretation, as we shall now show. Let T be a regular tetrahedron, as sketched in Figure 9.5.

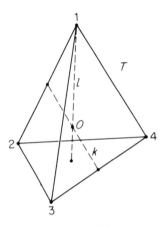

Figure 9.5

Each symmetry of T clearly carries the centroid O of T into itself. If a vertex, say 1, is also carried into itself, then evidently the symmetry is a rotation of T about the line l through O and 1. Hence, it is one of the permutations

$$(234), \quad (243).$$

Similarly, we may carry the other vertices into themselves by the rotations

$$(134), \quad (143), \quad (124), \quad (142), \quad (123), \quad (132).$$

One other type of symmetry of T is a rotation about a line k joining the midpoints of two opposite sides of T. The symmetries of this type are

$$(12)(34), \quad (14)(23), \quad (13)(24).$$

These are all the symmetries of T. Clearly each of the permutations listed above is even, and since they are 12 in number (including e), they form the alternating group A_4. We conclude that A_4 *is the group of symmetries of a regular tetrahedron*.

Exercises

1. List all the subgroups of A_4. Note that it has no subgroup of order 6.

2. Show that the cycle (12345) can be expressed as a product of 3-cycles (i.e., cycles of order 3). Why can't (1234) be expressed as a product of 3-cycles?

3. Prove that every even permutation in S_n, $n \geq 3$, can be expressed as a product of 3-cycles. [*Hint:* The product of two distinct transpositions is either a 3-cycle or a product of two 3-cycles.]

4. Prove that the subgroup G of S_8 generated by the two elements (1234)(5678) and (1638)(5274) is of order 8. Is G isomorphic to D_4?

*5. If a and b are cycles of the same order in S_n, prove that there exists some $c \in S_n$ such that $ac = cb$.

THEORETICAL PROJECT 1

1. Describe the group G of symmetries of a cube.

Partial solution: Clearly the center of the cube goes into itself under a symmetry. There are 13 lines of symmetry in the cube; 4 diagonals, 3 lines joining the centers of opposite faces, and 6 lines joining the midpoints of opposite sides.

2. Is G isomorphic to S_4? You may answer this question by observing that the four diagonals of the cube are carried into themselves by each symmetry.

3. Describe the group of symmetries of a regular octahedron. You may do this by observing that the regular octahedron is inscribed in a cube by joining midpoints of adjacent faces of a cube.

5. Normal Subgroups and Quotient Groups

Each subgroup H of a group G induces a partition $\{aH \mid a \in G\}$ of G into left cosets, and similarly for right cosets. We recall that $aH = \{a \cdot x \mid x \in H\}$ and $Ha = \{x \cdot a \mid x \in H\}$. By a similar argument to that used for Abelian groups (2.19), we may show that

9.13 $aH = bH$ iff $a^{-1}b \in H$, $Ha = Hb$ iff $ba^{-1} \in H$.

Corresponding to the subgroup $H = \{e,(12)\}$ of S_3, for example, are the left cosets

$$eH = H, \quad (23)H = \{(23),(132)\}, \quad (13)H = \{(13),(123)\}$$

and the right cosets

$$He = H, \quad H(23) = \{(23),(123)\}, \quad H(13) = \{(13),(132)\}.$$

We note that the partitions of G into left cosets and right cosets are different.

We recall that if H is a subgroup of an Abelian group G, then the partition G/H of G into cosets of H can be made into a group in a natural way. Can the same procedure be carried out for non-Abelian groups?

In trying to answer this question, we immediately have the problem of whether to use left or right cosets. Perhaps it makes no difference; so let us try to make

$$G/H = \{aH \mid a \in G\}$$

into a group by defining multiplication as follows:

9.14 $(aH) \cdot (bH) = (ab)H$ for all $aH, bH \in G/H$.

Is multiplication well-defined by 9.14? Thus, if

$$aH = a'H \text{ and } bH = b'H, \qquad \text{does } (ab)H = (a'b')H?$$

The answer is "no," as we can see by looking at the example above in which $G = S_3$ and $H = \{e, (12)\}$. We easily show that

$$(23)H = (132)H, \quad (13)H = (123)H, \quad \text{but } (23)(13)H \neq (132)(123)H.$$

The next question we ask is whether multiplication in G/H is ever well-defined by 9.14. For each $h \in H$, $aH = (ah)H$ and $(ab)H = (ahb)H$ iff $(ab)h' = ahb$ for some $h' \in H$; i.e., iff $hb = bh'$. Thus, we must have $Hb \subset bH$ for all $b \in G$ before multiplication can possibly be well-defined by 9.14. Since b^{-1} ranges overall of G as b ranges over G, and $Hb^{-1} \subset b^{-1}H$ is equivalent to $bH \subset Hb$, we must have $bH = Hb$ for all $b \in G$. In other words, the left and right coset partitioning of G by H must coincide.

A subgroup H of a group G is called *normal* (or *invariant*) iff

9.15 $bH = Hb$, or equivalently $H = b^{-1}Hb$, for all $b \in G$.

We do not mean by 9.15 that $bh = hb$ for all $h \in H$; rather, for every $h \in H$ there exists some $h' \in H$ such that $bh = h'b$, or, $b^{-1}hb \in H$ for every $h \in H$. By this definition, every subgroup of an Abelian group is normal. We now may prove the result hinted at by our remarks above.

9.16   Theorem. If H is a normal subgroup of a group G, then G/H is a group with multiplication defined by 9.14.

Proof: Multiplication is well-defined, as the reader may quickly verify. Since the mapping $G \xrightarrow{f} G/H$ defined by $f(a) = aH$ is an epimorphism of group G into the algebraic system $\{G/H; \cdot\}$, evidently G/H is also a group. ∎

As usual, we call G/H the *quotient group* of G by the normal subgroup H.

For example, the alternating subgroup A_n of S_n is normal. This is evident, since bhb^{-1} is an even permutation for all $b \in S_n$ and $h \in A_n$. Also, $bA_n = cA_n$ for all odd permutations b and c since $b^{-1}c$ is even. Therefore, the quotient group S_n/A_n has precisely two elements, A_n and bA_n, for any odd permutation b. Clearly S_n/A_n is isomorphic to $\{\mathbb{Z}_2; +\}$. Since S_n/A_n is of order 2, A_n is of order $(n!)/2$ by Lagrange's theorem.

Exercises

Find all the proper normal subgroups of each of the following groups.

1. S_3.   **2.** D_4.   **3.** D_5.

*4. D_6.   **5.** A_4.

6. The groups D_6 and A_4 are both of order 12. Are they isomorphic?

7. Prove 9.13.

8. Prove that multiplication is well-defined by 9.14 in G/H if H is a normal subgroup of G.

9. If $m < n$, then clearly S_m can be considered to be a subgroup of S_n. Prove that S_m is never a normal subgroup of S_n.

10. Prove that the center of a group G, $C(G)$, is a normal subgroup of G. (See Exercise 2, p. 167.)

11. Let set H consist of the eight elements ± 1, $\pm i$, $\pm j$, $\pm k$. Prove that H is a group if multiplication is defined as follows:

$$1 \cdot a = a, \quad (-a) \cdot b = a \cdot (-b) = -(a \cdot b), \quad (-a) \cdot (-b) = a \cdot b,$$

$$-(-a) = a$$

for all $a,b \in H$, and

$$i \cdot j = k, \qquad j \cdot k = i, \qquad k \cdot i = j,$$

$$j \cdot i = -k, \qquad k \cdot j = -i, \qquad i \cdot k = -j.$$

The group H is called the *quaternion group*.

12. List all the subgroups of the quaternion group, and show that they are all normal.

13. If G is a group, then the subgroup C of G generated by all elements of the form $aba^{-1}b^{-1}$, $a,b \in G$, is called the *commutator subgroup* of G. Prove that C is a normal subgroup of G and that G/C is an Abelian group.

14. Let H and K be normal subgroups of a group G. Prove that $H \cap K$ and $HK = \{a \cdot b \mid a \in H, b \in K\}$ are normal subgroups of G.

15. If H and K are normal subgroups of a group G such that $H \cap K = \{e\}$, then prove that the elements of H and K commute (i.e., $a \cdot b = b \cdot a$ for all $a \in H$, $b \in K$).

16. Let H be a subgroup of a group G. Define $C(H) = \{a \in G \mid ah = ha$ for all $h \in H\}$ and $N(H) = \{a \in G \mid aH = Ha\}$. Prove that $C(H)$ and $N(H)$ are subgroups of G, and that $C(H)$ is a normal subgroup of $N(H)$.

THEORETICAL PROJECT 2

9.17   Theorem. The alternating group A_n has no proper normal subgroup if $n > 4$.

Outline of proof: Let $G \neq \{e\}$ be a normal subgroup of A_n. If G contains some 3-cycle, say $(123) \in G$, then

$$(345)(123)(345)^{-1} = (345)(123)(354) = (124) \in G \text{ also.}$$

Continuing, it may be shown that every 3-cycle is in G. Hence, $G = A_n$ by Exercise 3, p. 178. The remainder of the proof is to show that G contains a 3-cycle. Let $a \in G$, $a \neq e$,

$$a = a_1 a_2 \ldots a_k, \qquad a_1, a_2, \ldots, a_k \text{ disjoint cycles.}$$

Case 1. Assume $a_1 = (123 \ldots m)$, $m \geq 4$. Then

$$(123)a(123)^{-1}a^{-1} = (123)a_1(132)a_1^{-1}$$

is a 3-cycle in G.

Case 2. Assume $a_1 = (123)$ and $a_2 = (456)$. Then

$$(345)a(345)^{-1}a^{-1} = (345)(123)(456)(354)(132)(465)$$

is a cycle in G of order 5. Hence, G contains a 3-cycle by Case 1.

Case 3. Assume a_1 is a 3-cycle and all other a_i are transpositions. Then a^2 is a 3-cycle in G.

Case 4. Assume all a_i are transpositions, with $a_1 = (12)$ and $a_2 = (34)$. Then

$$(123)a(123)^{-1}a^{-1} = (13)(24)$$

is in G. Also, $(125)(13)(24)(125)^{-1} = (23)(45)$ is in G. Hence,

$$(13)(24)(23)(45) = (13452)$$

is in G, and G contains a 3-cycle by Case 1.

The alternating group A_4 contains a proper normal subgroup

$$G = \{e, (12)(34), (13)(24), (14)(23)\}.$$

Where in the proof of 9.17 do you use the fact that $n > 4$?

6. Homomorphisms

If G and K are groups and $G \xrightarrow{f} K$ is a homomorphism, then clearly f maps the identity e of G into the identity e' of K and

$$f(x^n) = [f(x)]^n \quad \text{for all} \quad n \in \mathbb{Z}.$$

The *kernel* of f is defined as usual,

$$\ker f = \{x \in G \mid f(x) = e'\}.$$

9.18   Theorem. If G and K are groups and $G \xrightarrow{f} K$ is a homomorphism, then $\ker f$ is a normal subgroup of G.

Outline of proof: We easily show that $\ker f$ is a subgroup of G. If $b \in G$ and $h \in \ker f$, then $f(b^{-1}hb) = f(b^{-1})f(h)f(b) = [f(b)]^{-1}e'f(b) = e'$ and $b^{-1}hb \in \ker f$. It follows readily that $\ker f$ is normal. $\blacksquare$

The isomorphism theorem for Abelian groups (2.30) holds for any group, as stated below.

9.19   Isomorphism theorem. If G and K are groups and $G \xrightarrow{f} K$ is an epimorphism, then K is isomorphic to the quotient group $G/\ker f$ under the mapping $G/\ker f \xrightarrow{h} K$ defined by

$$h(a \ker f) = f(a) \quad \text{for all} \quad a \in G.$$

The reader may verify that the proof of the Abelian case carries over almost intact.

According to 9.19, every epimorphism $G \xrightarrow{f} K$ may be realized in the following fashion:

$$G \xrightarrow{g} G/H \xrightarrow{h} K, \qquad f = h \circ g,$$

for some normal subgroup H of G, where g is the natural homomorphism defined by $g(a) = aH$ and h is an isomorphism. In other words, up to isomorphisms the only homomorphic images of a group G are of the form G/H for some normal subgroup H of G.

Exercises

1. If a finite group G of even order n has a subgroup H of order $n/2$, then prove that H is a normal subgroup. Illustrate with the dihedral group D_n.

2. If G and K are groups and $G \xrightarrow{f} K$ is an epimorphism, prove that $f(N)$ is a normal subgroup of K for each normal subgroup N of G and $f^{-1}(H)$ is a normal subgroup of G for each normal subgroup H of K.

3. If H is a normal subgroup and K is any subgroup of a group G, prove that $HK = \{a \cdot b \mid a \in H, b \in K\}$ is a subgroup of G containing H and K.

4. Let H be a normal subgroup and K be any subgroup of a group G, as in Exercise 3. Define the mapping $K \xrightarrow{f} (HK)/H$ by $f(x) = xH$. Prove that f is an epimorphism. Show that ker $f = H \cap K$. Hence, prove that the groups $K/(H \cap K)$ and $(HK)/H$ are isomorphic.

5. Let H and K be normal subgroups of a group G, with $H \subset K$. Prove that K/H is a normal subgroup of G/H. Show that the mapping $G/H \xrightarrow{g} G/K$ defined by $g(xH) = xK$ is well-defined and has kernel K/H. Hence, prove that the groups $(G/H)/(K/H)$ and G/K are isomorphic.

*6. If n is an odd integer, prove that D_{2n} is isomorphic to $\mathbb{Z}_2 \times D_n$, where $\mathbb{Z}_2$ is the additive group of integers modulo 2.

7. Let H be a subgroup of a group G and $S = \{xH \mid x \in G\}$ be the partition of G into left cosets of H. Each $a \in G$ defines a mapping $S \xrightarrow{f_a} S$, $f_a(xH) = (ax)H$. Prove that each f_a is a permutation of S and that $K = \{f_a \mid a \in G\}$ is a group of permutations of S. Also prove that the mapping $G \xrightarrow{\varphi} K$ defined by $\varphi(a) = f_a$ is a homomorphism.

*8 Prove that the alternating group A_5 has no subgroup of order 15. [*Hint:* Use 9.17 and Exercise 7 above.]

7. Existence of Subgroups of a Finite Group

Although every subgroup H of a finite group G has a divisor of the order of G as its order, it is not true conversely that for every divisor k of the order of G there exists a subgroup H of order k. A simple example of this fact is that the alternating group A_4, a group of order 12, has no subgroup of order 6 as the reader may easily verify. However, there are always subgroups of prime power factors of the order of G according to the following classical theorem.

9.20   Theorem. If G is a finite group of order n and p is a prime factor of n, say $n = p^k t$ for some $k > 0$ and $(t,p) = 1$, then G has subgroups of order p^m for $m = 1,2, \ldots ,k$.

Outline of proof:† Let $m \leq k$ and $S = \{A \subset G \mid \#(A) = p^m\}$. Then $\#(S) = r$, the number of combinations of n things taken p^m at a time,

$$r = \binom{n}{p^m} = \frac{n!}{(p^m)!(n - p^m)!}.$$

It is a result of number theory that $p^{k-m} \mid r$, but $p^{k-m+1} \nmid r$. A relation $\sim$ may be defined in S by

$$A \sim B \text{ iff } A = xB \text{ for some } x \in G,$$

where $xB = \{x \cdot y \mid y \in B\}$ as usual. It is easily seen that $\sim$ is an equivalence relation. As such, it induces a partition $S/\sim$ of S. Let $S/\sim = \{S_1, S_2, \ldots, S_q\}$. If $p^{k-m+1} \mid \#(S_i)$ for each i, then evidently $p^{k-m+1} \mid r$ contrary to a remark above. Hence, $p^{k-m+1} \nmid \#(S_i)$ for some i, say for simplicity

$$p^{k-m+1} \nmid \#(S_1).$$

Let

$$S_1 = \{A_1, A_2, \ldots, A_u\}, \quad \text{so that } p^{k-m+1} \nmid u,$$

and

$$H = \{x \in G \mid xA_1 = A_1\}, \quad h = \#(H).$$

It is easily shown that H is a subgroup of G. If $A_i = bA_1$, then $A_i = bxA_1$ for each $x \in H$. Conversely, if $A_i = bA_1 = cA_1$ then $b^{-1}cA_1 = A_1$ and $c = bx$ for some $x \in H$. Therefore, if $G = \{b_1, b_2, \ldots, b_n\}$, each A_i of S_1 occurs exactly h times in the sequence $(b_1A_1, b_2A_1, \ldots, b_nA_1)$. Hence, $n = hu$ and $u \mid n$. Since $p^{k-m+1} \nmid u$, evidently $u \mid p^{k-m}t$. Consequently,

$$u \leq p^{k-m}t.$$

If $a \in A_1$ then $aH \subset A_1$ and therefore $h \leq p^m$. Hence, $n = hu \leq p^{k-m}tp^m = p^k t = n$ and consequently $h = p^m$. Thus H is a subgroup of order p^m. ∎

Subgroups of maximal prime power order of a finite group are called *Sylow groups* in honor of the Norwegian mathematician L. Sylow who discovered them in the 1870's. For example, the subgroups

$$\{e, (134), (143)\}, \quad \{e, (12)(34), (14)(23), (13)(24)\}$$

are Sylow subgroups of A_4.

If G is a finite group and p is a prime factor of the order of G, then G contains a subgroup H of order p. We know that H must be a cyclic group of order p, and hence some element of H has order p. These remarks prove the following result.

---

† As given by H. Wielandt, "Ein Beweis für die Existenz der Sylowgruppen," *Archiv der Math.*, **10** (1959), 401.

9.21   Theorem. If G is a finite group and p is a prime factor of the order of G, then G contains an element of order p.

Exercises

1. Elements b and c of a group G are said to be *conjugate* iff $b = xcx^{-1}$ for some $x \in G$, and we write $b \sim c$. Prove that $\sim$ is an equivalence relation in G. As such, $\sim$ induces a partition $G/\sim$ of G.

2. Let G be a finite group, $b \in G$, and $N(b)$ be the normalizer of b in G (see Exercise 3, p. 167). If $C(b)$ is the element of $G/\sim$ containing b, i.e., $C(b) = \{c \in G \mid b \sim c\}$, then prove that

$$\#(G) = \#[C(b)] \cdot \#[N(b)].$$

[*Hint:* By definition, $C(b) = \{xbx^{-1} \mid x \in G\}$. Let $\{a_1 N(b), a_2 N(b), \ldots, a_k N(b)\}$ be the partition of G into left cosets of $N(b)$. If $x \in a_i N(b)$, say $x = a_i d$, $d \in N(b)$, then $xbx^{-1} = a_i dbd^{-1}a_i^{-1} = a_i ba_i^{-1}$. If $x \in a_i N(b)$ and $y \in a_j N(b)$, with $i \neq j$, then $xbx^{-1} \neq yby^{-1}$. Hence, $\#[C(b)] = k$.] Note that we can count the number of elements in G by

$$\#(G) = \sum_{i=1}^{m} \frac{\#(G)}{\#[N(b_i)]},$$

where $G/\sim = \{C(b_1), C(b_2), \ldots C(b_m)\}$.

3. Prove that every group G of prime power order p^n has a proper center (as defined in Exercise 2, p. 167). [*Hint:* Let $G/\sim = \{C(b_1), C(b_2), \ldots, C(b_m)\}$ as in Exercise 2. Evidently $C(b_i) = \{b_i\}$ iff b_i is in the center of G. If b_i is not in the center, then $\#[C(b_i)] = p^{k_i}$ for some integer k_i in view of Lagrange's theorem and Exercise 2. Hence, $\#[C(b_i)]$ equals 1 or p^{k_i} for each i. Since

$$\#(G) = \#[C(b_1)] + \#[C(b_2)] + \ldots + \#[C(b_m)],$$

the number of b_i for which $C(b_i) = 1$ must be a multiple of p.]

4. Prove that every group G of order p^2, p a prime, is Abelian. [*Hint:* By Exercise 3, the center H of G is either of order p of p^2. If $\#(H) = p$, then $\#(G/H) = p$ and G/H is cyclic. And so on.]

5. Prove that every group of order 36 has a proper normal subgroup. [*Hint:* Use 9.20 and Exercise 7, p. 184.]

6. If group G has order $4p^n$, where $p > 2$ is a prime and $n > 1$, then prove that G has at least one proper normal subgroup. [*Hint:* See Exercise 5 above.]

THEORETICAL PROJECT 3

Describe all finite groups of order pq, where p and q are primes and $p < q$.

Partial solution: Let G be a group of order pq and H be a Sylow subgroup of order p. Also let $x \in G$ have order q. If H is not normal, then $x^i H x^{-i} \cap x^j H x^{-j} = \{e\}$ if $0 \leq i < j < q$; for otherwise $H = xHx^{-1}$ due to the fact that H is cyclic and every element other than e is a generator of H. Thus, there are $pq - q$ elements of order p in G, and $K = \{x^i \mid i = 0, 1, \ldots, q - 1\}$ must be the set of all elements of G of order q. Hence, K is a normal subgroup of G, and $yKy^{-1} = k$ for any $y \in G$ of order p. Thus, $yxy^{-1} = x^r$ for some positive integer $r < q$, and $y^2 x y^{-2} = yx^r y^{-1} = x^{r^2}, \ldots, y^p x y^{-p} = x^{r^p}$. Hence, $r^p \equiv 1 \pmod{q}$. In this case, G is a group generated by elements x and y such that $x^q = y^p = e$ and $yx = x^r y$ where r is some positive integer less than q for which $r^p \equiv 1 \pmod{q}$.

If H is normal, similar reasoning proves that $xyx^{-1} = y^s$ for some positive integer $s < p$ and $s^q \equiv 1 \pmod{p}$. Hence, $s \equiv 1 \pmod{p}$ and $s = 1$. In this case, G is cyclic.

For what choices of p and q is there a unique non-Abelian group of order pq? Illustrate.

chapter 10

Rings

Noncommutative rings entered into mathematics with the discovery in 1842 of quaternions by the famous Irish mathematician, physicist, and astronomer Sir W. Rowan Hamilton. Hamilton arrived at his system of quaternions after many fruitless years of searching for a field of coordinates for 3-dimensional space $\mathbb{R}^3$ analogous to the complex field of coordinates for the plane. While his system of quaternions was neither a field nor a coordinate system for $\mathbb{R}^3$, it lacked being a field only in that multiplication was not commutative, and it could be adapted in a useful way as a coordinate system for $\mathbb{R}^3$.

Shortly after the discovery of quaternions, the English mathematician Sir Arthur Cayley discovered the algebra of matrices. This discovery has had a profound influence on mathematics and on applications of mathematics to physics and other sciences in the past century. The algebra of matrices is an example of a ring, as we shall see in this chapter.

I. General Remarks

A *ring* is an algebraic system consisting of a set R of elements having two binary operations, addition and multiplication, such that $\{R; +\}$ is an Abelian group, multiplication is associative, and multiplication is distributive with respect to addition. If, furthermore, R contains a multiplicative identity element 1, with $1 \neq 0$, then R is called a *ring with unity* 1.

Commutative rings (C-rings) were studied in Chapter 3. The properties of rings developed in Section 1 of Chapter 3 are valid for any rings, not simply commutative rings, and will be used henceforth with no further comment.

As our first example of a noncommutative ring, let us describe Hamilton's quaternion ring D. In the first place, D is a 4-dimensional vector space over $\mathbb{R}$. Let

$$\{1,i,j,k\}$$

be a basis of D. We introduce a multiplication in D by first defining products of basis elements, as given in the table. Now each element of D has the form

$$a_1 1 + a_2 i + a_3 j + a_4 k, \quad a_r \in \mathbb{R},$$

and we define the product of two such elements by multiplying each term of the first by each term of the second, using the accompanying table to find

·	1	i	j	k
1	1	i	j	k
i	i	-1	k	$-j$
j	j	$-k$	-1	i
k	k	j	$-i$	-1

products of the basis elements. In particular,

$$(ai) \cdot (bj) = ab(i \cdot j) = abk,$$

and so on, for all $a,b \in \mathbb{R}$. Thus, we define

10.1 $(a_1 1 + a_2 i + a_3 j + a_4 k) \cdot (b_1 1 + b_2 i + b_3 j + b_4 k)$

$$= (a_1 b_1 - a_2 b_2 - a_3 b_3 - a_4 b_4)1 + (a_1 b_2 + a_2 b_1 + a_3 b_4 - a_4 b_3)i$$

$$+ (a_1 b_3 - a_2 b_4 + a_3 b_1 + a_4 b_2)j + (a_1 b_4 + a_2 b_3 - a_3 b_2 + a_4 b_1)k$$

for all $a_r, b_s \in \mathbb{R}$.

It may be verified that D is a ring with unity 1, although we shall postpone the details until later. Clearly D is not a C-ring since, in particular, $i \cdot j \neq j \cdot i$.

The mapping of $\mathbb{R}$ into D which maps a into $a1$ clearly is a monomorphism. If we identify $\mathbb{R}$ with its image $\{a1 \mid a \in \mathbb{R}\}$ under this mapping, then $\mathbb{R}$ is a subring of D and each element of D has the form

$$a_1 + a_2 i + a_3 j + a_4 k, \qquad a_r \in \mathbb{R}.$$

Also, $aq = qa$ for all $a \in \mathbb{R}$ and $q \in D$. The unity of $\mathbb{R}$ is now the unity of D also.

Each quaternion q has a *conjugate* $\bar{q}$ defined as follows:

10.2   If $q = a_1 + a_2 i + a_3 j + a_4 k$, then $\bar{q} = a_1 - a_2 i - a_3 j - a_4 k$.

Clearly $\bar{q} = 0$ iff $q = 0$ (i.e., $a_1 = a_2 = a_3 = a_4 = 0$). We easily verify the following properties of conjugates. If $q = a_1 + a_2 i + a_3 j + a_4 k$, then

10.3 $q + \bar{q} = 2a_1$ and $q \cdot \bar{q} = a_1^2 + a_2^2 + a_3^2 + a_4^2.$

10.4 $\bar{\bar{q}} = q, \quad \overline{p + q} = \bar{p} + \bar{q}, \quad \overline{p \cdot q} = \bar{q} \cdot \bar{p}$ for all $p,q \in D.$

We may define the *trace function* T and the *norm function* N for D just as we did for $\mathbb{C}$ and $\mathbb{Q}[\sqrt{n}]$; thus,

10.5 $T(q) = q + \bar{q}, \quad N(q) = q \cdot \bar{q}$ for all $q \in D.$

By 10.3, T and N are mappings of D into $\mathbb{R}$. By 10.4, we may show that

10.6 $T(p + q) = T(p) + T(q), \quad N(p \cdot q) = N(p) \cdot N(q)$ for all $p,q \in D.$

If $q \in D$, $q \neq 0$, then $q \cdot \bar{q} = N(q)$ and $q \cdot (\bar{q}/N(q)) = 1$. Similarly, $(\bar{q}/N(q)) \cdot q = 1$. Thus, each nonzero $q \in D$ has an *inverse* q^{-1} given by

10.7 $q^{-1} = \dfrac{1}{N(q)} \bar{q}.$

For example,

$$(2 - i + 3j)^{-1} = \frac{1}{14}(2 + i - 3j).$$

Also,

$$i^{-1} = -i, \qquad j^{-1} = -j, \qquad k^{-1} = -k.$$

A ring with unity such that every nonzero element has a multiplicative inverse is called a *division ring* (or *skew field*). By 10.7, D is a division ring. A commutative division ring is a field.

Since

$$q^2 - (q + \bar{q})q + q\bar{q} = 0 \text{ for each } q \in D,$$

evidently the quaternion $q = a_1 + a_2 i + a_3 j + a_4 k$ is a zero of the real polynomial

$$f(x) = x^2 - 2a_1 x + (a_1^2 + a_2^2 + a_3^2 + a_4^2).$$

Of course, $\bar{q}$ is also a zero of $f(x)$. Thus, every quaternion is a zero of a real second-degree polynomial.

For example, $2 - i + 3j$ and $2 + i - 3j$ are zeros of the real polynomial

$$x^2 - 4x + 14.$$

As another example, the polynomial

$$x^2 + 1$$

has as zeros i and $-i$; also j and $-j$; and also k and $-k$. Hence, the second-degree polynomial $x^2 + 1$ has at least six distinct zeros in D. Why doesn't this contradict Theorem 5.17? Actually, it is not difficult to show that $x^2 + 1$ has infinitely many zeros in D.

While a subring of a ring is defined as in Chapter 3, we must be careful in defining an ideal of a ring. A subring I of a ring R is called an *ideal* of R iff

$$rI \subset I \quad \text{and} \quad Ir \subset I \text{ for all } r \in R,$$

where $rI = \{rx \mid x \in I\}$ and similarly for Ir. Trivially, $\{0\}$ and R are ideals of of R. Every other ideal of R is called a *proper ideal*. We call a ring R *simple* iff R has no proper ideals.

Every division ring R is simple. For if I is a nonzero ideal of R and $a \in I$, $a \neq 0$, then $a^{-1}a = 1 \in I$. Hence, $r \cdot 1 = r$ is in I for each $r \in R$, and therefore $I = R$.

Just as with commutative rings, ideals enter naturally in ring theory in conjunction with homomorphisms. If R and S are rings and $R \xrightarrow{f} S$ is a homomorphism, then the kernel of f,

$$\ker f = \{a \in R \mid f(a) = 0\},$$

is an ideal of R. Clearly $\{\ker f; +\}$ is a subgroup of $\{R; +\}$. If $r \in R$ and $a \in \ker f$, then

$$f(ar) = f(a)f(r) = 0 \cdot f(r) = 0,$$

and similarly $f(ra) = 0$. Therefore, $(\ker f)r \subset \ker f$ and $r(\ker f) \subset \ker f$ for all $r \in R$, and $\ker f$ is an ideal of R.

On the other hand, if I is an ideal of ring R then, in particular, I is a subgroup of $\{R; +\}$ and

10.8 $R/I = \{a + I \mid a \in R\}$

is a quotient group with addition defined by

10.9 $(a + I) + (b + I) = (a + b) + I.$

In fact, R/I is a ring if we define multiplication in a similar way,

10.10 $(a + I) \cdot (b + I) = a \cdot b + I.$

We leave it for the reader to verify that multiplication is well-defined in R/I by 10.10 as long as I is an ideal of R. Since the mapping

10.11 $R \xrightarrow{h} R/I$ defined by $h(a) = a + I$

is an epimorphism by 10.9 and 10.10, and since R is a ring, it follows that R/I is a ring. We call R/I the *quotient ring* of R by the ideal I. The usual isomorphism theorem holds for rings (3.18).

10.12 Isomorphism theorem. If R and S are rings and $R \xrightarrow{f} S$ is an epimorphism, then the mapping $R/\ker f \xrightarrow{h} S$ defined by $h(a + \ker f) = f(a)$ is an isomorphism.

The *characteristic* of a ring R and of the elements of R is as defined in Section 4 of Chapter 3. Thus for each $r \in R$, ch $r = \#(A)$ if A is finite and ch $r = 0$ if A is infinite, where $A = \{nr \mid n \in \mathbb{Z}^+\}$. Another way of stating this is that ch r is the least positive integer n, if such exists, for which $nr = 0$. If no such n exists, ch $r = 0$. In turn ch R is the least positive integer n such that $nr = 0$ for all $r \in R$. If no such n exists, ch $R = 0$.

Exercises

1. Prove 10.3 and 10.4.

2. Prove 10.6 and 10.7.

3. Prove that $q \in D$ is a zero of $x^2 + 1$ iff $T(q) = 0$ and $N(q) = 1$. Hence exhibit several new zeros of $x^2 + 1$ in D. Prove that $x^2 + 1$ has an infinite number of zeros in D. Hence prove that there are an infinite number of subrings of D isomorphic to the complex number field $\mathbb{C}$.

4. If R is a ring such that $aR = R$ for every nonzero $a \in R$, prove that R is a division ring. [*Hint:* $ae = a$ for some $e \in R$. Then if $eb - b \neq 0$ for some $b \in R$, $(eb - b)R = R$, $(eb - b)c = e$ for some $c \in R$, and

$$0 = a(eb - b)c = ae = a,$$

contradiction. Is e the unity of R?]

5. Show that $I_n = \{a \in R \mid na = 0\}$ is an ideal of a ring R for every $n \in \mathbb{Z}^+$. Also show that $A_n = \{a \in R \mid n^k a = 0 \text{ for some } k > 0\}$ is an ideal of R for every $n \in \mathbb{Z}^+$. What can be said about the quotient ring R/A_n?

6. If R is a ring of characteristic $n > 1$ and $n = n_1 n_2$ where $n_i > 1$ and $(n_1, n_2) = 1$, then prove that R is isomorphic to a direct product $R_1 \times R_2$, where ch $R_i = n_i$, $i = 1, 2$.

7. Let R be a ring with unity such that $(x + 1)^3 = x^3 + 1$ for all $x \in R$.

Prove that R is isomorphic to a direct product of a Boolean ring and a ring of characteristic 3. Is the converse also true?

8. Let R be a ring such that $x^3 = x$ for all $x \in R$. Prove that R is isomorphic to a direct product of a Boolean ring and a ring of characteristic 3. [*Hint:* Prove $6x = 0$ for each $x \in R$. Then use Exercise 6.]

9. In a ring $\{R;+,\cdot\}$ let us define a new multiplication $\times$ by: $a \times b = a \cdot b - b \cdot a$ for all $a,b \in R$. Verify that the algebraic system $\{R;+,\times\}$ has all the properties of a ring except the multiplicative associative law. An algebraic system $\{S;+,\times\}$ is called a *Lie ring* iff (1) $\{S;+\}$ is an Abelian group, (2) $\times$ is distributive with respect to $+$, (3) $a^2 = 0$ for all $a \in S$, and (4) the *Jacobi identity* holds, i.e., $(a \times b) \times c + (b \times c) \times a + (c \times a) \times b = 0$ for all $a,b,c \in S$. Verify that $\{R;+,\times\}$ is in fact a Lie ring.

10. In a ring $\{R;+,\cdot\}$ let us define a new multiplication $\circ$ by: $a \circ b = a \cdot b + b \cdot a$ for all $a,b \in R$. Verify that the algebraic system $\{R;+,\circ\}$ is a Jordan ring. By definition, an algebraic system $\{S;+,\circ\}$ is a *Jordan ring* iff (1) $\{S;+\}$ is an Abelian group, (2) $\circ$ is distributive with respect to $+$, (3) $\circ$ is commutative, and (4) $[(a \circ a) \circ b] \circ a = (a \circ a) \circ (b \circ a)$ for all $a,b \in S$.

THEORETICAL PROJECT 1

Hamilton gave the following method of defining an operation of multiplication $(\times)$ in the vector space $V_3(\mathbb{R})$. Consider each vector $(a_1,a_2,a_3) \in V_3(\mathbb{R})$ to be the quaternion $a_1 i + a_2 j + a_3 k$,

$$(a_1,a_2,a_3) = a_1 i + a_2 j + a_3 k.$$

If the ordinary product of two quaternions is given by

$$(a_1 i + a_2 j + a_3 k) \cdot (b_1 i + b_2 j + b_3 k) = c_0 + c_1 i + c_2 j + c_3 k,$$

then define multiplication $(\times)$ in $V_3(\mathbb{R})$ by

$$(a_1 i + a_2 j + a_3 k) \times (b_1 i + b_2 j + b_3 k) = c_1 i + c_2 j + c_3 k.$$

For example, $(i - 2j + k) \cdot (j + 3k) = -1 - 7i - 3j + k$, and therefore

$$(i - 2j + k) \times (j + 3k) = -7i - 3j + k.$$

Prove that the system $\{V_3(\mathbb{R});+,\times)$ is a Lie ring. This system is the very useful 3-dimensional vector algebra used in calculus, physics, engineering, and so on.

2. Linear Transformations

The most common and most useful noncommutative rings are the rings of linear transformations of vector spaces and their isomorphic rings of matrices.

If V is a vector space over a field F, then a mapping $V \xrightarrow{f} V$ is called a *linear transformation* iff

10.13 $f(x + y) = f(x) + f(y)$ for all $x, y \in V$

and

10.14 $f(ax) = af(x)$ for all $x \in V$, $a \in F$.

Thus, f is a group homomorphism by 10.13 and f preserves scalar multiplication by 10.14. We shall denote by

$$L(V)$$

the set of all linear transformations of a vector space V.

We may combine 10.13 and 10.14, getting

$$f(ax + by) = f(ax) + f(by) = af(x) + bf(y)$$

for all $x, y \in V$, $a, b \in F$. More generally, we have for every $f \in L(V)$,

10.15 $f\left(\sum_{i=1}^{n} a_i x_i \right) = \sum_{i=1}^{n} a_i f(x_i)$ for all $x_i \in V$, $a_i \in F$.

Conversely, if $V \xrightarrow{f} V$ is a mapping for which 10.15 holds, then clearly both 10.13 and 10.14 hold, and $f \in L(V)$.

The sum and product of two mappings f and g of V into V are defined as previously:

10.16 $(f + g)(x) = f(x) + g(x)$ for all $x \in V$.

10.17 $(fg)(x) = f(g(x))$ for all $x \in V$.

Of course, fg is the usual composition of mappings (denoted by $f \circ g$ heretofore). Let us prove that if f and g are linear transformations then so are

$f + g$ and fg. That 10.13 holds for $f + g$ and fg follows from the computations below.

$$(f + g)(x + y) = f(x + y) + g(x + y) = [f(x) + f(y)] + [g(x) + g(y)]$$
$$= [f(x) + g(x)] + [f(y) + g(y)] = (f + g)(x)$$
$$+ (f + g)(y).$$
$$(fg)(x + y) = f[g(x + y)] = f[g(x) + g(y)]$$
$$= f[g(x)] + f[g(y)] = (fg)(x) + (fg)(y).$$

Also,

$$(f + g)(ax) = f(ax) + g(ax) = af(x) + ag(x)$$
$$= a[f(x) + g(x)] = a[(f + g)(x)]$$

and 10.14 holds for $f + g$. The reader may quickly verify that 10.14 also holds for fg. We may now state the following result.

   10.18   **Theorem.** For every vector space $V(F)$, the algebraic system $\{L(V); +, \cdot\}$ is a ring with unity.

   Outline of proof: The verification that $\{L(V); +\}$ is an Abelian group is straightforward, and hence is left to the reader for the most part. The zero element of $L(V)$ is denoted by 0 and defined by

$$0(x) = 0 \text{ for all } x \in V.$$

Clearly $f + 0 = f$ for all $f \in L(V)$. The negative of f, $-f$, is defined by

$$(-f)(x) = -f(x) \text{ for all } x \in V.$$

   We know that the composite operation $\circ$ is associative. That $(f + g)h = fh + gh$ for all $f, g, h \in L(V)$ follows from

$$[(f + g)h](x) = (f + g)[h(x)] = f[h(x)] + g[h(x)]$$
$$= (fh)(x) + (gh)(x) = (fh + gh)(x) \text{ for all } x \in V.$$

The other distributive law follows similarly. The unity $1 \in L(V)$ is the identity mapping

$$1(x) = x \text{ for all } x \in V. \quad \blacksquare$$

   The ring $L(V)$ can be made into a vector space over F by defining af for every $a \in F$ and $f \in L(V)$ as follows:

   10.19 $(af)(x) = a[f(x)]$ for all $x \in V.$

It is quickly shown that $af \in L(V)$ and that the usual properties are enjoyed by scalar multiplication in $L(V)$. Scalar multiplication is related to ordinary multiplication in $V(F)$ as follows.

10.20 $(af) \cdot g = f \cdot (ag) = a(f \cdot g)$ for all $a \in F$, $f,g \in L(V)$.

We leave the verification of 10.20 as an exercise.

A ring such as $L(V)$ which is also a vector space over a field F and has property 10.20 is called a *linear algebra* over F.

If the vector space $V(F)$ has finite dimension $n \geq 1$, then each $f \in L(V)$ is determined by what it does to an ordered basis $(x_1, x_2, \ldots, x_n)$ of V. That is, each element of V is a linear combination of the x_i's, and if

$$f(x_i) = y_i, \qquad i = 1, \ldots, n,$$

then

$$f\left(\sum_{i=1}^{n} a_i x_i\right) = \sum_{i=1}^{n} a_i y_i$$

by 10.15.

On the other hand, if $(x_1, x_2, \ldots, x_n)$ is an ordered basis of $V(F)$ and $(y_1, y_2, \ldots, y_n)$ is any ordered set of n elements of V, then define the mapping $V \xrightarrow{f} V$ by

$$(1) \qquad f\left(\sum_{i=1}^{n} a_i x_i\right) = \sum_{i=1}^{n} a_i y_i.$$

Since each vector of V is uniquely expressible as a linear combination of the x_i, f is well-defined by (1). Note that f maps x_i into y_i. Since

$$f\left(\sum_{i=1}^{n} a_i x_i + \sum_{i=1}^{n} b_i x_i\right) = f\left(\sum_{i=1}^{n} (a_i + b_i) x_i\right) = \sum_{i=1}^{n} (a_i + b_i) y_i$$

$$= \sum_{i=1}^{n} a_i y_i + \sum_{i=1}^{n} b_i y_i$$

$$= f\left(\sum_{i=1}^{n} a_i x_i\right) + f\left(\sum_{i=1}^{n} b_i x_i\right)$$

and

$$f\left(c \sum_{i=1}^{n} a_i x_i\right) = \sum_{i=1}^{n} c a_i y_i = cf\left(\sum_{i=1}^{n} a_i x_i\right)$$

f is a linear transformation of V.

For example, if $\{u_1, u_2, u_3\}$ is the usual unit basis of $V_3(\mathbb{R})$ and $y_1 = (\cos \theta, \sin \theta, 0)$, $y_2 = (-\sin \theta, \cos \theta, 0)$, $y_3 = (0,0,1) = u_3$, then there is a unique linear transformation f of $V_3(\mathbb{R})$ such that

$$f(u_1) = y_1, \qquad f(u_2) = y_2, \qquad f(u_3) = y_3.$$

Geometrically, f is a rotation in space about the z-axis and through an angle θ, as indicated in Figure 10.1. Thus, if $x = (a_1, a_2, a_3)$ then

$$f(x) = (a_1 \cos \theta - a_2 \sin \theta, \, a_1 \sin \theta + a_2 \cos \theta, \, a_3).$$

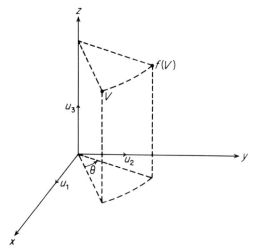

Figure 10.1

For each ordered basis $(x_1, x_2, \ldots, x_n)$ of an n-dimensional vector space $V(F)$, there exist linear transformations which map $n-1$ of the x_j's into 0 and the nth x_j into some x_i. Thus, define $e_{ij} \in L(V)$ by

10.21 $e_{ij}(x_k) = 0$ if $j \neq k$, $e_{ij}(x_j) = x_i$, $i, j, k = 1, 2, \ldots, n$.

Using the *Kronecker delta* δ_{ij} defined by

$$\delta_{ii} = 1, \quad \delta_{ij} = 0 \quad \text{if } i \neq j,$$

we can express 10.21 in the form

10.22 $e_{ij}(x_k) = \delta_{jk} x_i$, $i, j, k = 1, 2, \ldots, n$.

Hence, associated with each ordered basis $(x_1, x_2, \ldots, x_n)$ of V is a set

$$S = \{ e_{ij} \mid i, j = 1, 2, \ldots, n \}$$

of n^2 linear transformations of V.

The rule for multiplying the e_{ij} of 10.22 may be obtained as follows. Evidently

$$(e_{ij} \cdot e_{kl})(x_m) = e_{ij}(\delta_{lm} x_k) = \delta_{lm} e_{ij}(x_k) = \delta_{lm} \delta_{jk}(x_i),$$

from which it follows (since $\delta_{lm}(x_i) = e_{il}(x_m)$) that

10.23 $e_{ij} \cdot e_{kl} = \delta_{jk} e_{il}$, $i, j, k, l = 1, 2, \ldots, n$.

In other words,

$$e_{ij} \cdot e_{jk} = e_{ik}, \quad e_{ij} \cdot e_{kl} = 0 \quad \text{if } j \neq k.$$

Clearly $e_{11} + e_{22} + \ldots + e_{nn}$ is the unity of $L(V)$,

$$1 = e_{11} + e_{22} + \ldots + e_{nn},$$

since $(e_{11} + e_{22} + \ldots + e_{nn})(x_i) = x_i$ for each i.

Actually, S is an independent set of elements of the vector space $L(V)$ over F. For if

$$\sum_{i=1}^{n} \sum_{j=1}^{n} a_{ij} e_{ij} = 0$$

for some $a_{ij} \in F$, then

$$e_{kk}\left(\sum_{i=1}^{n} \sum_{j=1}^{n} a_{ij} e_{ij} \right) e_{ll} = a_{kl} e_{kl} = 0$$

by 10.23. Hence, $a_{kl} = 0$ for all k and l.

If f is any linear transformation of V, then $f(x_k)$ is a linear combination of the basis elements $x_1, x_2, \ldots, x_n$ for each k, i.e.,

$$f(x_k) = \sum_{i=1}^{n} a_{ik} x_i, \quad k = 1, 2, \ldots, n,$$

for some $a_{ik} \in F$. Since

$$\left(\sum_{i=1}^{n} \sum_{j=1}^{n} a_{ij} e_{ij} \right)(x_k) = \sum_{i=1}^{n} a_{ik} x_i, \quad k = 1, 2, \ldots, n,$$

also, evidently

10.24
$$f = \sum_{i=1}^{n} \sum_{j=1}^{n} a_{ij} e_{ij}.$$

That is, S is a set of generators of $L(V)$. Hence, S is a basis of the vector space $L(V)$. This proves the following result.

10.25   Theorem. If the vector space $V(F)$ has dimension n, then the vector space $L(V)$ has dimension n^2.

As an example, consider the vector space $V_2(\mathbb{Z}_2)$ and its unit basis $\{u_1, u_2\}$, where $u_1 = (1,0)$ and $u_2 = (0,1)$. The corresponding basis of $L(V_2)$ has four elements $e_{11}, e_{12}, e_{21}, e_{22}$ defined by:

$$e_{11}(u_1) = u_1, \quad e_{11}(u_2) = 0; \quad e_{12}(u_1) = 0, \quad e_{12}(u_2) = u_1$$
$$e_{21}(u_1) = u_2, \quad e_{21}(u_2) = 0; \quad e_{22}(u_1) = 0, \quad e_{22}(u_2) = u_2.$$

By 10.18,

$$L(V)_2 = \left\{ \sum_{i,j=1}^{2} a_{ij} e_{ij} \mid a_{ij} \in \mathbb{Z}_2 \right\}$$

is a ring with unity. Evidently $L(V_2)$ contains 16 elements, since it is a 4-dimensional vector space over $\mathbb{Z}_2$. The unity of $L(V_2)$ is $1 = e_{11} + e_{22}$. This ring is noncommutative, since, for example, $e_{11} \cdot e_{12} = e_{12}$ whereas $e_{12} \cdot e_{11} = 0$. The subspace

$$R = \{ae_{11} + be_{12} \,|\, a,b \in \mathbb{Z}_2\}$$

is actually a subring, since it is closed under multiplication. The ring R has four elements, and is also noncommutative since $e_{11}, e_{12} \in R$ and $e_{11}e_{12} \neq e_{12}e_{11}$ There is no noncommutative ring with fewer than four elements.

10.26   Theorem. If $V(F)$ is a finite-dimensional vector space, then $L(V)$ is a simple ring.

Outline of proof: Assume that $L(V)$ is generated by $S = \{e_{ij} \,|\, i,j = 1,2,\ldots,n\}$ as above. If I is a nonzero ideal of $L(V)$ and $f = \Sigma\, a_{ij}e_{ij} \in I$, $f \neq 0$, then some $a_{kl} \neq 0$. Hence,

$$a_{kl}^{-1}e_{ik}fe_{lj} = e_{ij} \in I \text{ for all } i \text{ and } j$$

and $I = R$. ∎

Exercises

1. If $V(F)$ is a vector space, prove that $af \in L(V)$ for all $a \in F$, $f \in L(V)$, and that the usual properties of scalar multiplication hold.

2. Prove 10.20.

3. Let G be any Abelian group and $H(G)$ be the set of all homomorphisms of G into G. If addition and multiplication are defined in $H(G)$ by 10.16 and 10.17, prove that $\{H(G); +, \cdot\}$ is a ring with unity.

4. Describe $H(G)$ of Exercise 3 in case: (1) $G = \mathbb{Z}$, (2) $G = \mathbb{Z} \times \mathbb{Z}$.

***5.** Let $V(F)$ be an n-dimensional vector space with ordered basis $(x_1, x_2, \ldots, x_n)$ and $\{e_{ji} \,|\, i,j = 1,2,\ldots,n\}$ be the associated basis of $L(V)$. If T is the subspace of $L(V)$ generated by $\{e_{ij} \,|\, i,j = 1,2,\ldots,n, \, i > j\}$, prove that T is a subring of $L(V)$. Show that $T^n = \{0\}$, i.e., that $a_1 \cdot a_2 \cdot \ldots \cdot a_n = 0$ for all $a_i \in T$. Illustrate in case $n = 3$.

***6.** Let f_θ be the rotation of $V_3(\mathbb{R})$ about the z-axis and through an angle θ (Figure 10.1), and g_φ be the rotation of $V_3(\mathbb{R})$ about the y-axis and through an angle φ. Represent $g_\varphi f_\theta$ in the form 10.24 relative to the basis (u_1, u_2, u_3).

***7.** Prove that there is no linear algebra S over R which is a division ring and a 3-dimensional vector space over R.

3. Matrix Rings

Associated with each n-dimensional vector space $V(F)$ is its ring of linear transformations $L(V)$. By choosing an ordered basis $(x_1, x_2, \ldots, x_n)$ of V and $e_{ij} \in L(V)$ defined by $e_{ij}(x_k) = \delta_{jk} x_i$, we saw that $L(V)$ was also a vector space over F with basis $S = \{e_{ij}\}$ and that the elements of S were multiplied according to the rule

$$e_{ij} e_{kl} = \delta_{jk} e_{il}.$$

If $f, g \in L(V)$ are given by

$$f = \sum_{i=1}^{n} \sum_{j=1}^{n} a_{ij} e_{ij}, \quad g = \sum_{i=1}^{n} \sum_{j=1}^{n} b_{ij} e_{ij}, \quad a_{ij}, b_{ij} \in F,$$

then

10.27
$$f + g = \sum_{i=1}^{n} \sum_{j=1}^{n} (a_{ij} + b_{ij}) e_{ij}$$

and

$$f \cdot g = \sum_{i=1}^{n} \sum_{j=1}^{n} \sum_{k=1}^{n} \sum_{l=1}^{n} a_{ij} b_{kl} \delta_{jk} e_{il},$$

or

$$f \cdot g = \sum_{i=1}^{n} \sum_{k=1}^{n} \sum_{l=1}^{n} a_{ik} b_{kl} e_{il}.$$

On interchanging the order of summation and replacing l by j, we have

10.28
$$f \cdot g = \sum_{i=1}^{n} \sum_{i=1}^{n} \left(\sum_{k=1}^{n} a_{ik} b_{kj} \right) e_{ij}.$$

A rectangular array of elements from a set F,

$$\begin{pmatrix} a_{11} & a_{12} & \cdots & a_{1n} \\ a_{21} & a_{22} & \cdots & a_{2n} \\ \cdots & \cdots & \cdots & \cdots \\ a_{m1} & a_{m2} & \cdots & a_{mn} \end{pmatrix}$$

having m rows and n columns, is called an $m \times n$ *matrix* over F. Its *i*th *row* is the n-tuple

$$(a_{i1}, a_{i2}, \ldots, a_{in})$$

and its *j*th *column* is the *m*-tuple

$$\begin{pmatrix} a_{1j} \\ a_{2j} \\ \cdot \\ \cdot \\ \cdot \\ a_{mj} \end{pmatrix}.$$

Note that a_{ij} is the element in the intersection of the *i*th row and *j*th column of the matrix.

If $\{F;+\}$ is an Abelian group then the set R of all $m \times n$ matrices over F can be considered to be the set F^{mn} of all ordered mn-tuples over F. As such, R is an Abelian group with addition carried out coordinatewise:

$$\begin{pmatrix} a_{11} & a_{12} & \cdots & a_{1n} \\ a_{21} & a_{22} & \cdots & a_{2n} \\ \cdots & & & \\ a_{m1} & a_{m2} & \cdots & a_{mn} \end{pmatrix} + \begin{pmatrix} b_{11} & b_{12} & \cdots & b_{1n} \\ b_{21} & b_{22} & \cdots & b_{2n} \\ \cdots & & & \\ b_{m1} & b_{m2} & \cdots & b_{mn} \end{pmatrix}$$

$$= \begin{pmatrix} a_{11}+b_{11} & a_{12}+b_{12} & \cdots & a_{1n}+b_{1n} \\ a_{21}+b_{21} & a_{22}+b_{22} & \cdots & a_{2n}+b_{2n} \\ \cdots & & & \\ a_{m1}+b_{m1} & a_{m2}+b_{m2} & \cdots & a_{mn}+b_{mn} \end{pmatrix}.$$

Denoting the matrices above by (a_{ij}) and (b_{ij}), we have

10.29 $$(a_{ij}) + (b_{ij}) = (a_{ij} + b_{ij}).$$

There is no natural way to define the product of two $m \times n$ matrices over F, even if F is a field, unless $m = n$. Of course, we could define multiplication coordinatewise once again, but the resulting algebraic system would be isomorphic to $\{F^{mn};+,\cdot\}$ and consequently would be nothing new.

Let F be a field and

$$(F)_n$$

denote the set of all $n \times n$ matrices (i.e., square matrices) over F. If

$$L(V) = \left\{ \sum_{i=1}^{n} \sum_{j=1}^{n} a_{ij} e_{ij} \mid a_{ij} \in F \right\}$$

is the ring of linear transformations of an *n*-dimensional vector space $V(F)$ discussed above, then there is a natural mapping

$$L(V) \xrightarrow{\sigma} (F)_n \quad \text{defined by} \quad \sigma\left(\sum_{i=1}^{n} \sum_{j=1}^{n} a_{ij} e_{ij} \right) = (a_{ij}).$$

Since the representation of each element of $L(V)$ in the form $\Sigma\, a_{ij}e_{ij}$ is unique, the mapping σ evidently is a bijection. Hence, we can make $(F)_n$ into a ring (in fact, a linear algebra) by carrying the operations of $L(V)$ over into $(F)_n$. Doing this, addition in $L(V)$ (10.27) carries over to addition in $(F)_n$ given by 10.29, and multiplication in $L(V)$ (10.28) carries over to

10.30
$$(a_{ij}) \cdot (b_{ij}) = \left(\sum_{k=1}^{n} a_{ik}b_{kj} \right)$$

in $(F)_n$. With these definitions of addition and multiplication, $(F)_n$ becomes a ring isomorphic to $L(V)$. Scalar multiplication in $L(V)$ carries over to

10.31
$$c(a_{ij}) = (ca_{ij})$$

in $(F)_n$, where $c \in F$. Then $(F)_n$ is a linear algebra isomorphic to $L(V)$. Clearly

$$0 = \begin{pmatrix} 0 & 0 & \cdots & 0 \\ 0 & 0 & \cdots & 0 \\ & \cdots & \cdots & \\ 0 & 0 & \cdots & 0 \end{pmatrix} \text{ and } I = (\delta_{ij}) = \begin{pmatrix} 1 & 0 & \cdots & 0 \\ 0 & 1 & \cdots & 0 \\ & \cdots & \cdots & \\ 0 & 0 & \cdots & 1 \end{pmatrix}$$

are the zero and unity, respectively, of $(F)_n$.

An easy way to remember 10.30 is to use inner products of row and column vectors of the matrices. Thus, if

$$x_i = (a_{i1}, a_{i2}, \ldots, a_{in}), \qquad y_j = \begin{pmatrix} b_{1j} \\ b_{2j} \\ \cdot \\ \cdot \\ \cdot \\ b_{nj} \end{pmatrix}$$

are the ith row of (a_{ij}) and jth column of (b_{ij}), respectively, then the inner product

$$x_i \cdot y_j = \sum_{k=1}^{n} a_{ik}b_{kj}$$

is the (i, j)th element of $(a_{ij}) \cdot (b_{ij})$,

$$(a_{ij}) \cdot (b_{ij}) = (x_i \cdot y_j).$$

If we let E_{ij} be the matrix of $(F)_n$ corresponding to e_{ij} in $L(V)$, then E_{ij} has 1 in the (i, j)th position and 0's elsewhere. Clearly $\{E_{ij}\}$ is a basis of the vector space $(F)_n$ over F; i.e.,

$$(a_{ij}) = \sum_{i=1}^{n} \sum_{j=1}^{n} a_{ij}E_{ij}.$$

The E_{ij} are multiplied in the same way the e_{ij} are,

$$E_{ij}E_{kl} = \delta_{jk}E_{il}.$$

For example, $(\mathbb{R})_2$ is the ring of all matrices of the form

$$\begin{pmatrix} a_{11} & a_{12} \\ a_{21} & a_{22} \end{pmatrix}, \qquad a_{ij} \in \mathbb{R}.$$

The matrices E_{ij} are given by

$$E_{11} = \begin{pmatrix} 1 & 0 \\ 0 & 0 \end{pmatrix}, \quad E_{12} = \begin{pmatrix} 0 & 1 \\ 0 & 0 \end{pmatrix}, \quad E_{21} = \begin{pmatrix} 0 & 0 \\ 1 & 0 \end{pmatrix}, \quad E_{22} = \begin{pmatrix} 0 & 0 \\ 0 & 1 \end{pmatrix}.$$

The zero and unity of $(\mathbb{R})_2$ are

$$\begin{pmatrix} 0 & 0 \\ 0 & 0 \end{pmatrix}, \quad \begin{pmatrix} 1 & 0 \\ 0 & 1 \end{pmatrix}.$$

We may use the fact that $(\mathbb{C})_2$ is a ring, where $\mathbb{C}$ is the complex number field, to prove that Hamilton's set

$$D = \{a_1 1 + a_2 i + a_3 j + a_4 k \mid a_i \in \mathbb{R}\}$$

of quaternions is a ring. By definition, D is a 4-dimensional vector space over $\mathbb{R}$ with a multiplication defined by 10.1. Let

$$A_1 = \begin{pmatrix} 1 & 0 \\ 0 & 1 \end{pmatrix}, \quad A_2 = \begin{pmatrix} \sqrt{-1} & 0 \\ 0 & -\sqrt{-1} \end{pmatrix},$$

$$A_3 = \begin{pmatrix} 0 & 1 \\ -1 & 0 \end{pmatrix}, \quad A_4 = \begin{pmatrix} 0 & \sqrt{-1} \\ \sqrt{-1} & 0 \end{pmatrix}.$$

(We use "$\sqrt{-1}$" in place of the usual symbol "i" in $\mathbb{C}$ since "i" is already used to denote one of the basis elements of D.) Then

$$\sum_{i=1}^4 a_i A_i = \begin{pmatrix} a_1 + a_2\sqrt{-1} & a_3 + a_4\sqrt{-1} \\ -a_3 + a_4\sqrt{-1} & a_1 - a_2\sqrt{-1} \end{pmatrix}, \qquad a_i \in \mathbb{R}.$$

Since the above matrix is zero iff $a_1 = a_2 = a_3 = a_4 = 0$, evidently $\{A_1, A_2, A_3, A_4\}^{\perp}$ in the vector space $(\mathbb{C})_2$ over $\mathbb{R}$. Let

$$S = \{a_1 A_1 + a_2 A_2 + a_3 A_3 + a_4 A_4 \mid a_i \in \mathbb{R}\}.$$

The reader may easily verify that S is closed under addition and multiplication and is, in fact, a ring with unity. The mapping $S \xrightarrow{f} D$ defined by

$$f\left(\sum_{i=1}^4 a_i A_i\right) = a_1 1 + a_2 i + a_3 j + a_4 k$$

may be shown to be a bijection preserving both addition and multiplication. Therefore, D is a ring. Since each nonzero $x \in D$ has an inverse $x^{-1} = \bar{x}/N(x)$, D is actually a division ring.

Exercises

1. Compute the following sums and products of the matrices $A,B,C \in (\mathbb{Q})_3$.

$$A = \begin{pmatrix} -2 & 1 & 0 \\ 3 & -1 & 5 \\ -1 & 1 & 4 \end{pmatrix}, \quad B = \begin{pmatrix} 4 & 1 & -2 \\ -6 & 2 & -6 \\ 2 & -2 & -8 \end{pmatrix},$$

$$C = \begin{pmatrix} -9 & -4 & 5 \\ -17 & -8 & 10 \\ 2 & 1 & -1 \end{pmatrix}.$$

(i) AB and BA.   (ii) AC and CA.

(iii) $(A + C)(A - C)$.   (iv) $BCB + CBC$.

(v) $(2A + B)^3$.

2. Show that $\mathbb{C}$ is isomorphic to a subring of $(\mathbb{R})_2$.

3. Let $R = (\mathbb{Q})_2$ and $A = \begin{pmatrix} -1 & 3 \\ 0 & 0 \end{pmatrix}$, $B = \begin{pmatrix} 2 & 0 \\ 1 & 0 \end{pmatrix}$. Describe each of the following sets of matrices.

(i) $\{X \in R \mid AX = 0\}$.   (ii) $\{Y \in R \mid YA = 0\}$.

(iii) $\{X \in R \mid XB = BX\}$.   (iv) $\{Y \in R \mid AYB = 0\}$.

4. If F is a field and $A = (a_{ij}) \in (F)_n$, then A is called a *diagonal matrix* iff $a_{ij} = 0$ for all i and j with $i \neq j$. Prove that $AB = BA$ for all diagonal matrices $A,B \in (F)_n$. For any diagonal matrix A, describe the set $S = \{X \in (F)_n \mid AX = XA\}$. Is S a subring of $(F)_n$?

5. The *center* $C(R)$ of a ring R is defined by

$$C(R) = \{a \in R \mid ax = xa \text{ for all } x \in R\}.$$

Prove that $C(R)$ is a subring of R. Describe $C(R)$ in case: (1) R is Hamilton's ring of quaternions; (2) $R = (F)_n$ where F is a field.

6. If F is a field and $A \in (F)_n$, say $A = (a_{ij})$, then the *trace* of A, $T(A)$, is defined by

$$T(A) = \sum_{i=1}^{n} a_{ii}.$$

Prove that $T(A + B) = T(A) + T(B)$, $T(cA) = cT(A)$, and $T(AB) = T(BA)$ for all $A,B \in (F)_n$ and $c \in F$.

7. Let $(x_1, \ldots, x_n)$ and $(y_1, \ldots, y_n)$ be two ordered bases of a vector space $V(F)$. Then each $f \in L(V)$ has associated with it two matrices A_f and B_f in $(F)_n$, one relative to the basis $(x_1, \ldots, x_n)$ and the other relative to the basis $(y_1, \ldots, y_n)$. Prove that there exists some $C \in (F)_n$ such that $B_f = CA_fC^{-1}$ for all $f \in L(V)$. Also prove that $T(A_f) = T(B_f)$ for all $f \in L(V)$. We may now define the *trace* if each $f \in L(V)$ to be $T(A_f)$ [or $T(B_f)$].

8. Prove that the set of all matrices in $(\mathbb{R})_2$ of the form

$$A(v) = h(v) \begin{pmatrix} 1 & -v \\ -v/c^2 & 1 \end{pmatrix}, \qquad -c < v < c,$$

where $h(v) = (1 - v^2/c^2)^{-1/2}$. is a multiplicative group (called the *Lorentz group*).

4. The Ring L(V)

We shall assume in this section that $V(F)$ is a finite-dimensional vector space and that $L(V)$ is its ring of linear transformations. For each subset S of V and each $f \in L(V)$, let

$$f(S) = \{f(x) \mid x \in S\}.$$

Clearly $f(S)$ is a subspace of V whenever S is a subspace. If S is a subspace and $\{x_1, x_2, \ldots, x_k\}$ is a basis of S, then

$$f(S) = Ff(x_1) + Ff(x_2) + \ldots + Ff(x_k),$$

that is, $\{f(x_1), f(x_2), \ldots, f(x_k)\}$ is a set of generators of $f(S)$. This set need not be linearly independent. However, since it is a set of generators of $f(S)$, some subset of it is a basis of $f(S)$. Hence,

10.32 $\dim f(S) \leq \dim S$ for every $f \in L(V)$ and subspace S of V.

The *rank* of $f \in L(V)$, $r(f)$, is defined by

10.33 $r(f) = \dim f(V)$.

If $r(f) = \dim V$, then f is called a *nonsingular* linear transformation, whereas, if $r(f) < \dim V$, then f is said to be *singular*.

For example, let $V_3(\mathbb{R})$ have its usual unit basis $\{u_1, u_2, u_3\}$ and let $f \in L(V_3)$ be defined by

$$f(u_1) = (0,1,1), \quad f(u_2) = (1,1,1), \quad f(u_3) = (1,0,0).$$

Then

$$f[(a,b,c)] = af(u_1) + bf(u_2) + cf(u_3) = (b + c, a + b, a + b).$$

Since $\{(0,1,1),(1,0,0)\}^{\perp}$ whereas $\{(0,1,1),(1,0,0),(1,1,1)\}^{\not\perp}$, evidently $r(f) = 2$ and f is singular. Note that $\ker f \neq \{0\}$, since, for example,

$$f[(1,-1,1)] = f(u_1) - f(u_2) + f(u_3) = (0,0,0).$$

The rank of a linear transformation f is closely related to the dimension of $\ker f$, as we shall show below. We first observe that $\ker f$ is a subspace of V; for $\ker f$ is an Abelian group, and $f(ax) = af(x) = 0$ for all $a \in F$, $x \in \ker f$. Since $\ker f$ is a subspace, each basis $\{x_1, x_2, \ldots, x_k\}$ of $\ker f$ can be extended to a basis $\{x_1, \ldots, x_k, \ldots, x_n\}$ of V. If $\ker f = \{0\}$, then $\{x_1, x_2, \ldots, x_n\}$ is simply any basis of V. Clearly

$$f(V) = Ff(x_{k+1}) + Ff(x_{k+2}) + \ldots + Ff(x_n),$$

for $f(x_i) = 0$ if $i \leq k$. In fact, $\{f(x_{k+1}), \ldots, f(x_n)\}$ is a basis of $f(V)$. For if

$$\sum_{i=k+1}^{n} c_i f(x_i) = 0 \text{ for some } c_i \in F, \text{ not all zero,}$$

then

$$f\left(\sum_{i=k+1}^{n} c_i x_i\right) = 0 \text{ and } \sum_{i=k+1}^{n} c_i x_i \in Fx_1 + \ldots + Fx_k = \ker f,$$

contrary to the independence of $\{x_1, x_2, \ldots, x_n\}$. Therefore, $\dim f(V) = n - k$, and we have proved the following result.

10.34 $r(f) + \dim (\ker f) = \dim V$ for all $f \in L(V)$.

The dimension of $\ker f$ is often referred to as the *nullity* of f.

If $f \in L(V)$ is nonsingular, then $r(f) = \dim V$ and $\dim (\ker f) = 0$, i.e., $\ker f = \{0\}$. Conversely, if $\ker f = \{0\}$ then $r(f) = \dim V$ by 10.34 and f is nonsingular. We state these observations as follows.

10.35 Theorem. For every $f \in L(V)$, f is nonsingular iff the mapping $V \xrightarrow{f} V$ is an isomorphism.

Returning to a nonzero $f \in L(V)$, a basis $\{x_1, x_2, \ldots, x_k\}$ of $\ker f$, and a basis $\{x_1, \ldots, x_k, \ldots, x_n\}$ of V, let us extend the independent set $\{f(x_{k+1}), \ldots, f(x_n)\}$ to a basis of V, say $\{y_1, \ldots, y_k, f(x_{k+1}), \ldots, f(x_n)\}$. If $z_1, \ldots, z_k$ are any k elements of V and $g \in L(V)$ is defined by

$$g(y_i) = z_i, \quad i = 1, \ldots, k, \quad g[f(x_j)] = x_j, \quad j = k + 1, \ldots, n,$$

then

$$(fgf)(x_i) = 0 = f(x_i) \text{ if } i = 1, \ldots, k,$$

and

$$(fgf)x_j = f(g[f(x_j)]) = f(x_j) \text{ if } j = k + 1, \ldots, n,$$

Therefore, $(fgf)(x_i) = f(x_i)$, $i = 1, \ldots, n$, and

10.36 $$fgf = f.$$

A ring R is called a *regular ring* iff for every $a \in R$ there exists some $b \in R$ such that $aba = a$. As a consequence of 10.36, we have proved:

10.37 Theorem. The ring $L(V)$ is a regular ring.

If $f \in L(V)$ is nonsingular, so that $V \xrightarrow{f} V$ is an isomorphism, then $V \xrightarrow{f^{-1}} V$ is also an isomorphism. It is easily shown that $f^{-1} \in L(V)$. Thus, f is a unit of $L(V)$. Conversely, if g is a unit of $L(V)$ and $g(x) = 0$ for some $x \in V$, then $x = g^{-1}g(x) = g^{-1}(0) = 0$. Hence, g is nonsingular by 10.35. Therefore,

$$U = \{f \in L(V) \mid f \text{ nonsingular}\}$$

is the group of units of $L(V)$.

Exercises

All vector spaces below are assumed to be finite-dimensional.

In each of Exercises 1–5, find the rank of the given linear transformation f of $V_3(\mathbb{R})$. $\{u_1, u_2, u_3\}$ is the usual unit basis of V_3. If f is singular, then find its kernel.

1. $f(u_1) = (2,1,-1)$, $f(u_2) = (1,1,2)$, $f(u_3) = (1,0,-3)$.

2. $f(u_1) = (0,0,0)$, $f(u_2) = (1,1,0)$, $f(u_3) = (-2,-2,0)$.

3. $f(u_1) = (1,1,1)$, $f(u_2) = (1,1,0)$, $f(u_3) = (5,5,-3)$.

4. $f(u_1) = (0,0,1)$, $f(u_2) = (0,1,1)$, $f(u_3) = (1,0,-1)$.

5. $f(u_1) = (8,11,-27)$, $f(u_2) = (4,3,-7)$, $f(u_3) = (2,-1,3)$.

6. Prove that $r(fg) \le r(f)$ and $r(fg) \le r(g)$ for all $f, g \in L(V)$.

7. Let vector space $V(F)$ have ordered basis $(x_1, x_2, \ldots, x_n)$. For each integer k, $1 \le k \le n$, let $f_k \in L(V)$ be defined by

$$f_k(x_i) = x_i \text{ if } i \le k, \qquad f_k(x_i) = 0 \text{ if } i > k.$$

Thus, $r(f_k) = k$, each f_k is an idempotent (i.e., $f_k \cdot f_k = f_k$), and $f_n = 1$. If $g \in L(V)$ has rank $k \geq 1$, then prove that there exist nonsingular $p,q \in L(V)$ such that $pgq = f_k$. [*Hint:* Let $\{y_1, \ldots, y_k, \ldots, y_n\}$ be a basis of V such that $\{g(y_1), \ldots, g(y_k)\}$ is a basis of $g(V)$ and $\{y_{k+1}, \ldots, y_n\}$ is a basis of ker g. Then select q so that it maps the x_i's into the y_i's, and so on.]

8. Prove that $r(f + g) \leq r(f) + r(g)$ for all $f,g \in L(V)$. Give examples to show that $r(f + g)$ can equal $r(f) + r(g)$, with $f \neq 0$ and $g \neq 0$.

*9. Prove that $r(fg) \geq r(f) + r(g) - \dim V$ for all $f,g \in L(V)$. Give an example, with $\dim V = 3$, in which $r(f) = r(g) = 2$ and $r(fg) = 1$.

10. If W is any subspace of V and $f \in L(V)$, then prove that $\dim W = \dim f(W) + \dim (W \cap \ker f)$.

*11. For each $f \in L(V)$, prove that $r(f) = r(f^2)$ iff there exists a subspace W of V such that $f(W) = W$ and $V = W + \ker f$.

*12. For each $f \in L(V)$, prove that $f^2 = f$ iff there exists a subspace W of V such that $\dim W = r(f)$ and $f(x) = x$ for all $x \in W$.

*13. For each $f \in L(V)$, prove that $f^m \neq 0$ for all $m \in \mathbb{Z}^+$ iff there exists a nonzero subspace W of V such that $f(W) = W$.

*14. Let $R = L(V)$ and $f,g \in R$. Prove that $g \in fR$ iff $g(V) \subseteq f(V)$.

*15. If a regular ring R has no nonzero divisors of zero, then prove that R is a division ring.

*16. A ring R is called *strongly regular* iff for every $a \in R$ there exists some $b \in R$ such that $a^2b = a$. Prove that a strongly regular ring has no nonzero nilpotent elements. Prove that a strongly regular ring is regular. Prove that every idempotent element of R is in the center of R.

THEORETICAL PROJECT 2

A subset A of a ring R is called *nil* if every element x of A is nilpotent, i.e., $x^n = 0$ for some $n \in \mathbb{Z}^+$.

1. Let A be an ideal of a ring R. If both A and R/A are nil, then prove that R is nil.

2. If A and B are nil ideals of a ring R, then prove that $A + B$ is also nil. [*Hint:* Use the fact that rings $(A + B)/A$ and $B/(A \cap B)$ are isomorphic.]

3. Prove that every ring R has a maximal nil ideal N.

The maximal nil ideal of a ring is called the *nil radical* of the ring.

4. If N is the radical of a ring R and A is an ideal of R with $A \subset N$, then prove that N/A is the nil radical of R/A.

THEORETICAL PROJECT 3

Let R be a ring with unity and $J = \{a \in R \mid (1 + ax)R = R$ for all $x \in R\}$.

1. Prove that J is an ideal of R. [*Hint:* If $a,b \in J$ and, for a given $x \in R$, $(1 + ax)d = 1$ and $(1 + bxd)e = 1$, then $(1 + (a + b)x)de = 1$. If for given $x,y \in R$, $(1 + axy)g = 1$ then $(1 + yax)(1 - ygax) = 1$.]

2. Prove that $R(1 + a) = R$ for all $a \in J$.

3. Prove that $J = \{a \in R \mid R(1 + xa) = R$ for all $x \in R\}$.

The ideal J is called the *Jacobson radical* of ring R.

4. Prove that the nil radical of R is contained in J.

5. Prove that J contains no nonzero idempotent elements.

6. If A is an ideal of ring R and $A \subset J$, then prove that J/A is the Jacobson radical of R/A.

chapter 11

Linear Equations and Determinants

Matrices were first introduced in mathematics to provide a systematic method of solving systems of linear equations. Under the guise of determinants, this method dates back to the seventeenth century. We shall show how to use determinants in solving systems of linear equations after studying the more general problem of the solvability of such systems.

1. Linear Equations Over a Field

If F is a field and $x_1, x_2, \ldots, x_n$ are unknowns, then the formal expression

11.1 $$a_1 x_1 + a_2 x_2 + \ldots + a_n x_n = b$$

where $a_1, a_2, \ldots, a_n, b \in F$, is called a *linear equation in n unknowns over F*. Using inner products, 11.1 has the form

11.2 $$\alpha \cdot \chi = b,$$

where

$$\alpha = (a_1, a_2, \ldots, a_n) \quad \text{and} \quad \chi = (x_1, x_2, \ldots, x_n).$$

If we replace the unknowns in 11.1 by elements of F, then 11.1 becomes a meaningful statement about elements of F. An n-tuple $(c_1, c_2, \ldots, c_n) \in F^n$ is called a *solution* of 11.1 iff the equation

$$a_1 c_1 + a_2 c_2 + \ldots + a_n c_n = b$$

is true. Using Greek letters for n-tuples, as we did above,

$$\gamma = (c_1, c_2, \ldots, c_n) \in F^n$$

is a solution of 11.2 iff

$$\alpha \cdot \gamma = b$$

is a true equation.

For example, the linear equation

$$3x_1 + 2x_2 = 4$$

in two unknowns over $\mathbb{Q}$ has $(2, -1) \in \mathbb{Q}^2$ as a solution, since

$$3 \cdot 2 + 2 \cdot (-1) = 4$$

is a true equation. In vector language, the equation

$$(3, 2) \cdot (x_1, x_2) = 4$$

has solution $(2, -1)$, since

$$(3, 2) \cdot (2, -1) = 4$$

is true. There are many other solutions of this equation; for example, $(0, 2)$ and $(\frac{4}{3}, 0)$ are solutions.

Every linear equation over a field F of the form 11.1 has a solution as long as some $a_i \neq 0$. For example, if $a_1 \neq 0$ then $(b/a_1, 0, \ldots, 0)$ is a solution of 11.1. If all $a_i = 0$, then 11.1 has a solution iff $b = 0$, in which case every n-tuple in F^n is a solution. If all $a_i = 0$ and $b \neq 0$, then 11.1 has no solution. We shall follow the usual custom of omitting the term $a_i x_i$ in 11.1 if $a_i = 0$. For example, we shall write

$$3x_1 + 5x_3 = 2 \text{ in place of } 3x_1 + 0x_2 + 5x_3 = 2.$$

The set of all solutions of a linear equation is called the *solution set* of the equation. To *solve* an equation is to find its solution set. For example, the linear equation $3x_1 + 2x_2 = 4$ in two unknowns over $\mathbb{Q}$ has solution set

$$\left\{ \left(r, \frac{4 - 3r}{2} \right) \,\middle|\, r \in \mathbb{Q} \right\}.$$

An equation of the form $0 = b$, where $b \neq 0$, has solution set $\varnothing$.

It is a simple matter to solve any given linear equation 11.1 over a field F. If some $a_i \neq 0$, say $a_k \neq 0$, then $\gamma = (c_1, c_2, \ldots, c_n) \in F^n$ is a solution of 11.1 iff

$$c_k = \frac{1}{a_k} (b - a_1 c_1 - \ldots - a_{j-1} c_{j-1} - a_{j+1} c_{j+1} - \ldots - a_n c_n).$$

Then

$$\{(c_1, c_2, \ldots, c_n) \mid c_i \in F, c_k \text{ as above}\}$$

is the solution set of 11.1.

An ordered set of linear equations in n unknowns over a field F is called a *system* of linear equations. Thus,

11.3
$$\begin{cases} a_{11}x_1 + a_{12}x_2 + \ldots + a_{1n}x^n = b_1 \\ a_{21}x_1 + a_{22}x_2 + \ldots + a_{2n}x_n = b_2, \\ \cdots\cdots\cdots\cdots\cdots\cdots\cdots \\ a_{m1}x_1 + a_{m2}x_2 + \ldots + a_{mn}x_n = b_m \end{cases} \quad a_{ij}, b_i \in F,$$

is called a system of m *linear equations in n unknowns over F*. Using the Σ-notation, 11.3 can be expressed as follows:

11.4
$$\sum_{j=1}^{n} a_{ij}x_j = b_i, \quad i = 1, 2, \ldots, m.$$

An n-tuple $\gamma \in F^n$ is called a *solution* of system 11.3 (or 11.4) iff γ is a solution of every equation of the system. The set of all solutions of 11.3 is called its *solution set*. If S_i is the solution set of the ith equation

$$a_{i1}x_1 + a_{i2}x_2 + \ldots + a_{in}x_n = b_i$$

of 11.3, then the solution set S of 11.3 is, by definition,

$$S = S_1 \cap S_2 \cap \ldots \cap S_n.$$

Associated with system 11.3 is the $m \times n$ matrix

$$A = \begin{pmatrix} a_{11} & a_{12} & \cdots & a_{1n} \\ a_{21} & a_{22} & \cdots & a_{2n} \\ \cdots\cdots\cdots\cdots\cdots \\ a_{m1} & a_{m2} & \cdots & a_{mn} \end{pmatrix}$$

of *coefficients* of the unknowns and the "column" vector

$$\beta = \begin{pmatrix} b_1 \\ b_2 \\ \cdot \\ \cdot \\ \cdot \\ b_m \end{pmatrix}$$

of *constant terms*. If we let

$$\alpha_i = (a_{i1} \quad a_{i2} \quad \cdots \quad a_{in})$$

be the ith row of matrix A, then 11.3 can be expressed in the form

11.5 $\alpha_i \cdot \chi = b_i, \quad i = 1, 2, \ldots, m,$

where χ is taken to be the "column" vector

$$\chi = \begin{pmatrix} x_1 \\ x_2 \\ \cdot \\ \cdot \\ \cdot \\ x_n \end{pmatrix}.$$

We can go one step further and express system 11.3 in the form

11.6 $A\chi = \beta,$

where $A\chi$ indicates vector-matrix multiplication, i.e., the row vectors of A are multiplied by the column vector χ:

$$A\chi = \begin{pmatrix} \alpha_1 \cdot \chi \\ \alpha_2 \cdot \chi \\ \cdot \\ \cdot \\ \cdot \\ \alpha_m \cdot \chi \end{pmatrix}.$$

For example, the system

$$\begin{cases} 2x_1 - 3x_2 + x_3 = 5 \\ 4x_1 + 7x_2 - 3x_3 = -6 \end{cases}$$

of two linear equations in three unknowns over $\mathbb{Q}$ can be expressed in the form

$$\begin{pmatrix} 2 & -3 & 1 \\ 4 & 7 & -3 \end{pmatrix} \begin{pmatrix} x_1 \\ x_2 \\ x_3 \end{pmatrix} = \begin{pmatrix} 5 \\ -6 \end{pmatrix}.$$

Two systems of linear equations in n unknowns over a field F are said to be *equivalent* iff their solution sets are equal. Evidently any two systems having empty solution sets are equivalent. We shall solve any given system by finding an equivalent system whose solution set is obvious.

For example, the system

$$\begin{cases} x_1 = 4 \\ x_2 = 2 \end{cases}$$

of two equations in two unknowns over $\mathbb{Q}$ has the obvious solution set $\{(4,2)\}$. Hence, any system of linear equations in two unknowns equivalent to the one above also has solution set $\{(4,2)\}$.

It is clear that we can change the order of the equations in a system without changing its solution set. Also, we can eliminate repetitions of equations as well as equations of the form $0 = 0$. A less obvious way of obtaining equivalent systems is as follows.

11.7   Theorem. The systems

$$(1) \qquad\qquad \alpha_i \cdot \chi = b_i, \qquad i = 1,2,\dots,m$$

and

$$(2) \qquad\qquad \alpha'_i \cdot \chi = b'_i, \qquad i = 1,2,\dots,m$$

of m linear equations in n unknowns over a field F are equivalent if $\alpha'_i = \alpha_i$ and $b'_i = b_i$ for $i = 1,2,\dots,m$, $i \ne k$, and

$$\alpha'_k = \sum_{i=1}^{m} d_i\alpha_i, \quad b'_k = \sum_{i=1}^{m} d_ib_i \quad \text{for some } d_i \in F,$$

with $d_k \ne 0$.

Outline of proof: By assumption, systems (1) and (2) have $m - 1$ equations in common; they differ only in their kth equations. Let S_1 be the solution set of system (1), S_2 of system (2). If $\gamma = (c_1,c_2,\dots,c_n) \in S_1$ then $\alpha_i \cdot \gamma = b_i$ for each i and

$$\alpha'_k \cdot \gamma = \sum_{i=1}^{m} d_i(\alpha_i \cdot \gamma) = \sum_{i=1}^{m} d_ib_i = b'_k.$$

Hence, $\gamma \in S_2$. Conversely, if $\gamma \in S_2$ then $\alpha'_i \cdot \gamma = b'_i$ for each i and therefore $\alpha_i \cdot \gamma = b_i$ for each $i \ne k$. Since

$$\alpha'_k \cdot \gamma = \sum_{i=1}^{m} d_i(\alpha_i \cdot \gamma) = b'_k = \sum_{i=1}^{m} d_ib_i$$

and $d_k \ne 0$, evidently $d_k(\alpha_k \cdot \gamma) = d_kb_k$ and $\alpha_k \cdot \gamma = b_k$. Hence, $\gamma \in S_1$. ∎

Theorem 11.7 may be used to find an echelon system equivalent to a given system of linear equations. A system

$$\sum_{j=1}^{n} a_{ij}x_j = b_i, \qquad i = 1,2,\dots,m$$

is called an *echelon system* iff there exist integers

$$0 < k_1 < k_2 < \dots < k_r \le n$$

such that

$$a_{ij} = 0 \text{ if } j < k_i, \quad a_{ik_i} \ne 0, \quad i = 1,2,\dots,r$$

and $a_{ij} = 0$ for all j if $i > r$, in case $r < m$. Thus, an echelon system of m linear equations in n unknowns has the form

$$a_{1k_1}x_{k_1} + a_{1\,k_1+1}x_{k_1+1} + \ldots + a_{1n}x_n = b_1$$
$$a_{2k_2}x_{k_2} + \ldots + a_{2n}x_n = b_2$$
$$\cdot$$
$$\cdot$$
$$\cdot$$
$$a_{rk_r}x_r + \ldots + a_{rn}x_n = b_r$$
$$0 = b_{r+1}$$
$$\cdot$$
$$\cdot$$
$$\cdot$$
$$0 = b_m.$$

For example,

11.9
$$\begin{cases} 3x_1 - x_2 + 4x_3 + 2x_4 = 3 \\ x_2 + 5x_3 - 3x_4 = 2 \\ x_4 = 1 \end{cases}$$

is an echelon system of three linear equations in four unknowns over $\mathbb{Q}$.

11.10 **Theorem.** An echelon system 11.8 of linear equations over a field F has a solution iff it contains no equation of the form $0 = b$ with $b \neq 0$.

Outline of proof: If 11.8 contains an equation $0 = b$ with $b \neq 0$, then clearly the solution set of 11.8 is $\emptyset$. Conversely, if system 11.8 contains no equation of the form $0 = b$ with $b \neq 0$, then let $c_i \in F$ be defined inductively as follows: c_j is any element of F if $c_j \neq k_1, k_2, \ldots, k_r$, while

$$c_{k_i} = \frac{1}{a_{ik_i}} \left(b_i - \sum_{j=k_i+1}^{n} a_{ij}c_j \right), \qquad i = r, r-1, \ldots, 1.$$

Then $(c_1, c_2, \ldots, c_n) \in F^n$ is a solution of 11.8 since it is a solution of each equation of 11.8. ∎

For example, $(c_1, c_2, c_3, c_4) \in \mathbb{Q}^4$ is a solution of 11.9 iff $c_4 = 1$, c_3 is any element of $\mathbb{Q}$, $c_2 = 2 - 5c_3 + 3$, and $c_1 = (3 + c_2 - 4c_3 - 2)/3$. In fact, it is clear that

$$\{(2 - 3c_3, 5 - 5c_3, c_3, 1) \mid c_3 \in \mathbb{Q}\}$$

is the solution set of 11.9.

Using Theorem 11.7, we can find an echelon system equivalent to any given system of linear equations. We shall illustrate how this is done by an example.

Consider the following system of four equations in four unknowns over $\mathbb{Q}$.

(1)
$$\begin{cases} 2x_1 - x_2 + 3x_3 + x_4 = 2 \\ x_1 \quad\;\; + x_3 + 2x_4 = \tfrac{3}{2} \\ 3x_1 - 2x_2 + 5x_3 + x_4 = \tfrac{9}{2} \\ 2x_2 - 2x_3 + 5x_4 = 0 \end{cases}$$

Labelling the equations of (1) by E_1, E_2, E_3, and E_4, the following system with equations E_1, $E_1 - 2E_2$, E_3, and E_4 is equivalent to (1) by 11.7.

(2)
$$\begin{cases} 2x_1 - x_2 + 3x_3 + x_4 = 2 \\ - x_2 + x_3 - 3x_4 = -1 \\ 3x_1 - 2x_2 + 5x_3 + x_4 = \tfrac{9}{2} \\ 2x_2 - 2x_3 + 5x_4 = 0 \end{cases}$$

In turn, labeling the equations of (2) by E_1, E_2, E_3, and E_4, system (3) below with equations E_1, E_2, $3E_1 - 2E_3$, and E_4 is equivalent to (2), and hence also to (1), by 11.7.

(3)
$$\begin{cases} 2x_1 - x_2 + 3x_3 + x_4 = 2 \\ x_2 + x_3 - 3x_4 = -1 \\ x_2 - x_3 + x_4 = -3 \\ 2x_2 - 2x_3 + 5x_4 = 0 \end{cases}$$

In turn, system (4) with equations E_1, E_2, $E_2 + E_3$, E_4 obtained from (3) is also equivalent to system (1).

(4)
$$\begin{cases} 2x_1 - x_2 + 3x_3 + x_4 = 2 \\ -x_2 + x_3 - 3x_4 = -1 \\ - 2x_4 = -4 \\ 2x_2 - 2x_3 + 5x_4 = 0 \end{cases}$$

In turn, system (5) with equations E_1, E_2, E_3, $2E_2 + E_4$ from (4) is equivalent to system (1).

(5)
$$\begin{cases} 2x_1 - x_2 + 3x_3 + x_4 = 2 \\ -x_2 + x_3 - 3x_4 = -1 \\ - 2x_4 = -4 \\ - x_4 = -2 \end{cases}$$

Finally, system (6) with equations E_1, E_2, E_3, $E_3 - 2E_4$ from (5) is equivalent to (1) and is in echelon form.

(6)
$$\begin{cases} 2x_1 - x_2 + 3x_3 + x_4 = 2 \\ - x_2 + x_3 - 3x_4 = -1 \\ - 2x_4 = -4 \\ 0 = 0 \end{cases}$$

System (6) has a solution by 11.10. The solution set of (6), and hence of (1) also, evidently is given by

$$\left\{ \left(\frac{-5 - 2c}{2}, -5 + c, c, 2 \right) \,\Big|\, c \in \mathbb{Q} \right\}.$$

Exercises

Solve each of the following systems of linear equations over the field $\mathbb{Q}$.

1. $\begin{cases} x_1 - 2x_2 = 1 \\ 2x_1 + x_2 = 3 \end{cases}$ 2. $\begin{cases} 3x_1 + x_2 = 5 \\ x_1 - x_2 = 2 \end{cases}$

3. $\begin{cases} 2x_1 + 4x_2 = 3 \\ x_1 + 2x_2 = 1 \end{cases}$ 4. $\begin{cases} 7x_1 - 2x_2 = 3 \\ -14x_1 + 4x_2 = -6 \end{cases}$

5. $\begin{cases} x_1 + x_2 - x_3 = 5 \\ 2x_1 - x_2 + x_3 = 7 \\ x_2 - x_3 = 1 \end{cases}$ 6. $\begin{cases} 3x_1 - x_2 + 2x_3 = 2 \\ x_2 - x_3 = 4 \\ -x_2 + x_3 = 1 \end{cases}$

7. $\begin{cases} x_1 + 2x_3 = 2 \\ 2x_1 + x_2 = 0 \\ x_3 - x_4 = 0 \\ 3x_1 + x_4 = 1 \end{cases}$ 8. $\begin{cases} x_1 - 2x_2 + x_3 + 2x_4 = 1 \\ x_1 - 2x_2 - x_3 + x_4 = 2 \\ x_4 = 3 \end{cases}$

Solve each of the following systems of linear equations over the stated field.

9. $\begin{cases} x_1 + x_3 = 1 \\ x_2 + x_3 = 0 \\ x_1 + x_4 = 1 \end{cases}$ over $\mathbb{Z}_2$

10. $\begin{cases} x_1 + x_3 = 1 \\ x_2 + x_3 = 0 \\ x_1 + x_4 = 1 \end{cases}$ over $\mathbb{Z}_5$

11. $\begin{cases} x_1 + 2x_2 + 2x_3 + x_4 = 2 \\ 2x_1 + 2x_2 + x_3 + x_4 = 1 \\ 2x_2 + x_4 = 1 \end{cases}$ over $\mathbb{Z}_3$

12. $\begin{cases} x_1 + 2x_2 + 2x_3 + x_4 = 2 \\ 2x_1 + 2x_2 + x_3 + x_4 = 1 \\ 2x_2 + x_4 = 1 \end{cases}$ over $\mathbb{Z}_7$

2. The Theory

A system of linear equations over a field F, say

11.4 $$\sum_{j=1}^{n} a_{ij}x_j = b_i, \qquad i = 1,2,\dots,m,$$

is said to be *compatible* iff whenever

$$\sum_{i=1}^{m} r_i a_{ij} = 0, \qquad j = 1,2,\dots,n,$$

for some $r_i \in F$, then also

$$\sum_{i=1}^{m} r_i b_i = 0.$$

Letting $\alpha_i = (a_{i1},a_{i2},\dots,a_{in})$ be the ith row of matrix (a_{ij}), system 11.4 is compatible iff

11.11   Whenever $\sum_{i=1}^{m} r_i \alpha_i = 0$ then also $\sum_{i=1}^{m} r_i b_i = 0$, $r_i \in F$.

11.12   **Theorem.** A system of linear equations over a field F has a solution iff it is compatible.

We can prove half of 11.12 easily. Thus, if 11.4 has a solution $(c_1,c_2,\dots,c_n) \in F^n$, then whenever $\sum_{i=1}^{m} r_i a_{ij} = 0, j = 1,2,\dots,n$, also

$$\sum_{i=1}^{m}\sum_{j=1}^{n} r_i a_{ij} c_j = \sum_{i=1}^{m} r_i b_i = 0.$$

Therefore, system 11.4 is compatible. The proof that a compatible system of linear equations has a solution will be given later.

Associated with system 11.4 is the matrix $A = (a_{ij})$ of coefficients of the unknowns and also the *augmented matrix*

11.13 $$\text{aug } A = \begin{pmatrix} a_{11} & a_{12} & \cdots & a_{1n} & b_1 \\ a_{21} & a_{22} & \cdots & a_{2n} & b_2 \\ \multicolumn{5}{c}{\dotfill} \\ a_{m1} & a_{m2} & \cdots & a_{mn} & b_m \end{pmatrix}.$$

Evidently aug A is an $m \times (n + 1)$ matrix over F.

The row vectors $\alpha_1, \alpha_2, \ldots, \alpha_m \in F^n$ of matrix A generate a subspace S of $V_n(F)$,

$$S = F\alpha_1 + F\alpha_2 + \ldots + F\alpha_m.$$

Similarly, the row vectors $\alpha_1', \alpha_2', \ldots, \alpha_m'$ of aug A, where

$$\alpha_i' = (a_{i1}, a_{i2}, \ldots, a_{in}, b_i) \in F^{n+1},$$

generate a subspace S' of $V_{n+1}(F)$,

$$S' = F\alpha_1' + F\alpha_2' + \ldots + F\alpha_m'.$$

There is a natural mapping $S' \xrightarrow{g} S$ defined by

11.14
$$g\left(\sum_{i=1}^{m} c_i\alpha_i'\right) = \sum_{i=1}^{m} c_i\alpha_i.$$

The mapping is well-defined; for if $\sum c_i\alpha_i' = \sum d_i\alpha_i'$ then evidently $\sum c_i\alpha_i = \sum d_i\alpha_i$. We leave it for the reader to verify that g is an epimorphism of vector space S' into S.

11.15   Theorem. The mapping $S' \xrightarrow{g} S$ defined by 11.14 is an isomorphism iff system 11.4 is compatible.

Proof: $\sum c_i\alpha_i' \in \ker g$ then $\sum c_i\alpha_i = 0$ and

(1)
$$\sum_{i=1}^{m} c_i a_{ij} = 0, \qquad j = 1, 2, \ldots, n.$$

Therefore, g is an isomorphism iff whenever (1) is satisfied for some $c_i \in F$ then also $\sum c_i b_i = 0$ and hence $\sum c_i\alpha_i' = 0$. ∎

Each $n \times n$ matrix $A = (a_{ij})$ over a field F has an associated linear transformation f of the vector space $V_n(F)$ relative to the usual unit basis $\{u_1, u_2, \ldots, u_n\}$. Thus, if $e_{ij} \in L(V_n)$ is defined by $e_{ij}(u_k) = \delta_{jk}u_i$ as in 10.22,

$$f = \sum_{i=1}^{n} \sum_{j=1}^{n} a_{ij}e_{ij}.$$

Now

$$f(u_j) = \sum_{i=1}^{n} a_{ij}u_i = (a_{1j}, a_{2j}, \ldots, a_{nj}) = \alpha_j,$$

the jth row vector of A, for each $j = 1, 2, \ldots, n$. Hence,

$$f(V_n) = F\alpha_1 + F\alpha_2 + \ldots + F\alpha_n$$

is the subspace of V_n generated by the row vectors of matrix A. Therefore, the rank of $f \in L(V_n)$ is simply the dimension of the subspace of V_n generated by the row vectors of A. For this reason, we call $r(f)$ the *row rank* of matrix A and denote it by $rr(A)$.

Since an isomorphism of vector spaces preserves dimension, we can also state 11.15 in the following form.

11.16   Theorem. A system of linear equations with matrix of coefficients A is compatible iff $rr(A) = rr(\text{aug } A)$.

The system 11.4 can also be expressed in terms of the column vectors of matrix $A = (a_{ij})$ as follows. If

$$\alpha^j = \begin{pmatrix} a_{1j} \\ a_{2j} \\ \cdot \\ \cdot \\ \cdot \\ a_{mj} \end{pmatrix}, \quad \beta = \begin{pmatrix} b_1 \\ b_2 \\ \cdot \\ \cdot \\ \cdot \\ b_m \end{pmatrix}, \quad \text{then } \alpha^j x_j = \begin{pmatrix} a_{1j}x_j \\ a_{2j}x_j \\ \cdot \\ \cdot \\ \cdot \\ a_{mj}x_j \end{pmatrix}$$

for each j and 11.4 has the form

11.17
$$\sum_{j=1}^{n} \alpha^j x_j = \beta.$$

Hence, $(c_1, c_2, \ldots, c_n) \in F^n$ is a solution of 11.4 iff

11.18
$$\sum_{j=1}^{n} \alpha^j c_j = \beta.$$

Note that we are now putting the scalars to the right of the vectors, to conform with the notation in 11.17.

If
$$T = \alpha^1 F + \alpha^2 F + \ldots + \alpha^n F$$

is the vector space generated by the column vectors of A, then dim T is called the *column rank* of A and is denoted by $cr(A)$. Let
$$T' = \alpha^1 F + \alpha^2 F + \ldots + \alpha^n F + \beta F$$

be the vector space generated by the column vectors of aug A. Clearly $T \subset T' \subset V_m(F)$, with $T = T'$ iff $cr(A) = cr(\text{aug } A)$. If system 11.4 has solution $(c_1, c_2, \ldots, c_n)$ then $\beta \in T$ and $T = T'$ by 11.18. Conversely, if $T = T'$ then $\beta \in T$ and $\beta = \sum \alpha^j c_j$ for some $c_i \in F$. Hence, $(c_1, c_2, \ldots, c_n)$ is a solution of 11.4. This proves the following result.

11.19   Theorem. A system of linear equations with matrix A of coefficients has a solution iff $cr(A) = cr(\text{aug } A)$.

Theorem 11.12 will follow from Theorems 11.16 and 11.19 once we establish the following result.

11.20   Theorem. For every $m \times n$ matrix A over a field F,

$$rr(A) = cr(A).$$

Proof: Let $\alpha_1, \alpha_2, \ldots, \alpha_m \in V_n(F)$ be the row vectors and $\alpha^1, \alpha^2, \ldots, \alpha^n \in V_m(F)$ be the column vectors of A. Since $\dim V_n = n$, $rr(A) \leq n$; and, similarly, $cr(A) \leq m$. We shall prove that $rr(A) \geq cr(A)$. An analogous argument, interchanging the roles of the rows and columns, will prove that $cr(A) \geq rr(A)$ and hence that $rr(A) = cr(A)$.

We first remark that if matrix A' is obtained from A by interchanging some of the rows of A, then $rr(A') = rr(A)$ and $cr(A') = cr(A)$. That $rr(A') = rr(A)$ is obvious; that $cr(A') = cr(A)$ follows from the observation that interchanging the ith and jth coordinates of all the vectors in a subspace of V_m does not change the dimension of the subspace.

If $rr(A) = k$, then we might as well assume that $\{\alpha_1, \alpha_2, \ldots, \alpha_k\}$ is a basis of the subspace $S = F\alpha_1 + F\alpha_2 + \ldots + F\alpha_m$ of $V_n(F)$. If

$$B = \begin{pmatrix} a_{11} & a_{12} & \cdots & a_{1n} \\ a_{21} & a_{22} & \cdots & a_{2n} \\ \cdots\cdots\cdots\cdots\cdots \\ a_{k1} & a_{k2} & \cdots & a_{kn} \end{pmatrix}$$

then B is a $k \times n$ matrix with row vectors $\alpha_1, \alpha_2, \ldots, \alpha_k$ and column vectors $\beta^1, \beta^2, \ldots, \beta^n \in V_k(F)$. Clearly $cr(B) \leq k$.

There is a natural mapping $T' \overset{g}{\longrightarrow} S'$ of the vector space $T' = \beta^1 F + \beta^2 F + \ldots + \beta^n F$ into the vector space $S' = \alpha^1 F + \alpha^2 F + \ldots + \alpha^n F$ defined by

$$g\left(\sum_{j=1}^{n} \beta^j c_j \right) = \sum_{j=1}^{n} \alpha^j c_j.$$

The mapping g is well-defined. For if $\sum \beta^j c_j = \sum \beta^j d_j$, then $\sum \beta^j(c_j - d_j) = 0$,

$$\sum_{j=1}^{n} a_{ij}(c_j - d_j) = 0, \qquad i = 1, 2, \ldots, k,$$

and

$$\alpha_i \cdot \gamma = 0, \qquad i = 1, 2, \ldots, k,$$

where

$$\gamma = (c_1 - d_1, c_2 - d_2, \ldots, c_n - d_n).$$

Since each α_r is a linear combination of the vectors $\alpha_1, \alpha_2, \ldots, \alpha_k$,

$$\alpha_r = \sum_{i=1}^{k} f_{ri} \alpha_i \text{ for some } f_{ri} \in F,$$

evidently

$$\alpha_r \cdot \gamma = \sum_{i=1}^{k} f_{ri}(\alpha_i \cdot \gamma) = 0 \text{ for each } r.$$

Hence,

$$\sum_{j=1}^{n} a_{ij}(c_j - d_j) = 0, \qquad i = 1,2,\ldots,m,$$

or

$$\sum_{j=1}^{n} \alpha^j(c_j - d_j) = 0,$$

and $\sum \alpha^j c_j = \sum \alpha^j d_j$. Thus, g is well-defined.

Clearly g is a surjection of T' into S'. Therefore, $k \geq \dim T' \geq \dim S'$ and $cr(A) \leq k = rr(A)$. ∎

In view of Theorem 11.20, we can define the *rank* of an $m \times n$ matrix A over a field to be either $rr(A)$ or $cr(A)$. Let us denote the rank of A by $r(A)$. If A is a square matrix, say $A \in (F)_n$, then the rank of A is the same as the rank of the associated linear transformation f of $V_n(F)$ and we have $r(A) = r(f)$. In particular, f, and hence A also, has an inverse iff $r(A) = r(f) = n$.

Exercises

Find the rank of each of the following matrices over $\mathbb{Q}$ by finding either its row rank or its column rank, whichever is easier.

1. $\begin{pmatrix} 2 & -1 \\ 0 & 2 \\ 1 & 3 \\ 4 & 1 \end{pmatrix}.$

2. $\begin{pmatrix} 2 & -1 & 4 & 1 \\ 3 & 5 & -1 & 2 \\ 5 & 17 & -11 & 4 \end{pmatrix}.$

3. $\begin{pmatrix} 1 & 1 & 0 \\ 0 & 1 & 1 \\ 1 & 1 & 1 \end{pmatrix}.$

4. $\begin{pmatrix} -1 & 0 & 1 & 0 \\ 2 & 0 & 0 & -2 \\ 0 & 3 & 0 & 3 \\ 4 & 1 & -1 & 2 \end{pmatrix}.$

5. $\begin{pmatrix} 1 & 3 & 2 & 3 & 0 & 0 \\ -1 & -3 & 2 & 1 & -4 & -4 \\ 2 & 6 & -1 & 1 & 5 & 3 \end{pmatrix}.$

6. If in system 11.4 we have $m < n$ and $r(A) = m$, does the system necessarily have a solution? Prove your answer.

7. If in system 11.4 we have $m > n$ and $r(A) = n$, does the system necessarily have a solution? Prove your answer.

8. If in system 11.4 we have $m = n$ and $r(A) = n$, prove that the system has a unique solution.

3. The Solution Set of a System of Linear Equations

Associated with the system

11.4 $$\sum_{j=1}^{n} a_{ij}x_j = b_i, \qquad i = 1, 2, \ldots, m,$$

of m linear equations in n unknowns over a field F is the *homogeneous system*

11.21 $$\sum_{j=1}^{n} a_{ij}x_j = 0, \qquad i = 1, 2, \ldots, m.$$

System 11.21 always has the *trivial solution* $(0, 0, \ldots, 0) \in F^n$. If S is the solution set of 11.21 and $\gamma = (c_1, c_2, \ldots, c_n)$, $\delta = (d_1, d_2, \ldots, d_n)$ are in S and $k \in F$, then $\gamma + \delta$ and $k\gamma$ are also in S since

$$\sum_{j=1}^{n} a_{ij}(c_j + d_j) = \sum_{j=1}^{n} a_{ij}c_j + \sum_{j=1}^{n} a_{ij}d_j = 0, \qquad i = 1, 2, \ldots, m,$$

and

$$\sum_{j=1}^{n} a_{ij}(kc_j) = k \sum_{j=1}^{n} a_{ij}c_j = 0, \qquad i = 1, 2, \ldots, m.$$

Therefore, S is a *subspace* of $V_n(F)$.

In describing the solution set of 11.21, it is convenient to express the system in the form

11.22 $$\alpha^1 x_1 + \alpha^2 x_2 + \ldots + \alpha^n x_n = 0,$$

where $\alpha^1, \alpha^2, \ldots, \alpha^n$ are the column vectors of the $m \times n$ matrix $A = (a_{ij})$. Let $k = r(A)$. If $k = n$, then $\{\alpha^1, \alpha^2, \ldots, \alpha^n\}^{\perp}$ and the only solution of 11.22, and hence also of 11.21, is the trivial one.

If $k < n$, let us assume that the unknowns $x_1, x_2, \ldots, x_n$ are ordered so that the first k columns of A are independent, i.e., so that $\{\alpha^1, \alpha^2, \ldots, \alpha^k\}^{\perp}$.

Then every other column is a linear combination of the first k columns,

11.23 $\alpha^j = \sum\limits_{r=1}^{k} \alpha^r d_{jr}$ for some $d_{jr} \in F$, $j = k + 1, \ldots, n$.

Let $\gamma_j \in V_n(F)$ be defined by

11.24 $\gamma_j = (d_{j1} - \delta_{j1}, d_{j2} - \delta_{j2}, \ldots, d_{jn} - \delta_{jn}), j = k + 1, \ldots, n,$

where $d_{ji} = 0$ if $i > k$ and δ_{ij} is the usual Kronecker delta. Thus,

$$\gamma_{k+1} = (d_{k+1\ 1}, \ldots, d_{k+1\ k}, -1, 0, \ldots, 0)$$

$$\gamma_{k+2} = (d_{k+2\ 1}, \ldots, d_{k+2\ k}, 0, -1, 0, \ldots, 0)$$

$$\cdots\cdots\cdots\cdots\cdots\cdots\cdots\cdots\cdots\cdots\cdots\cdots$$

$$\gamma_n = (d_{n1}, \ldots, d_{nk}, 0, \ldots, 0, -1)$$

Clearly $\{\gamma_{k+1}, \gamma_{k+2}, \ldots, \gamma_n\}^\perp$.
We may now solve system 11.21 as follows.

11.25   Theorem. The homogeneous system of linear equations 11.21 has solution set S given by
$$S = F\gamma_{k+1} + \ldots + F\gamma_n$$
where the γ_j are defined by 11.24.

Proof: That each $\gamma_j \in S$ follows from 11.23, since

$$\sum_{r=1}^{n} a_{ir}(d_{jr} - \delta_{jr}) = \sum_{r=1}^{k} a_{ir}d_{jr} - a_{ij} = 0, \qquad i = 1, 2, \ldots, m.$$

Hence, $S \supset F\gamma_{k+1} + \ldots + F\gamma_n$.
On the other hand, if $\gamma = (d_1, d_2, \ldots, d_n)$ is in S, then so is

$$\gamma' = \gamma + \sum_{j=k+1}^{n} d_j\gamma_j$$

since S is a vector space. Now $d_{ji} - \delta_{ji} = -\delta_{ji}$ if $i > k$, and therefore $\gamma' = (c_1, \ldots, c_k, 0, \ldots, 0)$ for some $c_i \in F$. Hence,

$$\alpha^1 c_1 + \ldots + \alpha^k c_k = 0$$

by 11.22, and all $c_i = 0$ due to the independence of $\{\alpha^1, \ldots, \alpha^k\}$. Consequently $\gamma' = 0$ and

$$\gamma = -\sum_{j=k+1}^{n} d_j\gamma_j.$$

We conclude that $S \subset F\gamma_{k+1} + \ldots + F\gamma_n.$ ∎

Since $\{\gamma_{k+1}, \ldots, \gamma_n\}^{\perp}$, evidently dim $S = n - k$. We therefore have the following corollary of 11.25.

11.26   Corollary. Let

$$\sum_{j=1}^{n} a_{ij}x_j = 0, \qquad i = 1,2,\ldots,m$$

be a homogeneous system of linear equations over a field F and $A = (a_{ij})$ be its matrix of coefficients. Then the solution set of the system is a subspace of $V_n(F)$ of dimension $n - r(A)$.

According to this result, the homogeneous system 11.21 always has a nontrivial solution if $r(A) < n$. If, for example, $m < n$ then $r(A) \leq m$ and the system has a nontrivial solution. That is, a *homogeneous system containing more unknowns than equations always has a nontrivial solution.*

It is now easy to describe the solution set of any system of linear equations.

11.27   Theorem. Let

(1) $$\sum_{j=1}^{n} a_{ij}x_j = b_i, \qquad i = 1,2,\ldots,m,$$

be a compatible system of linear equations over a field F and

(2) $$\sum_{j=1}^{n} a_{ij}x_j = 0, \qquad i = 1,2,\ldots,m,$$

be its associated homogeneous system. If S is the solution set of system (2) and γ is any solution of system (1), then $\gamma + S$ is the solution set of (1).

Proof: If $\gamma = (c_1, c_2, \ldots, c_n)$ and $\delta = (d_1, d_2, \ldots, d_n) \in S$, then

$$\sum_j a_{ij}(c_j + d_j) = \sum_j a_{ij}c_j + \sum_j a_{ij}d_j = \sum_j a_{ij}c_j = b_i$$

for each i. Hence, $\gamma + \delta$ is a solution of (1). Conversely, if $\varepsilon = (e_1, e_2, \ldots, e_n)$ is a solution of (1) then $\sum_j a_{ij}(e_j - c_j) = \sum_j a_{ij}e_j - \sum_j a_{ij}c_j = b_i - b_i = 0$ for each i. Hence, $\varepsilon - \gamma \in S$ and $\varepsilon \in \gamma + S$. ∎

Exercises

Solve each of the following systems of linear equations over $\mathbb{Q}$ by first solving the associated homogeneous system.

1. $2x - 3y + z = 7$

2. $\begin{cases} x + y - 2z = 0 \\ 2x + y + z = 4 \end{cases}$

3. $\begin{cases} 2x - y = 4 \\ x + 2y = 7 \\ 3x - 4y = 1 \end{cases}$

4. $\begin{cases} x + y - 2z = 7 \\ 2x - y - z = -1 \\ y - z = 5 \end{cases}$

Solve each of the following systems of linear equations over the stated field.

5. $\begin{cases} x + 2y + z = 0 \\ 2x + 2y + z = 1 \end{cases}$ over $\mathbb{Z}_3$

6. $\begin{cases} x + y + z + w = 0 \\ y + z + w = 1 \\ x + y + w = 0 \end{cases}$ over $\mathbb{Z}_2$

7. $\begin{cases} x + 2y + 3z + 2w = 2 \\ y + 4z + 6w = 6 \\ 2x + y + 3w = 0 \end{cases}$ over $\mathbb{Z}_7$

8. $\begin{cases} x + y + z = 0 \\ x + 2y + 2z = 1 \\ x + 3y + 3z = 2 \end{cases}$ over $\mathbb{Z}_5$

9. Let F be a field and $A, B \in (F)_n$ be such that $r(A) = m$, $r(B) = n$, and $BA = C = (c_{ij})$ where $c_{ij} = 0$ if $i < j$ and $c_{ii} = 1$ if $i \leq m$. If $A = (a_{ij})$, then solve the system of linear equations

$$\sum_{j=1}^{n} a_{ij} x_j = 0, \qquad i = 1, 2, \ldots, n.$$

4. Determinants

If F is a field and $(F)_n$ is the algebra of all $n \times n$ matrices over F, then the *determinant* det A of each $A = (a_{ij})$ in $(F)_n$ is defined as follows:

11.28 $\det A = \sum_{\sigma \in S_n} \text{sgn } \sigma \, a_{1\sigma(1)} a_{2\sigma(2)} \cdots a_{n\sigma(n)}$

For each permutation $\sigma \in S_n$, the *sign* of σ is defined by

$$\text{sgn } \sigma = \begin{cases} 1 & \text{if } \sigma \text{ is even,} \\ -1 & \text{if } \sigma \text{ is odd.} \end{cases}$$

For example, $S_2 = \{\varepsilon, (12)\}$ where ε is the identity permutation and

if $A = \begin{pmatrix} a_{11} & a_{12} \\ a_{21} & a_{22} \end{pmatrix}$ then det $A = a_{11}a_{22} - a_{12}a_{21}$.

Next, $S_3 = \{\varepsilon, (12), (13), (23), (123), (132)\}$ and if $A = (a_{ij})$

$\det A = a_{11}a_{22}a_{33} - a_{12}a_{21}a_{33} - a_{13}a_{22}a_{31} - a_{11}a_{23}a_{32} + a_{12}a_{23}a_{31} + a_{13}a_{21}a_{32}.$

If $n > 3$, then much labor is needed to write down det A, since the sum in 11.28 has $n!$ terms. For example, if $A \in (F)_5$ then det A has 120 terms. Fortunately, general properties of determinants soon to be stated will greatly simplify the actual computation of det A for any given matrix $A \in (F)_n$.

For each $A = (a_{ij}) \in (F)_n$, the *transpose* of A is denoted by A^T and defined by $A^T = (a_{ji})$. Thus, the ith row (column) of A is the ith column (row) of A^T for each i. Since sgn $\sigma = $ sgn σ^{-1} for each $\sigma \in S_n$ and

$$a_{1\sigma(1)}a_{2\sigma(2)} \cdots a_{n\sigma(n)} = a_{\tau(1)1}a_{\tau(2)2} \cdots a_{\tau(n)n}$$

if $\tau = \sigma^{-1}$, evidently

11.29   det $A^T = $ det A for all $A \in (F)_n$.

Some basic properties of the mapping $(F)_n \xrightarrow{\text{det}} F$ are given below.

11.30   **Theorem.** If $A,B,C,D \in (F)_n$ are given in terms of their row vectors by

$$A = \begin{pmatrix} \alpha_1 \\ \vdots \\ \alpha_i \\ \vdots \\ \alpha_j \\ \vdots \\ \alpha_n \end{pmatrix} \quad B = \begin{pmatrix} \alpha_1 \\ \vdots \\ c\alpha_i \\ \vdots \\ \alpha_j \\ \vdots \\ \alpha_n \end{pmatrix}, \quad C = \begin{pmatrix} \alpha_1 \\ \vdots \\ \alpha_j \\ \vdots \\ \alpha_i \\ \vdots \\ \alpha_n \end{pmatrix}, \quad D = \begin{pmatrix} \alpha_1 \\ \vdots \\ \alpha_i + c\alpha_j \\ \vdots \\ \alpha_j \\ \vdots \\ \alpha_n \end{pmatrix}$$

for some $c \in F$ and $i \neq j$, then

(1) det $B = c$ det A,
(2) det $C = -$det A,
(3) det $D = $ det A.

Outline of proof: (1) is evident, since each a_{ij} in 11.28 is replaced by ca_{ij}. To prove (2), let $C = (c_{ij})$. Then a representative element in the sum defining det C is

$$f = \text{sgn } \sigma \, c_{1\sigma(1)} \cdots c_{i\sigma(i)} \cdots c_{j\sigma(j)} \cdots c_{n\sigma(n)}.$$

Since $c_{rs} = a_{rs}$ if $r \neq i$ or j while $c_{is} = a_{js}$ and $c_{js} = a_{is}$, evidently

$$f = -\text{sgn } \tau \, a_{1\tau(1)} \cdots a_{i\tau(i)} \cdots a_{j\tau(j)} \cdots a_{n\tau(n)}$$

where $\tau = \sigma(ij)$, and (2) follows.

Before proving (3), we note that if the *i*th and *j*th rows of matrix A are equal then, $A = C$ and det $A = -$det A, 2 det $A = 0$, and hence det $A = 0$. Thus, a corollary of (2) is that

11.31   det $A = 0$ if two rows (columns) of A are equal.

The above proof of 11.31 fails if ch $F = 2$ (why?). However, 11.31 may be proved directly from 11.28 in this case.

To prove 11.30(3), we have

$$\det D = \sum_{\sigma \in S_n} \text{sgn } \sigma \, a_{1\sigma(1)} \cdots (a_{i\sigma(i)} + ca_{j\sigma(i)}) \cdots a_{j\sigma(j)} \cdots a_{n\sigma(n)}$$

$$= \sum_{\sigma \in S_n} \text{sgn } \sigma \, a_{1\sigma(1)} \cdots a_{i\sigma(i)} \cdots a_{j\sigma(j)} \cdots a_{n\sigma(n)}$$

$$+ c \sum_{\sigma \in S_n} \text{sgn } \sigma \, a_{1\sigma(1)} \cdots a_{j\sigma(i)} \cdots a_{j\sigma(j)} \cdots a_{n\sigma(n)}$$

$$= \det A + 0$$

in view of 11.31. ∎

While the results of 11.30 were stated in terms of rows, analogous results hold for columns because of 11.29.

How many of the terms of det A contain the element a_{rs}? The answer clearly is $(n - 1)!$, since that many permutations $\sigma \in S_n$ are such that $\sigma(r) = s$. If a_{rs} is factored out of these terms, the resulting sum a'_{rs} is given by:

11.32 $a'_{rs} = \sum \text{sgn } \sigma \, a_{1\sigma(1)} \cdots a_{r-1\,\sigma(r-1)} a_{r+1\,\sigma(r+1)} \cdots a_{n\sigma(n)},$

the sum taken over all $\sigma \in S_n$ for which $\sigma(r) = s$. If we let A_{rs} be the submatrix of A obtained by striking out the rth row and sth column of A,

11.33 $A_{rs} =$

$$\begin{pmatrix} a_{11} & \cdots & a_{1\,s-1} & a_{1\,s+1} & \cdots & a_{1n} \\ \cdot & & \cdot & \cdot & & \cdot \\ \cdot & & \cdot & \cdot & & \cdot \\ \cdot & & \cdot & \cdot & & \cdot \\ a_{r-1\,1} & \cdots & a_{r-1\,s-1} & a_{r-1\,s+1} & \cdots & a_{r-1\,n} \\ a_{r+1\,1} & \cdots & a_{r+1\,s-1} & a_{r+1\,s+1} & \cdots & a_{r+1\,n} \\ \cdot & & \cdot & \cdot & & \cdot \\ \cdot & & \cdot & \cdot & & \cdot \\ \cdot & & \cdot & \cdot & & \cdot \\ a_{n1} & \cdots & a_{n\,s-1} & a_{n\,s+1} & \cdots & a_{nn} \end{pmatrix}$$

then we have

11.34
$$a'_{rs} = (-1)^{r+s} \det A_{rs}.$$

Outline of proof: Clearly 11.34 is true if $r = s$, for then a'_{rs} is precisely $\det A_{rs}$ which is the same as $(-1)^{2r} \det A_{rs}$. If $r < n$ and $s = r + 1$, then form the matrix B from A by interchanging the rth and $(r + 1)$st columns of A. By 11.30(2), $\det B = -\det A$. Clearly $B_{rr} = A_{r\,r+1}$, $b'_{rr} = -a'_{r\,r+1}$, and therefore $a'_{rs} = -\det B_{rr} = (-1)^{r+r+1} \det A_{r\,r+1}$. A continuation of this process for $s = r - 1, r + 2, r - 2$, and so on, proves 11.34. ∎

The element a'_{rs} defined in 11.32 is called the *cofactor* of a_{rs} in matrix $A = (a_{ij})$. By 11.34, the cofactor a'_{rs} is either plus or minus the determinant of the *minor matrix* A_{rs} of A.

Each term of $\det A$ has precisely one of the elements $a_{r1}, a_{r2}, \ldots, a_{rn}$ as a factor. Therefore, for any fixed r,

11.35
$$\det A = \sum_{j=1}^{n} a_{rj} a'_{rj}.$$

Similarly, for any fixed s,

11.36
$$\det A = \sum_{i=1}^{n} a_{is} a'_{is}.$$

Expression 11.35 is called the *expansion of* $\det A$ *by minors of the* rth *row*; 11.36 the *expansion of* $\det A$ *by minors of the* sth *column*.

If, for example,

$$A = \begin{pmatrix} 3 & -1 & 2 \\ 2 & 1 & 4 \\ -1 & 3 & 1 \end{pmatrix}$$

is in $(\mathbb{Q})_3$, then the expansion of $\det A$ by minors of the second row is as follows:

$$\det A = 2 \cdot (-1)^{2+1} \det \begin{pmatrix} -1 & 2 \\ 3 & 1 \end{pmatrix} + 1 \cdot (-1)^{2+2} \det \begin{pmatrix} 3 & 2 \\ -1 & 1 \end{pmatrix}$$

$$+ 4 \cdot (-1)^{2+3} \det \begin{pmatrix} 3 & -1 \\ -1 & 3 \end{pmatrix}$$

$$= -2(-1 - 6) + (3 + 2) - 4(9 - 1) = -13.$$

Formulas 11.30–11.36 can considerably reduce the work involved in finding $\det A$, $A \in (F)_n$. The scheme is to use 11.30(3) to get all the elements except one in some row (column) equal to zero, and then use 11.35 (11.36) on this row (column). This reduces the problem to that of finding the determinant of an $(n - 1) \times (n - 1)$ matrix B. We may then continue the process with B.

For example, let $A \in (\mathbb{Q})_4$ be the matrix

$$A = \begin{pmatrix} 5 & -3 & 8 & 9 \\ 1 & 4 & -1 & 5 \\ -1 & 1 & 3 & 7 \\ 4 & -3 & 4 & 5 \end{pmatrix}.$$

If we multiply the second row of A by -5, 1, and -4 and add the resulting vectors to the first, third, and fourth rows, respectively, of A, we obtain the matrix

$$B = \begin{pmatrix} 0 & -23 & 13 & -16 \\ 1 & 4 & -1 & 5 \\ 0 & 5 & 2 & 12 \\ 0 & -19 & 8 & -15 \end{pmatrix}$$

having the same determinant as A by 11.30(3). Expanding det B by minors of the first column, we have

$$\det A = \det B = 1 \cdot (-1)^{2+1} \det B_{21},$$

where

$$B_{21} = \begin{pmatrix} -23 & 13 & -16 \\ 5 & 2 & 12 \\ -19 & 8 & -15 \end{pmatrix}.$$

On multiplying the second column of B_{21} by $-\frac{5}{2}$ and -6 and adding the resulting vectors to the first and third columns, respectively, of B_{21}, we obtain the matrix

$$= \begin{pmatrix} \dfrac{-111}{2} & 13 & -94 \\ 0 & 2 & 0 \\ -39 & 8 & -63 \end{pmatrix}$$

having the same determinant as B_{21} by 11.30(3). Expanding det C by minors of the second row, we have

$$\det A = -\det B_{21} = -2 \cdot (-1)^{2+2} \det \begin{pmatrix} \dfrac{-111}{2} & -94 \\ -39 & -63 \end{pmatrix} = 339.$$

Exercises

Find the determinant of each of the following matrices.

1. $\begin{pmatrix} 2 & 1 & 4 \\ 1 & 2 & -1 \\ 3 & 1 & 1 \end{pmatrix}$ in $(\mathbb{Q})_3$

2. $\begin{pmatrix} i-1 & i & 1 \\ 2 & 2+i & 1 \\ -i & 0 & 1 \end{pmatrix}$ in $(\mathbb{C})_3$

3. $\begin{pmatrix} 0 & 1 & 2 & 1 \\ 2 & 1 & 1 & 3 \\ 3 & 2 & 0 & 2 \\ 1 & 4 & 1 & 4 \end{pmatrix}$ in $(\mathbb{Z}_5)_4$

4. $\begin{pmatrix} -1 & 1 & 3 & 2 \\ 0 & 2 & -2 & 1 \\ 3 & -3 & 1 & 4 \\ 2 & 2 & -1 & 1 \end{pmatrix}$ in $(\mathbb{Q})_4$

5. $\begin{pmatrix} 4 & -1 & 0 & 1 & 0 \\ 2 & 0 & 0 & 2 & 0 \\ 3 & -3 & 1 & 0 & 1 \\ 4 & 0 & 0 & 1 & 2 \\ 5 & 1 & 5 & 1 & 0 \end{pmatrix}$ in $(\mathbb{Q})_5$

6. $\begin{pmatrix} 1 & 0 & 1 & 1 & 1 \\ 1 & 1 & 0 & 1 & 1 \\ 1 & 1 & 1 & 0 & 1 \\ 1 & 1 & 1 & 1 & 0 \\ 0 & 1 & 1 & 1 & 1 \end{pmatrix}$ in $(\mathbb{Z}_2)_5$

7. Prove that if the matrix $A = (a_{ij}) \in (F)_n$ is in triangular form (i.e., $a_{ij} = 0$ for all $i > j$, or $a_{ij} = 0$ for all $i < j$), then $\det A = a_{11} \cdot a_{22} \cdot \ldots \cdot a_{nn}$.

8. If $A \in (F)_3$ is given by

$$A = \begin{pmatrix} 1 & a & a^2 \\ 1 & b & b^2 \\ 1 & c & c^2 \end{pmatrix}$$

show that $\det A = (b - c)(c - a)(a - b)$. Generalize.

9. If $A \in (F)_3$ is given by

$$A = \begin{pmatrix} x & 1 & 1 \\ 1 & x & 1 \\ 1 & 1 & x \end{pmatrix}$$

show that $\det A = (x - 1)^2(x + 2)$. Generalize.

10. Let $A = (a_{ij}) \in (F)_n$ be given by: $a_{ij} = 1$ if $i \neq j$, $a_{ii} = 0$. Prove that $\det A = (-1)^n(1 - n)$.

5. Further Properties of Determinants

Again we let F be a field, $(F)_n$ be the ring of all $n \times n$ matrices over F, and $\det A$ be the determinant of any $A \in (F)_n$. Clearly $\det I = 1$, where I is the identity matrix.

If in the matrix $A = (a_{ij})$ we replace the rth row by the vector $(k_1, k_2, \ldots, k_n)$ thus yielding the matrix B, then, by 11.35,

$$\det B = \sum_{j=1}^{n} k_j a'_{rj}.$$

Here a'_{rj} is the cofactor of a_{rj} in B, and hence also in A. In particular, if $k_j = a_{ij}, j = 1, 2, \ldots, n$, for some $i \neq r$, then the ith and rth rows of B are equal and $\det B = 0$ by 11.31. Therefore,

11.37
$$\sum_{j=1}^{n} a_{ij} a'_{rj} = \begin{cases} \det A & \text{if } i = r, \\ 0 & \text{if } i \neq r. \end{cases}$$

Working with columns instead of rows, we have the analogous result

11.38
$$\sum_{i=1}^{n} a_{ij} a'_{is} = \begin{cases} \det A & \text{if } j = s, \\ 0 & \text{if } j \neq s. \end{cases}$$

The transpose of the matrix (a'_{ij}) made up of the cofactors of $A = (a_{ij})$ is called the *adjoint* of A and is denoted by adj A. Thus

$$\text{adj } A = \begin{pmatrix} a'_{11} & a'_{21} & \cdots & a'_{n1} \\ a'_{12} & a'_{22} & \cdots & a'_{n2} \\ \cdots\cdots\cdots\cdots\cdots \\ a'_{1n} & a'_{2n} & \cdots & a'_{nn} \end{pmatrix}.$$

The usefulness of adj A stems from the following result.

11.39 Theorem. For each $A \in (F)_n$,

$$A \cdot \text{adj } A = \text{adj } A \cdot A = (\det A)I.$$

This follows directly from 11.37 and 11.38.

If $\det A \neq 0$, then the matrix A has a multiplicative inverse A^{-1} given by

$$A^{-1} = \frac{1}{\det A} \text{adj } A$$

according to 11.39.

For example, if $A \in (W)_2$ is given by

$$A = \begin{pmatrix} 2 & 3 \\ 1 & 3 \end{pmatrix},$$

then the cofactors of A are; $a'_{11} = 3$, $a'_{12} = -1$, $a'_{21} = -3$, $a'_{22} = 2$. Hence,

$$\text{adj } A = \begin{pmatrix} 3 & -3 \\ -1 & 2 \end{pmatrix}$$

and

$$A \cdot \text{adj } A = \text{adj } A \cdot A = \begin{pmatrix} 3 & 0 \\ 0 & 3 \end{pmatrix} = 3I.$$

This is as expected from 11.39, since $\det A = 3$. Thus,

$$A^{-1} = \begin{pmatrix} 1 & -1 \\ -\frac{1}{3} & \frac{2}{3} \end{pmatrix}.$$

As another example, if $A \in (\mathbb{Q})_3$ is given by

$$A = \begin{pmatrix} 1 & 1 & 1 \\ 1 & 2 & 1 \\ -3 & 0 & 1 \end{pmatrix}, \quad \text{then adj } A = \begin{pmatrix} 2 & -1 & -1 \\ -4 & 4 & 0 \\ 6 & -3 & 1 \end{pmatrix}.$$

It is easily verified that $A \cdot \text{adj } A = 4I$, and therefore

$$A^{-1} = \begin{pmatrix} \frac{1}{2} & \frac{1}{4} & -\frac{1}{4} \\ -1 & 1 & 0 \\ \frac{3}{2} & -\frac{3}{4} & \frac{1}{4} \end{pmatrix}.$$

The determinant and rank of a matrix are related in the following way.

11.40   Theorem. *If A is an $m \times n$ matrix over a field F, then $r(A)$ is the largest integer k such that some $k \times k$ submatrix of A has nonzero determinant.*

Proof: Let k be the largest integer such that some $k \times k$ submatrix of A has nonzero determinant. We may assume that the $k \times k$ submatrix B in the upper left corner of A has nonzero determinant. For, by interchanging rows or columns of A, if necessary, any $k \times k$ submatrix of A can be moved to the upper left corner of the resulting matrix. Since the procedure of interchanging rows (columns) of a matrix does not change the rank of the matrix, we need only prove the theorem for the new matrix thus formed.

So let $A = (a_{ij})$ and $B = (a_{ij}) \in (F)_k$ be the upper left corner of A. By assumption, $\det B \neq 0$ and therefore $r(B) = k$ by our previous remarks. Hence, the first k rows of A are linearly independent and $r(A) \geq k$. If $k = m$ or $k = n$ then necessarily $r(A) = k$ and the theorem is proved.

If $k < m$ and $k < n$, then form the $(k + 1) \times (k + 1)$ matrix C_j as follows:

$$C_j = \begin{pmatrix} a_{11} & a_{12} & \cdots & a_{1k} & a_{1j} \\ a_{21} & a_{22} & \cdots & a_{2k} & a_{2j} \\ \cdots & \cdots & \cdots & \cdots & \cdots \\ a_{k1} & a_{k2} & \cdots & a_{kk} & a_{kj} \\ a_{k+1\,1} & a_{k+1\,2} & \cdots & a_{k+1\,k} & a_{k+1\,j} \end{pmatrix}$$

If $j \leq k$, $\det C_j = 0$ since two columns of C_j are equal; if $j > k$, $\det C_j = 0$ since C_j is a $(k + 1) \times (k + 1)$ submatrix of A. Expanding $\det C_j$ by minors of the last column, we obtain

(1)
$$\sum_{i=1}^{k+1} c_i a_{ij} = 0, \qquad j = 1, 2, \ldots, n,$$

where c_i is the cofactor of a_{ij} in C_j, and $c_{k+1} = \det B \neq 0$. Clearly the numbers $c_1, c_2, \ldots, c_{k+1}$ do not depend on j; they are the same for any choice of j between 1 and n. If we let $\alpha_1, \alpha_2, \ldots, \alpha_m$ be the m row vectors of A, then the n equations of (1) can be expressed in the compact form

(2)
$$\sum_{i=1}^{k+1} c_i \alpha_i = 0.$$

Since $c_{k+1} \neq 0$, equation (2) shows that α_{k+1} is a linear combination of $\alpha_1, \alpha_2,$ $\ldots, \alpha_k$.

In place of the last row of C_j, we can just as well put

$$(a_{r1}, a_{r2}, \ldots, a_{rk}, a_{rj})$$

where r is any integer greater than k. If we do this, then by exactly the same argument as above, we can show that the vector α_r is a linear combination of the vectors $\alpha_1, \alpha_2, \ldots, \alpha_k$. Therefore, $rr(A) \leq k$. Since $r(A) = rr(A)$, we have $r(A) = k$. ∎

Let us illustrate how 11.40 can be used to find the rank of a matrix. If $A \in (\mathbb{Q})_4$ is given by

$$A = \begin{pmatrix} 3 & 1 & 4 & 8 \\ -1 & 2 & 0 & 6 \\ 2 & 1 & 3 & 7 \\ 4 & 1 & -1 & -9 \end{pmatrix}$$

then we may add a multiple of a given row (column) of A to another row (column) of A without affecting the determinant of A or any submatrix of A containing the given row (column). Holding the second column of A fixed, and adding the proper multiples of it to the other columns of A, we obtain

$$B = \begin{pmatrix} 0 & 1 & 0 & 0 \\ -7 & 2 & -8 & -10 \\ -1 & 1 & -1 & -1 \\ 1 & 1 & -5 & -17 \end{pmatrix}.$$

Since

$$\det B = -\det \begin{pmatrix} -7 & -8 & -10 \\ -1 & -1 & -1 \\ 1 & -5 & -17 \end{pmatrix} = 0,$$

evidently $r(B) < 4$ and also $r(A) < 4$. Now

$$\det \begin{pmatrix} 0 & 1 & 0 \\ -7 & 2 & -8 \\ -1 & 1 & -1 \end{pmatrix} \neq 0,$$

and hence $r(B) = 3$ by 11.40. Thus, $r(A) = 3$.

Exercises

Find the rank of each of the following matrices over $\mathbb{Q}$. If the matrix has an inverse, find it also.

1. $\begin{pmatrix} -3 & 2 \\ 5 & -4 \end{pmatrix}.$

2. $\begin{pmatrix} 3 & 2 & 0 & 5 \\ 1 & -2 & 8 & 7 \\ -2 & 1 & -7 & -8 \end{pmatrix}.$

3. $\begin{pmatrix} 1 & 2 & 1 \\ -1 & 1 & 1 \\ 0 & -2 & -1 \end{pmatrix}.$

4. $\begin{pmatrix} 1 & 0 & 0 & 0 \\ -1 & 2 & 0 & 0 \\ 1 & -1 & 3 & 0 \\ 1 & 0 & 0 & 1 \end{pmatrix}.$

5. $\begin{pmatrix} 1 & 1 & 1 & 1 \\ 1 & 2 & 3 & 4 \\ 1 & 3 & 6 & 10 \\ 3 & 6 & 10 & 15 \end{pmatrix}$

6. $\begin{pmatrix} 1 & 2 & 3 & 2 & 6 \\ 0 & -1 & 1 & 1 & -7 \\ 1 & 0 & 1 & 2 & 0 \\ -1 & 1 & 0 & -2 & 3 \end{pmatrix}.$

7. Let F be a field, with ch $F \neq 2$. Show that $(AB)^T = B^T A^T$ for all $A, B \in (F)_n$. Call $A \in (F)_n$ *symmetric* iff $A^T = A$ and *skew-symmetric* iff $A^T = -A$. Show that $A + A^T$ and AA^T are symmetric, and $A - A^T$ is skew-symmetric, for all $A \in (F)_n$. Show that AB is symmetric iff $AB = BA$. Prove that every A in $(F)_n$ may be uniquely expressed as a sum of a symmetric and a skew-symmetric matrix.

8. If $A = (a_{ij}) \in (\mathbb{C})_n$, then let $\bar{A} = (\bar{a}_{ij})$ and $A^* = (\bar{A})^T$. Call $A \in (\mathbb{C})_n$ *hermitian* iff $A^* = A$ and *skew-hermitian* iff $A^* = -A$. Obtain results for hermitian and skew-hermitian matrices similar to those of Exercise 7.

6. Determinants and Systems of Linear Equations

As we indicated in the beginning of this chapter, determinants arose in mathematics as a systematic device for solving systems of linear equations. We shall show how determinants are used in solving systems of linear equations in this section.

Let

11.40
$$\sum_{j=1}^{n} a_{ij}x_j = b_i, \qquad i = 1,2, \ldots ,m,$$

be a system of m linear equations in n unknowns over a field F, and let $A = (a_{ij})$ be its matrix of coefficients. We assume that system 11.4 is compatible, and hence that $r(A) = r(\text{aug } A)$ by 11.16. If $r(A) = k$, then we may assume that the $k \times k$ submatrix B in the upper left corner of A has nonzero determinant and hence has an inverse. Otherwise, we could reorder the equations and unknowns of 11.4 until this was so.

If $r(A) = r(B) = k$, where B is the $k \times k$ submatrix of A in the upper left corner, then the solution set of 11.4 is equal to the solution set of system

11.41
$$\sum_{j=1}^{n} a_{ij}x_j = b_i, \qquad i = 1,2, \ldots ,k$$

consisting of the first k equations of 11.4. For clearly each solution of 11.4 is also a solution of 11.41. On the other hand, if $\gamma = (c_1,c_2, \ldots ,c_n)$ is a solution of 11.41, then

$$\alpha_i \cdot \gamma = b_i, \qquad i = 1,2, \ldots ,k,$$

where $\alpha_1, \ldots ,\alpha_m$ are the m row vectors of A. Since each $\alpha_r, r > k$, is a linear combination of $\alpha_1,\alpha_2, \ldots ,\alpha_k$, say $\alpha_r = d_1\alpha_1 + \ldots + d_k\alpha_k$, and $b_r = d_1b_1 + \ldots + d_kb_k$ by the compatibility of system 11.4, evidently

$$\alpha_r \cdot \gamma = \sum_{i=1}^{k} d_i(\alpha_i \cdot \gamma) = \sum_{i=1}^{k} d_ib_i = b_r.$$

That is, γ is a solution of 11.4.

Finally, we solve system 11.41 by replacing the unknowns $x_{k+1}, \ldots ,x_n$ by arbitrary elements $t_{k+1}, \ldots ,t_n$ of F and transposing these terms to the right side of the equation as follows:

11.42
$$\sum_{j=1}^{k} a_{ij}x_j = b_i - \sum_{j=k+1}^{n} a_{ij}t_j, \qquad i = 1,2, \ldots ,k.$$

Thus, if $(c_1,c_2, \ldots ,c_k)$ is a solution of 11.42 then $(c_1, \ldots ,c_k,t_{k+1}, \ldots ,t_n)$ is a solution of 11.41. Conversely, if $(c_1,c_2, \ldots ,c_n)$ is a solution of 11.41 then $(c_1,c_2, \ldots ,c_k)$ is a solution of 11.42 if we let $t_j = c_j, j = k + 1, \ldots ,n$.

System 11.42 may be expressed in the form

11.43 $$B\chi = \delta,$$

where $B = (a_{ij}) \in (F)_k$ is nonsingular (i.e., det $B \neq 0$) and

$$\chi = \begin{pmatrix} x_1 \\ x_2 \\ \cdot \\ \cdot \\ \cdot \\ x_k \end{pmatrix}, \qquad \delta = \begin{pmatrix} d_1 \\ d_2 \\ \cdot \\ \cdot \\ \cdot \\ d_k \end{pmatrix}.$$

We have used $d_i = b_i - (a_{i\,k+1}t_{k+1} + \ldots + a_{in}t_n)$, $i = 1, \ldots, k$, in 11.43. Since B has an inverse B^{-1} given by $(\text{adj } B)/\det B$, we can formally solve 11.43 as follows:

$$B^{-1}(B\chi) = B^{-1}\delta$$
$$(B^{-1}B)\chi = B^{-1}\delta$$

11.44 $$\chi = B^{-1}\delta.$$

Thus, $B^{-1}\delta$ is the unique solution of 11.43. Recalling that adj $B = (a'_{ij})T$ where a'_{ij} is the cofactor of a_{ij} in B, we can write 11.44 in the form

11.45 $$x_j = \frac{1}{\det B} \sum_{i=1}^{k} d_i a'_{ij}, \qquad j = 1, 2, \ldots, k.$$

Classically, this solution was expressed in the following way.

11.46   *Cramer's rule.* If the matrix $B = (a_{ij}) \in (F)_k$ is nonsingular, then the system of linear equations

$$\sum_{j=1}^{k} a_{ij}x_j = d_i, \qquad i = 1, 2, \ldots, k$$

has a unique solution given by

$$x_j = \frac{\det B_j}{\det B}, \qquad j = 1, \ldots, k$$

where B_j is the matrix obtained from B by replacing the jth column of B by the vector

$$\begin{pmatrix} d_1 \\ d_2 \\ \cdot \\ \cdot \\ \cdot \\ d_k \end{pmatrix}.$$

Consider, for example, the following system of equations over $\mathbb{Q}$.

(1)
$$\begin{cases} x_1 + x_2 - 2x_3 + x_4 = 2 \\ 2x_1 + 3x_2 + x_3 - x_4 = -4 \\ x_1 + 3x_2 + 8x_3 + 2x_4 = 7 \\ x_1 + 2x_2 + 3x_3 + 5x_4 = 15 \end{cases}$$

For this system,

$$A = \begin{pmatrix} 1 & 1 & -2 & 1 \\ 2 & 3 & 1 & -1 \\ 1 & 3 & 8 & 2 \\ 1 & 2 & 3 & 5 \end{pmatrix}, \quad \text{aug } A = \begin{pmatrix} 1 & 1 & -2 & 1 & 2 \\ 2 & 3 & 1 & -1 & -4 \\ 1 & 3 & 8 & 2 & 7 \\ 1 & 2 & 3 & 5 & 15 \end{pmatrix}.$$

We find $r(\text{aug } A)$, and also $r(A)$, by the usual method. Adding multiples of the first column of aug A to the other columns so as to obtain zeros in the first row, we get the following matrix having the same rank as aug A:

$$C_1 = \begin{pmatrix} 1 & 0 & 0 & 0 & 0 \\ 2 & 1 & 5 & -3 & -8 \\ 1 & 2 & 10 & 1 & 5 \\ 1 & 1 & 5 & 4 & 13 \end{pmatrix}.$$

Adding the proper multiples of the second column of C_1 to other columns, we obtain

$$C_2 = \begin{pmatrix} 1 & 0 & 0 & 0 & 0 \\ 2 & 1 & 0 & 0 & 0 \\ 1 & 2 & 0 & 7 & 21 \\ 1 & 1 & 0 & 7 & 21 \end{pmatrix}$$

having the same rank as C_1. Finally, multiplying the fourth column of C_2 by -3 and adding it to the fifth column, we obtain

$$C_3 = \begin{pmatrix} 1 & 0 & 0 & 0 & 0 \\ 2 & 1 & 0 & 0 & 0 \\ 1 & 2 & 0 & 7 & 0 \\ 1 & 1 & 0 & 7 & 0 \end{pmatrix}.$$

having the same rank as C_2. Clearly $cr(C_3) = 3$, and hence $r(\text{aug } A) = 3$. The first four columns of the C_i are from matrix A, and hence it is apparent that $r(A) = 3$ also. Hence, by 11.16, system (1) has a solution.

By looking at C_3, it is clear that interchanging the x_3 and x_4 terms in system (3) will yield a system

$$
(2) \quad
\begin{cases}
x_1 + x_2 + x_4 - 2x_3 = 2 \\
2x_1 + 3x_2 - x_4 + x_3 = -4 \\
x_1 + 3x_2 + 2x_4 + 8x_3 = 7 \\
x_1 + 2x_2 + 5x_4 + 3x_3 = 15
\end{cases}
$$

with matrix coefficients of

$$
A = \begin{pmatrix}
1 & 1 & 1 & -2 \\
2 & 3 & -1 & 1 \\
1 & 3 & 2 & 8 \\
1 & 2 & 5 & 3
\end{pmatrix}
$$

such that $r(A) = 3$ and the 3×3 matrix

$$
B = \begin{pmatrix}
1 & 1 & 1 \\
2 & 3 & -1 \\
1 & 3 & 2
\end{pmatrix}
$$

in the upper left corner is nonsingular. In fact, we see that $\det B = 7$.

To solve (2), we need only solve the system

$$
(3) \quad
\begin{cases}
x_1 + x_2 + x_4 = 2 + 2t \\
2x_1 + 3x_2 - x_4 = -4 - t \\
x_1 + 3x_2 + 2x_4 = 7 - 8t
\end{cases}
$$

The B_j of Cramer's rule are as follows:

$$
B_1 = \begin{pmatrix}
2 + 2t & 1 & 1 \\
-4 - t & 3 & -1 \\
7 - 8t & 3 & 2
\end{pmatrix}, \quad
B_2 = \begin{pmatrix}
1 & 2 + 2t & 1 \\
2 & -4 - t & -1 \\
1 & 7 - 8t & 2
\end{pmatrix},
$$

$$
B_3 = \begin{pmatrix}
1 & 1 & 2 + 2t \\
2 & 3 & -4 - t \\
1 & 3 & 7 - 8t
\end{pmatrix}.
$$

Hence, the solution is given by

$$x_1 = \frac{\det B_1}{7}, \qquad x_2 = \frac{\det B_2}{7}, \qquad x_3 = \frac{\det B_3}{7}.$$

Rather than carrying out the details above, let us solve (3) by 11.44. We quickly check that

$$\operatorname{adj} B = \begin{pmatrix} 9 & 1 & -4 \\ -5 & 1 & 3 \\ 3 & -2 & 1 \end{pmatrix}.$$

Hence,

$$\begin{pmatrix} x_1 \\ x_2 \\ x_4 \end{pmatrix} = \frac{1}{7} \begin{pmatrix} 9 & 1 & -4 \\ -5 & 1 & 3 \\ 3 & -2 & 1 \end{pmatrix} \begin{pmatrix} 2 + 2t \\ -4 - t \\ 7 - 8t \end{pmatrix}$$

$$= \frac{1}{7} \begin{pmatrix} -14 + 49t \\ 7 - 35t \\ 21 \end{pmatrix} = \begin{pmatrix} -2 + 7t \\ 1 - 5t \\ 3 \end{pmatrix}.$$

Thus, the solution set of (1) is

$$\{(-2 + 7t, 1 - 5t, t, 3) \mid t \in \mathbb{Q}\}.$$

Exercises

Solve each of the following systems of linear equations over the field $\mathbb{Q}$.

1.
$$\begin{cases} 6x_1 + x_2 + 3x_3 = 2 \\ 2x_1 - x_2 + 2x_3 = -1 \\ x_1 + 2x_2 - x_3 = 1 \end{cases}$$

2.
$$\begin{cases} x_2 + x_3 = 4 \\ x_1 + x_3 = -1 \\ x_1 + x_2 = 3 \end{cases}$$

3.
$$\begin{cases} 3x_1 + x_2 - x_3 = -1 \\ 2x_1 - 3x_3 = -4 \\ x_1 + 3x_2 + 9x_3 = 1 \end{cases}$$

4.
$$\begin{cases} 6x_1 + 2x_2 + 3x_3 = -2 \\ 3x_1 + x_2 + 2x_3 = 0 \\ 3x_1 + x_2 = -4 \end{cases}$$

5.
$$\begin{cases} x_1 + x_2 + x_3 + x_4 = -1 \\ x_1 + 2x_2 + 3x_3 + 4x_4 = 1 \\ x_1 + 3x_2 + 6x_3 + 10x_4 = 1 \\ x_1 + 4x_2 + 10x_3 + 20x_4 = -1 \end{cases}$$

6.
$$\begin{cases} -x_1 + x_3 + 2x_4 = -9 \\ x_1 + x_2 - x_3 + 3x_4 = -17 \\ 4x_1 - x_2 + 2x_3 + x_4 = 4 \\ 4x_1 - 3x_2 + 8x_3 + 5x_4 = -2 \end{cases}$$

$$7. \quad \begin{cases} x_1 + 2x_2 - x_3 + 2x_4 = 3 \\ -x_1 - 3x_2 + 2x_3 + x_4 = -1 \\ -x_1 - 5x_2 + 4x_3 + 7x_4 = 3 \\ x_1 + 6x_2 - 5x_3 - 10x_4 = -4 \end{cases}$$

$$8. \quad \begin{cases} x_1 \quad + x_3 \qquad\qquad = 2 \\ \quad x_2 \quad + x_4 \qquad = -1 \\ x_1 \qquad\qquad + x_5 = 3 \\ \quad x_2 \qquad\qquad + x_5 = 7 \\ \quad x_3 + x_4 \qquad = -1 \end{cases}$$

$$9. \quad \begin{cases} x_1 - x_3 \qquad + 2x_5 = 8 \\ x_2 + 2x_3 + x_4 \qquad = 3 \\ x_1 - 3x_2 \qquad - x_5 = -1 \\ x_1 - 8x_2 + 4x_3 + x_4 - 7x_5 = -16 \\ 4x_1 - 11x_2 - 5x_3 - 2x_4 - x_5 = -1 \end{cases}$$

$$10. \quad \begin{cases} x_1 \quad + 2x_3 \qquad\qquad = 0 \\ \quad x_2 \quad - x_4 \qquad = 0 \\ \quad x_3 \quad + x_5 = 0 \\ x_1 - x_2 \qquad\qquad = 0 \\ \quad x_4 - 2x_5 = 0 \end{cases}$$

Solve each of the following systems of linear equations over the field $\mathbb{Z}_3$.

$$11. \quad \begin{cases} x_1 + 2x_2 + x_3 + x_4 = 2 \\ 2x_1 + x_2 + 2x_3 + x_4 = 0 \\ x_1 + x_2 + 2x_3 + x_4 = 1 \\ 2x_1 \qquad\qquad + x_4 = 2 \end{cases}$$

$$12. \quad \begin{cases} x_1 \quad + 2x_3 \qquad + x_5 = 1 \\ x_1 + x_2 \qquad\qquad + x_5 = 0 \\ x_1 \qquad + x_3 + x_4 \qquad = 0 \\ x_2 + 2x_3 + 2x_4 + x_5 = 0 \\ x_1 + x_2 + 2x_3 + x_4 \qquad = 2 \end{cases}$$

chapter 12

Lattices

The operations of union and intersection in the set $\mathscr{P}(A)$ of all subsets of a set A make $\mathscr{P}(A)$ into a type of algebraic system called a *lattice*. Other examples of lattices are the set of all subgroups of a group and the set of all ideals of a ring, with appropriate operations of union and intersection. Such algebraic systems are the topic of this chapter.

1. Posets

A relation α in a set S is called a *partial ordering* iff (1) α is reflexive, (2) α is transitive, and (3) α is antisymmetric (i.e., whenever $a \, \alpha \, b$ and $b \, \alpha \, a$, then $a = b$). A set S with a partial ordering α is called a *partially ordered set*, abbreviated *poset*. We shall speak of the poset $\{S;\alpha\}$ when we wish to indicate its partial ordering α. If T is a subset of S, then clearly $\{T;\alpha\}$ is also a poset.

The first example of a poset that comes to mind is $\{\mathscr{P}(A); \subset\}$. In this example, the partial ordering is set inclusion. Since $\{T; \subset\}$ is also a poset where T is any subset of $\mathscr{P}(A)$, evidently the sets of all subgroups of a group, of all ideals of a ring, and of all subspaces of a vector space are examples of posets partially ordered by set inclusion.

If $\{S;\alpha\}$ is a poset, then so is $\{S;\varkappa\}$ where the relation $\varkappa$ is defined in the obvious way: for $a,b \in S$,

$$a \, \varkappa \, b \quad \text{iff} \quad b \, \alpha \, a.$$

We call poset $\{S;\varkappa\}$ the *dual* of poset $\{S;\alpha\}$.

A poset $\{S;\alpha\}$ is called a *chain* (or a *linearly ordered set*) iff either $a \,\alpha\, b$ or $b \,\alpha\, a$ for all $a,b \in S$. Thus any two elements of a chain are comparable. The poset $\{\mathscr{P}(A); \subset\}$ is not a chain if $\#(A) > 1$. For example, if $A = \{1,2,3\}$ and $a = \{1,2\}$, $b = \{2,3\}$, then neither $a \subset b$ nor $b \subset a$ holds. However, if $S = \{\varnothing,\{1\},\{1,2\},\{1,2,3\}\}$, then $\{S: \subset\}$ is a chain. As another example, $\{\mathbb{Z}; \leq\}$ is a chain where $\leq$ is the usual ordering of integers.

The most common symbol for the partial ordering in a poset other than $\mathscr{P}(A)$ is $\leq$. When we omit mentioning the symbol for the partial ordering in a poset S, it is tacitly understood to be $\leq$. Then the relations $<$ and $>$

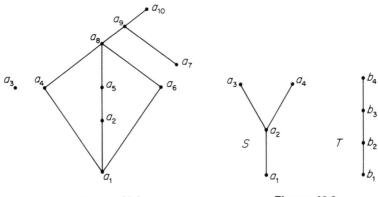

Figure 12.1   **Figure 12.2**

in S have the usual meaning: $a < b$ iff $a \leq b$ and $a \neq b$, $a > b$ iff $b < a$. It is to be noted that $<$ and $>$ are not partial orderings in S.

A finite poset can be represented by a diagram, as illustrated in Figure 12.1. In the poset $S = \{a_1,a_2, \ldots ,a_{10}\}$, we understand $x \leq y$ iff there is a rising path joining x to y (moving from x to y). Thus, $a_1 \leq a_4$, $a_1 \leq a_5$, $a_2 \leq a_9$, $a_6 \leq a_{10}$, and so on. However, $a_8 \not\leq a_7$ since the path joining a_8 to a_7 is not always rising. For the same reason, $a_7 \not\leq a_8$. That is, a_7 and a_8 are not comparable by the relation $\leq$. Evidently $x \leq a_3$ or $a_3 \leq x$ for no $x \neq a_3$ in S. While S is not a chain, each of the subsets $\{a_1,a_2,a_5,a_8,a_9,a_{10}\}$, $\{a_6,a_8,a_{10}\}$, $\{a_7,a_9\}$, $\{a_3\}$ of S is.

If $\{S; \leq\}$ and $\{T; \leq\}$ are posets, then a mapping $S \xrightarrow{f} T$ is said to be *order-preserving* iff whenever $a \leq b$ in S, then also $f(a) \leq f(b)$ in T. For example, if the posets S and T are as shown in Figure 12.2 and the mapping $S \xrightarrow{f} T$ is defined by $f(a_i) = b_i$, then f is order-preserving. However, although f is a bijection, the mapping $T \xrightarrow{f^{-1}} S$ is not order-preserving.

A bijection $S \xrightarrow{f} T$ of poset S into poset T is called an *isomorphism* iff the mappings $S \xrightarrow{f} T$ and $T \xrightarrow{f^{-1}} S$ are both order-preserving. Clearly, the diagrams of isomorphic posets must branch in exactly the same way.

If A is a subset of a poset $\{S;\alpha\}$, then $u \in S$ is called an *upper bound* of A iff $a \, \alpha \, u$ for all $a \in A$. In case u is an upper bound of A and $u \in A$, then clearly u is the *greatest element* of A. Dually, if $B \subset S$ and $v \in S$ with $v \, \alpha \, b$ for all $b \in B$, then v is called a *lower bound* of set B; and if $v \in B$ then v is the *least element* of B. If a poset S has a least element, we shall call it the "zero element" of S; and if S has a greatest element, we shall call it the "all element" of S. For example, the poset $\mathscr{P}(A)$ of all subsets of a set A has zero element $\varnothing$ and all element A.

Associated with each subset A of a poset $\{S;\alpha\}$ are the sets $A' = \{x \in S \mid a \, \alpha \, x$ for all $a \in A\}$ of all upper bounds of A and $A'' = \{y \in S \mid y \, \alpha \, a$ for all $a \in A\}$ of all lower bounds of A. If $A' \neq \varnothing$ and A' has a least element u, then u is called the *least upper bound* (lub) of set A; and if $A'' \neq \varnothing$ and A'' has a greatest element v, then v is called the *greatest lower bound* (glb) of set A. Of course, not every subset of S has to have a lub or glb.

According to the definition above, an upper bound of a subset A of a poset $\{S;\alpha\}$ is a lower bound of A considered as a subset of the dual poset $\{S;\varkappa\}$, and vice versa. In particular, glb A in $\{S;\alpha\}$ is the same as lub A in $\{S;\varkappa\}$, if either exists, and vice versa.

Exercises

1. Draw a diagram of the poset $\mathscr{P}(S)$ in case (i) $S = \{a,b\}$ (ii) $S = \{a,b,c\}$.

2. Draw a diagram of the poset of all subgroups of the symmetric group S_3.

3. Draw a diagram of the poset of all subspaces of the vector space $V_3(\mathbb{Z}_2)$.

2. Lattices

Every one-element subset $\{a\}$ of a poset $\{L;\alpha\}$ has a lub, namely a, and a glb, also a. If every two-element subset of L has a lub and a glb, then the poset L is called a *lattice*. The operations of "union," denoted by $\cup$, and "intersection," denoted by $\cap$, are defined in a lattice L as follows:

$$a \cup b = \text{lub } \{a,b\}, \qquad a \cap b = \text{glb } \{a,b\} \text{ for all } a,b \in L,$$

For example, if S is a set and $\{\mathscr{P}(S); \subset\}$ is the poset of all subsets of S, then the set $\{A,B\}$ has a lub, namely the set-theoretic union of A and B, $A \cup B$, and a glb, namely the set-theoretic intersection of A and B, $A \cap B$, for all $A,B \in \mathcal{P}(S)$. It is this example, of course, that motivated our choice of symbols above for lub $\{a,b\}$ and glb $\{a,b\}$.

As a second example, let G be a group and $L(G)$ be the set of all subgroups of G. For any two subgroups A and B of G, there is a unique least subgroup of G containing both A and B, namely the subgroup generated by the elements of A and B. Clearly this is the subgroup $A \cup B = $ lub $\{A,B\}$. Evidently glb $\{A,B\} = A \cap B$, the set-theoretic intersection of A and B. Thus, $L(G)$ is a lattice.

A third example of a lattice is afforded by the set $L(V)$ of all subspaces of a vector space $V(F)$ over a field F. Then for any two subspaces A and B of V, $A + B = \{a + b \mid a \in A, b \in B\}$ is the lub of $\{A,B\}$ and the set-theoretic intersection $A \cap B$ is the glb of $\{A,B\}$. Thus, $L(V)$ is a lattice.

If R is a ring and $L(R)$ is the set of all ideals of R, then for all $A,B \in L(R)$, $A + B = $ lub $\{A,B\}$ and $A \cap B = $ glb $\{A,B\}$. Therefore, $L(R)$ is a lattice.

In each of the examples above, the partial ordering is set inclusion $\subset$. A somewhat different example is the set $\mathbb{Z}^+$ of positive integers with order relation "is a factor of," denoted by $|$. The reader easily verifies that $\{\mathbb{Z}^+; | \}$ is a poset. Do lub $\{a,b\}$ and glb $\{a,b\}$ exist for all $a,b \in \mathbb{Z}^+$? By definition, lub $\{a,b\}$ is an integer c such that $a \mid c$ and $b \mid c$, such that if $a \mid d$ and $b \mid d$ then $c \mid d$. That is, lub $\{a,b\} = [a,b]$, the lcm of a and b. Similarly, glb $\{a,b\} = (a,b)$, the gcd of a and b. Thus, $\{\mathbb{Z}^+; | \}$ is a lattice in which $a \cup b = [a,b]$ and $a \cap b = (a,b)$.

By definition, a lattice is an algebraic system $\{L; \leq, \cup, \cap\}$ composed of a set L, a partial ordering $\leq$, and two operations $\cup$ and $\cap$ defined in terms of the partial ordering. The operations of a lattice have the following properties.

12.1   Theorem. If $\{L; \leq, \cup, \cap\}$ is a lattice, then:

(1) $\cup$ and $\cap$ are commutative operations.
(2) $\cup$ and $\cap$ are associative operations.
(3) $\cup$ and $\cap$ are idempotent operations; i.e.,

$$a \cap a = a, \quad a \cup a = a \quad \text{for all } a \in L.$$

(4) $\cup$ and $\cap$ are absorptive operations; i.e.,

$$a \cap (a \cup b) = a, \quad a \cup (a \cap b) = a \quad \text{for all } a,b \in L.$$

Outline of proof: (1) and (3) are obvious. To prove that $a \cup (b \cup c) = (a \cup b) \cup c$, we have $a \leq a \cup b \leq (a \cup b) \cup c$, $b \leq a \cup b \leq (a \cup b) \cup c$, and $c \leq (a \cup b) \cup c$. Hence, $b \cup c \leq (a \cup b) \cup c$ and $a \cup (b \cup c) \leq (a \cup b) \cup c$. Similarly, we may show that $(a \cup b) \cup c \leq a \cup (b \cup c)$. Therefore, $a \cup (b \cup c) = (a \cup b) \cup c$. This proves part of (2). The other part is proved dually.

To prove (4), we have from $a \leq a \cup b$ and $a \leq a$ that $a \leq a \cap (a \cup b)$. On the other hand, $a \cap (a \cup b) = $ glb $\{a, a \cup b\} \leq a$. Therefore, $a = a \cap (a \cup b)$. Dually, $a \cup (a \cap b) = a$. ∎

The converse of the above theorem is also true in the following sense.

12.2 Theorem. If $\{L; \cup, \cap\}$ is an algebriac system with operations $\cup$ and $\cap$ which are: (1) commutative, (2) associative, (3) idempotent, and (4) absorptive, then $\{L; \leq, \cup, \cap\}$ is a lattice with partial ordering defined by

$$a \leq b \text{ iff } a \cap b = a, \quad \text{for all } a,b \in L.$$

Outline of proof: We first observe that $a \cap b = a$ iff $a \cup b = b$. For if $a \cap b = a$ then $a \cup b = b \cup a = b \cup (a \cap b) = b$ by (1) and (4). Conversely, if $a \cup b = b$ then $a \cap b = a \cap (a \cup b) = a$ by (4).

Since $a \cap a = a$, $a \leq a$ and $\leq$ is reflexive. If $a \leq b$ and $b \leq c$, so that $a \cap b = a$ and $b \cap c = b$, then $a \cap c = (a \cap b) \cap c = a \cap (b \cap c) = a \cap b = a$ and $a \leq c$. Hence, $\leq$ is transitive. Clearly $\leq$ is antisymmetric. Thus, $\{L; \leq\}$ is a poset.

To prove that $a \cup b = $ lub $\{a,b\}$, we have already shown that $a \leq a \cup b$ and $b \leq b \cup a = a \cup b$. Hence, $a \cup b$ is an upper bound of $\{a,b\}$. If $a \leq x$ and $b \leq x$ for some $x \in L$, then $a \cup x = x$, $b \cup x = x$, and therefore $(a \cup b) \cup x = a \cup (b \cup x) = a \cup x = x$. Hence, $a \cup b \leq x$ and $a \cup b = $ lub $\{a,b\}$.

The proof that $a \cap b = $ glb $\{a,b\}$ is similar to the one above. ∎

If poset $\{L; \leq\}$ is a lattice then so is the dual poset $\{L; \geq\}$. The bijection $L \xrightarrow{\varphi} L$ defined by $\varphi(a) = a$ carries lub $\{a,b\}$ in $\{L; \leq\}$ into glb $\{a,b\}$ in $\{L; \geq\}$, and vice versa. Consequently, every property of a lattice has a dual property obtained by interchanging $\cup$ and $\cap$. In other words, the four defining properties of a lattice, 12.1(1)–12.1(4), are self-dual. Thus, the following duality principle holds in a lattice: *every theorem about a lattice has a dual theorem obtained by interchanging $\leq$ and $\geq$, and $\cup$ and $\cap$.*

If a lattice L has a zero element 0 and an all element I, then clearly 0 and I are dual to each other; i.e., $0 \leq a \leq I$ and $I \geq a \geq 0$ for all $a \in L$. Thus,

$$a \cap 0 = 0, \quad a \cup I = I, \quad a \cup 0 = a \quad a \cap I = a \quad \text{for all } a \in L.$$

Note that the dual of a property involving 0 or I is obtained by interchanging 0 and I as well as $\cup$ and $\cap$.

A poset $\{L; \leq\}$ is called a *complete lattice* iff every nonempty subset of L has both a lub and a glb. Clearly, a complete lattice is a lattice. If L is a complete lattice and $A \subset L$, then we shall use the notation $\bigcup_{a \in A} a$ for lub A and $\bigcap_{a \in A} a$ for glb A.

Evidently a complete lattice L has a zero element 0 and an all element I given by

$$0 = \bigcap_{a \in L} a, \qquad I = \bigcup_{a \in L} a.$$

It is sufficient to know that every subset of L has a glb or lub in order to know that L is a complete lattice, as the following theorem shows.

12.3   Theorem. Let L be a poset containing an all element I (or, dually, a zero element 0). If every subset of L has a glb (or, dually, a lub), then L is a complete lattice.

Proof: For each $A \subset L$, let $A' = \{b \in L \mid a \leq b$ for all $a \in A\}$. We know that $A' \neq \varnothing$, since $I \in A'$. By assumption, A' has a glb a'. Clearly $a' = \text{lub } A$. The dual is proved similarly. ∎

If, for example, S is a set and L is a subset of $\mathscr{P}(S)$ such that $S \in L$ and L is closed under the operation of set-theoretic intersection (i.e., $\bigcap_{A \in T} A \in L$ for every subset T of L), then L is a complete lattice by 12.3. For this reason, the set $L(G)$ of all subgroups of a group G, the set $L(R)$ of all ideals of a ring R, and the set $L(V)$ of all subspaces of a vector space V are complete lattices.

A subset M of a lattice L is called a *sublattice* of L iff it is closed under the operations $\cup$ and $\cap$ of L. Thus, M is a sublattice of L iff for all $a,b \in M$, the lub and glb of $\{a,b\}$ in L are also in M. A complete sublattice of a complete lattice is defined in a similar way.

We must realize that a subset M of a lattice L can be a lattice without being a sublattice of L. That is, each pair $\{a,b\}$ of elements of M might have a lub and a glb in M which are not always the lub and glb of $\{a,b\}$ in L. For example, the lattice $L(G)$ of subgroups of a group G is not usually a sublattice of the lattice $\mathscr{P}(G)$ of all subsets of G, although $L(G)$ is a subset of $\mathscr{P}(G)$. Thus, the set-theoretic union of two subgroups of G is not usually a subgroup of G.

Exercises

1. Show that lattice $L(S_3)$ is not a sublattice of $\mathscr{P}(S_3)$.

2. Show that the lattice of ideals of $\mathbb{Z}_8$ is a sublattice of $\mathscr{P}(\mathbb{Z}_8)$. Generalize.

3. If L is a lattice, then prove that $a \cap (b \cup c) \geq (a \cap b) \cup (a \cap c)$ and $a \cup (b \cap c) \leq (a \cup b) \cap (a \cup c)$ for all $a,b,c \in L$.

4. Let L be the set of all continuous functions with domain $[0,1] = \{x \in \mathbb{R} \mid 0 \leq x \leq 1\}$ and range contained in $\mathbb{R}$. Define the relation $\leq$ in L

by: $f \leq g$ iff $f(x) \leq g(x)$ for all $x \in [0,1]$. Prove that L is a lattice. Is it a complete lattice?

5. If L is a lattice and $a,b, \in L$ with $a \leq b$, then define an *interval* $[a,b]$ in L by: $[a,b] = \{x \in L \mid a \leq x \leq b\}$. Prove that each interval of a lattice L is a sublattice of L.

6. Let L and S be posets and $L \xrightarrow{f} S$ be an order-preserving surjection. If L is a lattice, is S necessarily a lattice? Prove your answer.

7. Prove that every finite subset of a lattice has a lub and a glb.

8. Give an example of a finite poset with a zero element and an all element which is not a lattice.

3. Modular and Complemented Lattices

The lattice $L(R)$ of ideals of a ring R has the following property: if $A,B,C \in L(R)$, with $B \subset A$, then

$$A \cap (B + C) = B + (A \cap C).$$

Proof: Clearly $B + (A \cap C) \subset A \cap (B + C)$. If $x \in A \cap (B + C)$ then $x \in A$ and $x = b + c$ for some $b \in B$ and $c \in C$. Since $B \subset A$, $c = x - b \in A$ and therefore $c \in A \cap C$. Thus, $x \in B + (A \cap C)$. We conclude that $A \cap (B + C) \subset B + (A \cap C)$. ∎

A lattice L is called *modular* iff

12.4 $a \cap (b \cup c) = b \cup (a \cap c)$ whenever $b \leq a$, $a,b,c \in L$.

By the proof above, the lattice $L(R)$ of ideals of a ring R is modular. The same proof shows that the lattices $L(V)$ of all subspaces of a vector space V and $L(G)$ of all subgroups of an Abelian group G are also modular.

The modular law is self-dual; that is, if we interchange $\cup$ and $\cap$, and $\leq$ and $\geq$, in 12.4, thereby obtaining that $a \cup (b \cap c) = b \cap (a \cup c)$ whenever $b \geq a$, we simply get back 12.4 (with a and b interchanged). Therefore, the principle of duality holds for a modular lattice. Clearly every sublattice of a modular lattice is modular.

Not all the lattices arising naturally in mathematics are modular. For example, the lattice $L(G)$ of subgroups of a group G is not usually modular.

This is demonstrated by Figure 12.3, which represents the lattice $L(A_4)$ of all subgroups of the alternating group A_4. The subgroups of A_4 are: $0 = \{e\}, I = A_4$,

$$a_1 = \{e,(12)(34)\}, \qquad a_2 = \{e,(13)(24)\},$$
$$a_3 = \{e,(14)(23)\}, \qquad a_4 = \{e,(123),(132)\},$$
$$a_5 = \{e,(124),(142)\}, \qquad a_6 = \{e,(234),(243)\},$$

and $b = \{e,(12)(34),(13)(24),(14)(23)\}$. We see that $L(A_4)$ is not modular as follows: $a_3 \leq b$, whereas

$$b \cap (a_3 \cup a_4) = b \cap I = b \neq a_3 = a_3 \cup 0 = a_3 \cup (b \cap a_4).$$

Evidently the poset of Figure 12.4 is a lattice. It is nonmodular, since $c \geq b$ whereas $c \cap (b \cup d) = c \cap e = c \neq b = b \cup a = b \cup (c \cap d)$. It is

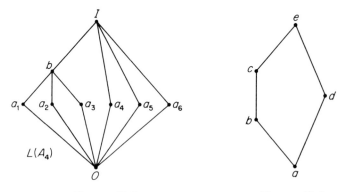

Figure 12.3   **Figure 12.4**

easily shown that $S = \{0,a_3,a_4,b,I\}$ is a sublattice of $L(A_4)$ isomorphic to the lattice of Figure 12.4. This remark illustrates the following theorem.

12.5   Theorem. A lattice L is modular iff it contains no five-element sublattice of the form of Figure 12.4.

Outline of proof: We need only show that every nonmodular lattice L contains a sublattice of the form of Figure 12.4. Lattice L must contain elements b, c, and d with $b < c$ such that $b \cup (c \cap d) < c \cap (b \cup d)$. It is easily shown that $\{c \cap d, d, b \cup (c \cap d), c \cap (b \cup d), b \cup d\}$ is a sublattice of L of the form of Figure 12.4. ∎

A lattice L containing a zero element 0 and an all element I is called a *complemented lattice* iff for every $a \in L$ there exists at least one $b \in L$ such that

12.6 $a \cup b = I, a \cap b = 0.$

In other words, L is complemented iff each $a \in L$ is contained in some four-element sublattice of the form $\{a,b,0,I\}$. Clearly 12.6 is a self-dual property of a lattice.

In any lattice L containing 0 and I, elements a and b are called *complements* of each other if they satisfy 12.6. Evidently 0 and I are complements of each other.

It is easily verified that $L(A_4)$, shown in Figure 12.3, is a complemented lattice. Thus, each element of the set $\{a_1,a_2,a_3,b\}$ is a complement of each element of the set $\{a_4,a_5,a_6\}$.

The lattice $L(V)$ of all subspaces of a vector space V over a field F is modular, as we remarked above. This lattice is also complemented. That is, for each subspace A of V there exists some subspace B of V such that $A \cap B = \{0\}$ and $A + B = V$. If $\dim V = n < \infty$ and $\dim A = k$, then each basis $\{x_1,x_2,\ldots,x_k\}$ of A can be extended to a basis $\{x_1,x_2,\ldots,x_k, x_{k+1},\ldots,x_n\}$ of V. The subspace $B = Fx_{k+1} + \ldots + Fx_n$ clearly is a complement of A. We shall omit the proof that $L(V)$ is complemented in case V is an inifinite-dimensional vector space.

Exercises

1. Is the lattice of Figure 12.5 modular? Complemented? Prove your answers.

2. If L is a modular lattice then prove that

$$a \cap b = [(a \cap b) \cup (a \cap c)] \cap [(a \cap b) \cup (b \cap c)]$$

for all $a,b,c \in L$.

3. Prove that the set $L_n(G)$ of normal subgroups of a group G is a modular lattice. [*Hint:* See Exercise 14, p. 181.]

4. If L is a poset and $a,b \in L$, then b is called a *cover* of a iff $a < b$ whereas $a < x < b$ for no $x \in L$. Thus, if b is a cover of a then the interval $[a,b]$ is simply the set $\{a,b\}$. A lattice L is called *semi-modular* iff whenever a covers $a \cap b$ then also $a \cup b$ covers b in L. Prove that a modular lattice is semimodular. Use Figure 12.5 to show that a semimodular lattice is not necessarily modular.

*5. Let L be a modular lattice and $b_1,b_2,\ldots,b_n$, $c_1,c_2,\ldots,c_n$ be elements of L such that $b_i \leq c_j$ for all i and j as long as $i \neq j$. Prove that

$$\bigcup_{i=1}^{n} (b_i \cap c_i) = \left(\bigcup_{i=1}^{n} b_i\right) \cap \left(\bigcap_{i=1}^{n} c_i\right).$$

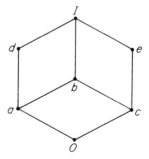

Figure 12.5

THEORETICAL PROJECT 1

Prove the following theorem.

12.7 Theorem. If L is a modular lattice, then the intervals $[a \cap b, a]$ and $[b, a \cup b]$ are isomorphic for all $a, b \in L$.

Outline of proof: Define the mapping $[a \cap b, a] \xrightarrow{f} [b, a \cup b]$ by $f(x) = x \cup b$. Show that $[b, a \cup b] \xrightarrow{f^{-1}} [a \cap b, a]$ is defined by $f^{-1}(y) = y \cap a$.

6. Let L be a modular lattice with 0 and let $x, y, z \in L$. Prove:
   (a) If $x \cap y = 0$ and $z \cap (x \cup y) = 0$, then $x \cap (y \cup z) = 0$.
   (b) If $x \cap y = 0$ and $x \cap (y \cup z) \neq 0$, then $z \cap (x \cup y) \neq 0$.

4. Distributive Lattices

A lattice L is called *distributive* iff

12.8 $a \cap (b \cup c) = (a \cap b) \cup (a \cap c)$ for all $a, b, c \in L$.

Evidently 12.8 is a stronger condition than the modular law (12.4); that is, every distributive lattice is modular. That a modular lattice need not be distributive is shown by the lattice of Figure 12.6, for which

$$a = a \cap (b \cup c) \neq (a \cap b) \cup (a \cap c) = d.$$

If L is a distributive lattice and $a, b, c \in L$, then

$$(a \cup b) \cap (a \cup c) = [(a \cup b) \cap a] \cup [(a \cup b) \cap c] = a \cup [(a \cup b) \cap c]$$
$$= a \cup [(a \cap c) \cup (b \cap c)] = [a \cup (a \cap c)] \cup (b \cap c)$$
$$= a \cup (b \cap c);$$

that is,

12.9 $a \cup (b \cap c) = (a \cup b) \cap (a \cup c)$ for all $a, b, c \in L$.

Dually, we may prove 12.8 from 12.9. Thus, $\cap$ is distributive with respect to $\cup$ and $\cup$ is distributive with respect to $\cap$ in a distributive lattice. Consequently, distributivity is a self-dual property of a lattice. Clearly a sublattice of a distributive lattice is distributive.

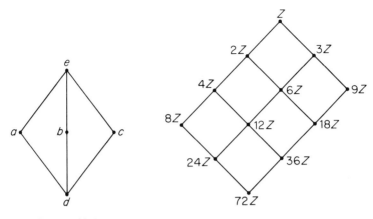

Figure 12.6   **Figure 12.7**

A common example of a distributive lattice is the lattice $L(R)$ of all ideals of a principal ideal domain R. By 7.8(5), this lattice is distributive. Thus, for example, $L(\mathbb{Z})$ is a distributive lattice. The interval $[72\mathbb{Z},\mathbb{Z}]$ of this lattice is shown in Figure 12.7. Of course, this interval is also a distributive lattice. This lattice is not complemented, since, for example, $6\mathbb{Z}$ has no complement.

A lattice L which is both distributive and complemented is called a *Boolean algebra*. The prototype of a Boolean algebra is the lattice $\mathscr{P}(S)$ of all subsets of a set S. For in the first place each $A \in \mathscr{P}(S)$ has a complement $A' = \{x \in S \mid x \notin A\}$. To prove the distributive law 12.7 for $\mathscr{P}(S)$, we need only show that $A \cap (B \cup C) \subset (A \cap B) \cup (A \cap C)$ for all $A,B,C \in \mathscr{P}(S)$ (see Exercise 3, p.248). To show this, let $x \in A \cap (B \cup C)$. Then $x \in A$ and either $x \in B$ or $x \in C$. Hence, either $x \in A \cap B$ or $x \in A \cap C$. Thus, $A \cap (B \cup C) \subset (A \cap B) \cup (A \cap C)$.

If L is a Boolean algebra, then each $a \in L$ has a unique complement. For if x and y are complements of a, so that $a \cup x = a \cup y = I$ and $a \cap x = a \cap y = 0$, then $x = x \cap (a \cup y) = (x \cap a) \cup (x \cap y) = x \cap y$ and, similarly, $y = x \cap y$. Hence, $x = y$. The unique complement of a will be denoted by a'. Clearly $0' = I$ and $I' = 0$. Also, $(a')' = a$ for each $a \in L$.

12.10 Theorem. If L is a Boolean algebra, then the mapping $L \xrightarrow{\gamma} L$ defined by $\gamma(a) = a'$ is a dual isomorphism, i.e., an isomorphism between $\{L;\leq\}$ and its dual $\{L;\geq\}$.

Proof: Since $\gamma^2 = \gamma \circ \gamma$ is the identity mapping of L, evidently γ is a bijection. If $a \leq b$ then $a \cap b' = 0$ and $b' = b' \cap (a \cup a') = (b' \cap a) \cup (b' \cap a') = b' \cap a'$. Hence $a' \geq b'$. Thus, γ is an order-preserving mapping of $\{L;\leq\}$ into $\{L;\geq\}$. Similarly, γ is an order-preserving mapping of $\{L;\geq\}$ into $\{L;\leq\}$. Consequently, γ is a dual isomorphism. ∎

The fact that the mapping $L \xrightarrow{\gamma} L$ above is a dual isomorphism leads to the following property of a Boolean algebra L.

12.11 $(a \cup b)' = a' \cap b', (a \cap b)' = a' \cup b'$ for all $a,b \in L$.

George Boole, after whom Boolean algebras were named, was an English mathematician of the nineteenth century. In the book *An Investigation of the Laws of Thought* (1854) Boole introduced his algebraic system in order to formally study logic. We shall not describe the application of Boolean algebras to logic, but rather refer the interested reader to any one of the appropriate books listed in the bibliography.

Exercises

1. Let L be a distributive lattice. Prove that if $a,b,c \in L$ are such that $a \cap c = b \cap c$ and $a \cup c = b \cup c$ then $a = b$.

2. Let L be a Boolean algebra. Prove that

$$(a \cap b') \cup (a' \cap b) = (a \cup b) \cap (a' \cup b')$$

for all $a,b \in L$.

3. Let R be a ring with unity and $L = \{e \in R \mid e^2 - e, ex = xe \text{ for all } x \in R\}$. Define operations $\cap$ and $\cup$ in L by: $e \cap f = ef, e \cup f = e + f - ef$. Prove that L is closed under $\cap$ and $\cup$, and that $\{L; \cap, \cup\}$ is a Boolean algebra.

4. Prove that the lattice of ideals of a regular ring R is distributive.

THEORETICAL PROJECT 2

Operations of addition and multiplication may be defined in a Boolean algebra L as follows: $a + b = (a \cap b') \cup (a' \cap b), a \cdot b = a \cap b$ for all $a,b \in L$. Prove that $\{L; +, \cdot\}$ is a Boolean ring with unity.

Operations of union and intersection may be defined in a Boolean ring with unity R as follows: $a \cup b = a + b + ab$, $a \cap b = a \cdot b$ for all $a,b \in R$. Prove that $\{R; \cup, \cap\}$ is a Boolean algebra.

Let each Boolean algebra A have associated with it a Boolean ring $R(A)$ and each Boolean ring with unity B have associated with it a Boolean algebra $L(B)$ as above. Prove that $L(R(A))$ is isomorphic to A and $R(L(B))$ is isomorphic to B for every Boolean algebra A and every Boolean ring with unity B.

appendix

Natural Numbers
and Integers

I. The Natural Numbers

The set
$$\mathbb{N} = \{0,1,2,\ldots\}$$
of natural numbers may be characterized by the following three properties, called the Peano† axioms.

A1. The set $\mathbb{N}$ consists of an element 0 and at least one other element.

If we let
$$\mathbb{N}^* = \{x \in \mathbb{N} \mid x \neq 0\},$$
then $\mathbb{N}^* \neq \varnothing$ by A.1. Clearly $\mathbb{N} = \mathbb{N}^* \cup \{0\}$ and $\mathbb{N}^* \cap \{0\} = \varnothing$.

A.2 There exists a bijection $\mathbb{N} \xrightarrow{\ *\ } \mathbb{N}^*$.

Intuitively, we think of n^* as the *successor* of each $n \in \mathbb{N}$. By A.2, each $n \in \mathbb{N}$ has a unique successor n^*, and every $n \neq 0$ is the successor of some natural number.

A.3 If $S \subset \mathbb{N}$, if $0 \in S$, and if $n^* \in S$ for every $n \in S$, then $S = \mathbb{N}$.

---

† Axioms for $\mathbb{N}$ were first given by the Italian mathematician G. Peano in 1889.

Axiom A.3 is known as the *principle of mathematical induction.*

We assume that the reader is familiar with the usual symbols for the natural numbers: $0* = 1$, $1* = 2$, $2* = 3$, $3* = 4$, and so on.

Operations of addition and multiplication may be defined in $\mathbb{N}$ as follows: for all $m,n \in \mathbb{N}$,

A.4 $n + 0 = n, \quad n + m* = (n + m)*.$

A.5 $n \cdot 0 = 0, \quad n \cdot m* = (n \cdot m) + n.$

These are *recursive definitions* in the sense that $n + m*$ is well-defined only if $n + m$ is, and similarly for $n \cdot m*$. That addition and multiplication are uniquely defined by A.4 and A.5 is a consequence of the following theorem.

A.6   Recursion theorem. Let S be a nonempty set, a be any element of S, and $S \overset{f}{\longrightarrow} S$ be any mapping. Then there exists a unique mapping $\mathbb{N} \overset{h}{\longrightarrow} S$ such that

$$h(0) = a, \quad h(n*) = f(h(n)) \quad \text{for all } n \in \mathbb{N}.$$

Proof: Let

$$T = \{A \in \mathscr{P}(\mathbb{N} \times S) \mid (0,a) \in A, \quad \text{and } (n*,f(x)) \in A \text{ for every } (n,x) \in A\}$$

Clearly $\mathbb{N} \times S \in T$, so that $T \neq \varnothing$. Let h be the intersection of all the sets of T. Evidently $h \neq \varnothing$, since every set in T contains the element $(0,a)$. Does h define a mapping of $\mathbb{N}$ into S? That is, for each $n \in \mathbb{N}$ is there a unique $x \in S$ such that $(n,x) \in h$? It is immediate from A.3 and the definition of T that for every $n \in \mathbb{N}$ there exists some $x \in S$ such that $(n,x) \in h$. Let

$$K = \{n \in \mathbb{N} \mid (n,x) \in h \text{ for one and only one } x \in S\}.$$

Is $0 \in K$? If not, $(0,b) \in h$ for some $b \neq a$. However, in this case $h' = \{(m,y) \in h \mid (m,y) \neq (0,b)\}$ is in T and $h' \nsubseteq h$, contrary to the fact that h is the intersection of all sets of T. Thus, $0 \in K$. A similar argument proves that $n* \in K$ for every $n \in K$. Therefore, $K = \mathbb{N}$ by A.3. Thus, h defines a mapping $\mathbb{N} \overset{h}{\longrightarrow} S$, where $h(n) = x$ iff $(n,x) \in h$. Clearly $h(0) = a$, and $h(n*) = f(h(n))$ if $h(n) = x$ by the definition of set T. Also, h is unique since it is the intersection of all sets of T. ∎

We apply A.6 to the problem of defining addition in $\mathbb{N}$ as follows. Let the set S of A.6 equal $\mathbb{N}$, and the mapping f be the successor mapping $f(x) = x*$. Then for every $n \in \mathbb{N}$ there exists a unique mapping $\mathbb{N} \overset{h}{\longrightarrow} \mathbb{N}$ such that

$$h(0) = n, \quad h(m*) = f(h(m)) = [h(m)]*.$$

We now define $n + m = h(m)$ for all $m \in \mathbb{N}$. Thus,

$$n + 0 = n, \quad n + m^* = (n + m)^* \quad \text{for all } m \in \mathbb{N}.$$

Since this addition is uniquely defined for every $n \in \mathbb{N}$. it is well-defined for all $m,n \in \mathbb{N}$. We note that $n + 0^* = n^*$, i.e.,

$$n^* = n + 1 \text{ for all } n \in \mathbb{N}.$$

The recursion theorem may be used in a similar fashion to prove that multiplication in $\mathbb{N}$ is well-defined by A.5.

A.7   Theorem. The operations of addition and multiplication in $\mathbb{N}$ have the following properties:

(i) Addition and multiplication are associative.
(ii) Addition and multiplication are commutative.
(iii) Multiplication is distributive with respect to addition.
(iv) The cancellation laws hold, i.e.,

$$\text{if } m + k = n + k \qquad \text{then } m = n.$$
$$\text{if } m \cdot k = n \cdot k \quad \text{and } k \neq 0 \quad \text{then } m = n.$$

Outline of proof: To prove that addition is associative, let m and n be any given elements of $\mathbb{N}$ and

$$S = \{k \in \mathbb{N} \mid (m + n) + k = m + (n + k)\}.$$

Clearly $0 \in S$. If $k \in S$, so that $(m + n) + k = m + (n + k)$, then

$$(m + n) + k^* = [(m + n) + k]^* = [m + (n + k)]^*$$
$$= m + (n + k)^* = m + (n + k^*)$$

and $k^* \in S$. Hence, $S = \mathbb{N}$ by A.3, and addition is associative.

To prove that addition is commutative, we first prove that

(1) $$0 + m = m \text{ for all } m \in \mathbb{N}.$$

If $S = \{m \in \mathbb{N} \mid 0 + m = m\}$, then evidently $0 \in S$. If $m \in S$, then $0 + m^* = (0 + m)^* = m^*$ and $m^* \in S$. Hence, $S = \mathbb{N}$ and (1) is proved. If $1 + m = m + 1$ for some $m \in \mathbb{N}$. then $1 + m^* = 1 + (m + 1) = (1 + m) + 1 = (m + 1) + 1 = m^* + 1$. Hence,

(2) $$1 + m = m + 1 \text{ for all } m \in \mathbb{N}$$

It is now an easy matter to prove that for any given $m \in \mathbb{N}$,

(3) $$n + m = m + n \text{ for all } n \in \mathbb{N}.$$

Thus, (3) holds if $n = 0$ or $n = 1$ by (1) and (2). If $n + m = m + n$ for some $n \in \mathbb{N}$, then $n^* + m = (n + 1) + m = n + (1 + m) = n + (m + 1) = (n + m) + 1 = (m + n) + 1 = m + (n + 1) = m + n^*$. Hence, (3) follows by mathematical induction. Therefore, addition is commutative.

The distributive law may be proved by showing, as above, that

$$S = \{k \in \mathbb{N} \mid (m + n) \cdot k = m \cdot k + n \cdot k\}$$

equals $\mathbb{N}$ for any $m,n \in \mathbb{N}$. Finally, the commutative and associative laws of multiplication may be established in a similar manner. ∎

The order relation "greater than or equal to" ($\geq$) in $\mathbb{N}$ is defined as follows.

A.8 $m \geq n$ iff $m = k + n$ for some $k \in \mathbb{N}$.

Since $m = 0 + m$, $m \geq m$ and the relation $\geq$ is reflexive. It is easily shown that $\geq$ is transitive and antisymmetric (i.e., if $m \geq n$ and $n \geq m$ then $n = m$).

Other relations in $\mathbb{N}$ are "less than or equal to" ($\leq$), "less than" ($<$), and "greater than" ($>$). Thus, $m \leq n$ iff $n \geq m$; $m > n$ iff $m \geq n$ and $m \neq n$; $m < n$ iff $n > m$.

An important addition property of the order relation $\geq$ in $\mathbb{N}$ is that it is *linear;* i.e.,

A.9   For all $m,n \in \mathbb{N}$, either $m \geq n$ or $n \geq m$.

Proof: We note first of all that $n \geq 0$ for all $n \in \mathbb{N}$. For any given $m \in \mathbb{N}$, let

$$S = \{n \in \mathbb{N} \mid n \leq m\}, \qquad T = \{n \in \mathbb{N} \mid n \geq m\}.$$

We may prove A.9 by showing that $S \cup T = \mathbb{N}$. Clearly $0 \in S \cup T$, since $0 \in S$. If $n \in S \cup T$, then either $n \in S$ or $n \in T$. If $n \in S$, $n \notin T$, then $n < m$ and $n^* \leq m$ so that $n^* \in S$. If $n \in T$, then evidently $n^* \in T$ also. Therefore, $S \cup T = \mathbb{N}$ by A.3. ∎

Similar arguments may be used to prove the following properties of $>$: for all $m,n \in \mathbb{N}$,

A.10 $m > n$ iff $m + k > n + k$ for some $k \in \mathbb{N}$.

A.11 $m > n$ iff $m \cdot k > n \cdot k$ for some nonzero $k \in \mathbb{N}$.

The above properties are still valid if $>$ is replaced by $<$, $\geq$, or $\leq$.

The set $\mathbb{N}$ has the following property relative to its order relation $\geq$.

A.12   Well-ordering of $\mathbb{N}$*.* Every nonempty subset S of $\mathbb{N}$ has a least element.

Proof: Let $T = \{n \in \mathbb{N} \mid n \le m \text{ for all } m \in S\}$. Clearly $0 \in T$. It is equally clear that $T \ne \mathbb{N}$; for if $m \in S$ then $m + 1 \notin T$. Hence, in view of A.3, there must exist some $n \in T$ such that $n + 1 \notin T$. Evidently $n \in S$; for otherwise $n < m$ for all $m \in S$ and therefore $n + 1 \le m$ for all $m \in S$ and $n + 1 \in T$. Consequently, n is the least element of S. ∎

2. Counting

Two sets A and B are said to be *equipotent*, $A \sim B$, iff there exists a bijection $A \longrightarrow B$. Starting with a set S, equipotence is easily shown to be an equivalence relation in the set $\mathscr{P}(S)$ of all subsets of S. Thus, the identity mapping $A \longrightarrow A$ shows that $A \sim A$. If $A \xrightarrow{f} B$ and $B \xrightarrow{g} C$ are bijections, then so is $A \xrightarrow{g \circ f} C$. Hence, $\sim$ is transitive. And so on.

For each natural number k, we can form the set

$$\mathbb{N}_k = \{n \in \mathbb{N} \mid n < k\}.$$

For example, $\mathbb{N}_0 = \varnothing, \mathbb{N}_1 = \{0\}$, $\mathbb{N}_2 = \{0,1\}$, and $\mathbb{N}_3 = \{0,1,2\}$.

A.13   Theorem. $\mathbb{N}_k \sim \mathbb{N}_m$ iff $k = m$.

Proof: We shall prove that if $m < k$ then $\mathbb{N}_k$ is not equipotent with any subset of $\mathbb{N}_m$. This will prove A.13. To this end, let
$S = \{k \in \mathbb{N} \mid \mathbb{N}_k \text{ is not equipotent to a subset of } \mathbb{N}_m \text{ for any } m < k\}$.
Clearly $0,1 \in S$. If $k \in S$ then $k + 1 \in S$ also. For otherwise, there would exist some $m + 1 < k + 1$ and some injection $\mathbb{N}_{k+1} \xrightarrow{f} \mathbb{N}_{m+1}$. Now if $f(x) \ne m$ for all $x \in \mathbb{N}_k$, then the mapping $\mathbb{N}_k \xrightarrow{f'} \mathbb{N}_m$ defined by $f'(x) = f(x)$, $x \in \mathbb{N}_k$, would be an injection, contrary to the assumption that $k \in S$. Therefore, $f(n) = m$ for some $n \in \mathbb{N}_k$. Since f is an injection and $n \ne k$, $f(k) \ne m$; i.e., $f(k) \in \mathbb{N}_m$. Then the mapping $\mathbb{N}_k \xrightarrow{g} \mathbb{N}_m$ defined by $g(x) = f(x)$ if $x \in \mathbb{N}_k$, $x \ne n$, $g(n) = f(k)$, would be an injection. Again, this would be contrary to the choice of k. Therefore, $k + 1 \in S$ and $S = \mathbb{N}$ by A_3. ∎

A set A is called a *finite set* iff $A \sim \mathbb{N}_k$ for some $k \in \mathbb{N}$. By A.13, there is a unique $k \in \mathbb{N}$ such that $A \sim \mathbb{N}_k$ if A is a finite set. We call k the *number of elements* in A, and write

$$\#(A) = k \text{ iff } A \sim \mathbb{N}_k.$$

By this definition, $\varnothing$ is a finite set with $\#(\varnothing) = 0$.

If a set A is not equipotent to $\mathbb{N}_k$ for any $k \in \mathbb{N}$, then A is called an *infinite set* and we write $\#(A) = \infty$. It is apparent that $\mathbb{N}$ is an infinite set. For if $\mathbb{N} \sim \mathbb{N}_k$ for some $k \in \mathbb{N}$, then there would exist an injection $\mathbb{N}_{k+1} \longrightarrow \mathbb{N}_k$, contrary to our remarks in the proof of A.13. The set $\mathbb{N}$, or any set equipotent to $\mathbb{N}$, is called a *countably infinite set*. There are other uncountably infinite sets which we will not discuss here.

If B is a finite set and $A \subset B$, then A is also a finite set. For if $\#(B) = k$, there is an injection $A \longrightarrow \mathbb{N}_k$. If n is the least element of $\mathbb{N}$ for which there exists an injection $A \xrightarrow{f} \mathbb{N}_n$, then f must be a bijection. Otherwise, if $f(A) \neq \mathbb{N}_n$ a new injection $A \xrightarrow{g} \mathbb{N}_{n-1}$ can be defined as in the proof of A.13. This contradicts the choice of n. Hence, $\#(A) = n \leq \#(B)$. Clearly $\#(A) = \#(B)$ iff $A = B$.

We leave the proofs of the following facts about finite sets to the reader.

A.14   If $A \cap B = \varnothing$ then $\#(A \cup B) = \#(A) + \#(B)$.

A.15 $$\#(A \times B) = \#(A) \cdot \#(B).$$

Each nonempty finite set A is equipotent to $\mathbb{N}_{k+1}$ for some $k \in \mathbb{N}$, and therefore there exists a bijection $\mathbb{N}_{k+1} \xrightarrow{f} A$. Since $\mathbb{N}_{k+1} = \{0,1,\ldots,k\}$, evidently $A = \{f(0), f(1), \ldots, f(k)\}$. If we let $f(0) = a_0, f(1) = a_1, \ldots, f(k) = a_k$, then $A = \{a_0, a_1, \ldots, a_k\}$. We can also express A in the form $A = \{b_1, b_2, \ldots, b_{k+1}\}$ by letting $b_i = a_{i+1}$ for each i.

3. The Integers

We know from our previous mathematical experience that the set $\mathbb{N}$ of natural numbers can be enlarged to the set of integers, a set consisting of natural numbers and their negatives. Let us indicate briefly how the set of integers can be derived from $\mathbb{N}$ in the setting of this book.

The first step in the derivation is to consider the set $\mathbb{N} \times \mathbb{N}$ of all ordered pairs of natural numbers. Essentially what we are going to do is to consider elements of the form $(1,0)$, $(2,0)$, $(3,0)$, and so on, as positive integers, elements of the form $(0,1)$, $(0,2)$, $(0,3)$, and so on, as negative integers, and $(0,0)$ as zero. Every other element of $\mathbb{N} \times \mathbb{N}$ will be taken to be equivalent to one of those indicated above in a natural way. Thus, (3,1) will be equivalent to (2,0) and (4,9) to (0,5). In more formal language, let us define the relation $\backsim$ in $\mathbb{N} \times \mathbb{N}$ as follows:†

$$(a,m) \backsim (b,n) \text{ iff } a + n = b + m.$$

It is easily verified that $\backsim$ is an equivalence relation in $\mathbb{N} \times \mathbb{N}$. For example, if $(a,m) \backsim (b,n)$ and $(b,n) \backsim (c,p)$ then $a + n = b + m$ and $b + p = c + n$. Hence, $(a + n) + p = (b + m) + p = (b + p) + m = (c + n) + m$ and therefore $(a + p) + n = (c + m) + n$, $a + p = c + n$, and $(a,n) \backsim (c,p)$. This shows that $\backsim$ is transitive.

Since $\backsim$ is an equivalence relation, it induces a partition $\mathbb{N} \times \mathbb{N}/\backsim$ of $\mathbb{N} \times \mathbb{N}$. Thus, each element $x/\backsim$ of $\mathbb{N} \times \mathbb{N}/\backsim$ has the form

$$x/\backsim = \{y \in \mathbb{N} \times \mathbb{N} \mid x \backsim y\}.$$

For example,

$$(4,9)/\backsim = \{(0,5),(1,6),(2,7),(3,8), \dots \}.$$

The elements of $\mathbb{N} \times \mathbb{N}/\backsim$ are called *integers*. We shall discard the cumbersome symbol $\mathbb{N} \times \mathbb{N}/\backsim$ for the set of all integers, using in its place henceforth the symbol

$$\mathbb{Z}.$$

Operations of addition $(+)$ and multiplication $(\cdot)$ are defined in $\mathbb{Z}$ as follows:

$$(a,m)/\backsim + (b,n)/\backsim = (a + b, m + n)/\backsim$$
$$(a,m)/\backsim \cdot (b,n)/\backsim = (ab + mn, an + bm)/\backsim .$$

We should verify that these operations are well-defined, since the sum and product of two sets are defined in terms of particular elements of the sets. Thus, if $(a,m)/\backsim = (a',m')/\backsim$ and $(b,n)/\backsim = (b',n')/\backsim$, is $(a + b, m + n)/\backsim = (a' + b', m' + n')/\backsim$? And is $(ab + mn, an + bm)/\backsim = (a'b' + m'n', a'n' + b'm')/\backsim$? By what is given, $a + m' = a' + m$ and $b + n' = b' + n$. From these equations, it is a straightforward calculation to verify that

$$(a + b) + (m' + n') = (a' + b') + (m + n)$$

and

$$(ab + mn) + (a'n' + b'm') = (a'b' + m'n') + (an + bm).$$

This will prove that the operations above are well-defined in $\mathbb{Z}$.

It may now be proved that the properties of addition and multiplication in $\mathbb{N}$ carry over to $\mathbb{Z}$. That is, addition and multiplication are associative and commutative, and multiplication is distributive with respect to addition in $\mathbb{Z}$. Furthermore,

$$0 = (a,a)/\backsim \qquad \text{and} \qquad 1 = (a + 1, a)/\backsim$$

---

† In set notation, $\backsim$ is the following subset of $(\mathbb{N} \times \mathbb{N}) \times (\mathbb{N} \times \mathbb{N})$:

$$\backsim = \{((a,m),(b,n)) \in (\mathbb{N} \times \mathbb{N}) \times (\mathbb{N} \times \mathbb{N}) \mid a + n = b + m\}.$$

are identity elements of addition and multiplication, respectively, in $\mathbb{Z}$. The cancellation laws also hold in $\mathbb{Z}$. The one new property that $\mathbb{Z}$ has is that addition is inversive; that is, each element of $\mathbb{Z}$ has an additive inverse.

If $x = (a,m)/\sim$, then define $-x = (m,a)/\sim$. Then

$$x + (-x) = (-x) + x = (a + m, a + m)/\sim = 0.$$

Thus, $-x$ is the additive inverse of x for each $x \in \mathbb{Z}$.

The order relation $\geq$ is defined in $\mathbb{Z}$ as follows:

$$(a,m)/\sim \geq (b,n)/\sim \quad \text{iff } a + n \geq b + m.$$

Again, it should be verified that $\geq$ is well-defined. The other relations $>$, $\leq$, and $<$ are defined in terms of $\geq$ as usual. It may be shown that $\mathbb{Z}$ is linearly ordered by $\geq$; i.e., $x \geq y$ or $y \geq x$ for all $x,y \in \mathbb{Z}$. Also, for $x, y \in \mathbb{Z}$,

   (i) $x > y$ iff $x + z > y + z$ for some $z \in \mathbb{Z}$.

   (ii) $x > y$ iff $x \cdot z > y \cdot z$ for some $z > 0$, $z \in \mathbb{Z}$.

An element x of $\mathbb{Z}$ is called a *positive integer* iff $x > 0$. Clearly $(a,m)/\sim > 0$ iff $a > m$. Thus each positive integer has the form $(m + k, m)/\sim$ (or, $(k,0)/\sim$) for some natural number $k > 0$. We recall that the integer 0 is defined by $0 = (m,m)/\sim$. Let

$$\mathbb{N}' = \{x \in \mathbb{Z} \mid x \geq 0\}.$$

Since $(m + k, m)/\sim = (n + l, n)/\sim$ iff $k = l$, evidently the mapping $\mathbb{N} \xrightarrow{f} \mathbb{N}'$ defined by

$$f(k) = (k,0)/\sim$$

is a bijection. It may be shown that the mapping f also preserves addition and multiplication ,that is,

$$f(k + m) = f(k) + f(m), \quad f(k \cdot m) = f(k) \cdot f(m) \quad \text{for all } k,m \in \mathbb{N}.$$

In addition, it may be shown that $f(k) \geq f(m)$ iff $k \geq m$ for all $k,m \in \mathbb{N}$. Thus, we cannot distinguish between $\mathbb{N}$ and $\mathbb{N}'$ as far as their operations and relations are concerned. We say that $\mathbb{N}$ and $\mathbb{N}'$ are algebraically equivalent for this reason. We may identify $\mathbb{N}$ and $\mathbb{N}'$ in this book, since we are interested only in the algebraic properties (i.e., those related to the operations and relations) of the sets, not in the nature of their elements. If we let $\mathbb{N}^- = \{-x \mid x \in \mathbb{N}\}$, then

$$\underset{\parallel}{\mathbb{Z}} = \mathbb{N} \cup \mathbb{N}^-.$$

The *absolute value* is a mapping $\mathbb{Z} \longrightarrow \mathbb{N}$ defined by

$$|x| = x \text{ if } x \in \mathbb{N}; \quad |x| = -x \text{ if } x \in \mathbb{N}^-.$$

It may be proved that

$$|x + y| \leq |x| + |y|, \quad |x \cdot y| = |x| \cdot |y| \quad \text{for all } x,y \in \mathbb{Z}.$$

Bibliography

Albert, A. A., *Fundamental Concepts of Higher Algebra*. Chicago: University of Chicago Press, 1956.

Birkhoff, G. and S. Maclane, *A Brief Survey of Modern Algebra*. New York: The Macmillan Company, 1953.

Erdélyi, A., *Operational Calculus and Generalized Functions*. New York: Holt, Rinehart & Winston, Inc., 1962.

Fuchs, L., *Abelian Groups*. Publishing House of The Hungarian Academy of Sciences, 1958.

Hall, M., *The Theory of Groups*. New York: The Macmillan Company, 1959.

Halmos, P. R., *Finite-Dimensional Vector Spaces*. Princeton, N.J.: D. Van Nostrand Co., Inc., 1958.

————, *Naive Set Theory*. Princeton, N.J.: D. Van Nostrand Co., Inc., 1960.

Hardy, G. H. and E. M. Wright, *An Introduction to the Theory of Numbers* (4th ed.). Oxford: Clarendon Press, 1960.

Herstein, I. N., *Topics in Algebra*. New York: Blaisdell Publishing Company, 1964.

Jacobson, N., *Lectures in Abstract Algebra*, vol. 1. Princeton, N.J.: D. Van Nostrand Co., Inc., 1951.

Kaplansky, I., *Infinite Abelian Groups*. Ann Arbor, Mich.: The University of Michigan Press, 1954.

Kurosh, A. G., *Lectures on General Algebra*. New York: Chelsea Publishing Company, 1963.

264

Ledermann, W., *Introduction to the Theory of Finite Groups*. Edinburgh: Oliver and Boyd, 1957.

McCoy, N. H., *Rings and Ideals*, Carus Monograph Series, no. 8. LaSalle, Ill.: Open Court Publishing Co., 1948.

Sawyer, W. W., *A Concrete Approach to Abstract Algebra*. San Francisco: W. H. Freeman & Co., 1959.

Van der Waerden, B. L., *Modern Algebra*, vol. 1. New York: Ungar Publishing Company, 1949.

Whitesitt, J. E., *Boolean Algebra and Its Applications*. Reading, Mass.: Addison-Wesley Publishing Co., 1961.

Zariski, O. and P. Samuel, *Commutative Algebra*, vol. 1. Princeton, N.J.: D. Van Nostrand Co., Inc., 1958.

Index

A

Abelian group, 29
Absolute value, 14, 73, 263
  of a complex number, 114
Absorptive operation, 246
Adjoint of a matrix, 233
Algebraic extension of a field, 104, 107
Algebraic system, 11
  element, 103
Algebraic variety, 99
Algebraically closed field, 111
Antisymmetric relation, 3
Archimedean property, 22
Argument of a complex number, 115
Arithmetic, 15
  fundamental theorem, 17
Associative operation, 9
Augmented matrix, 218

B

Basis, of a vector space, 148
Bijection, 5
Bilinear, 155
Boolean algebra, 253
  ring, 54

C

Cancellation law, 12, 30, 166
Cartesian product, 3
  of groups, 43, 167
Cauchy's inequality, 158
Cayley's theorem, 170

Center:
  of a group, 167
  of a ring, 204
Chain, 244
Characteristic, 61, 192
Circle group, 115
Cofactor, 229
Column rank of a matrix, 220
Commutative operation, 9
Commutative ring, 52
Compatible system, 218
Complement, 251
Completeness property, 21
Complex number field, 110
  plane, 113
Composite of mappings, 7
Congruence modulo n, 38
Conjugate:
  complex numbers, 111
  elements of a group, 186
  quadratic numbers, 131
  quaternions, 189
Constructible number, 26
Construction problems of antiquity, 27
Convolution ring, 56
Coset, 35
  left, 166
  right, 166
Cramer's rule, 238
Cycle, 173
Cyclic group, 48
  module, 160

D

de Moivre's theorem, 115
Dense, 22

Dependent set of vectors, 147
Determinant, 226
Dihedral group, 171
Dimension, of a vector space, 151
Distributive operation, 10
Divisible group, 51
Division process, 15, 83
Division ring, 190
Divisor, 16, 83
   of zero, 65
Domain of a mapping, 5
Dual of a poset, 243
   of a lattice, 247

E

Echelon system, 214
Eisenstein's theorem, 92
Empty set, 2
Epimorphism:
   of a group, 41
   of a ring, 59
Equipotent sets, 260
Equivalence relation, 3
Equivalent system, 213
Euclidean domain, 130
Euclidean space, 157
Euclid's algorithm, 19

F

Factor, 16, 83
   theorem, 87
Fermat, 18
   theorem, 68
Field, 66
   algebraically closed, 111
   algebraic extension, 104
   Galois, 108
   ordered, 71
   of quotients, 68, 93
   real, 24
Finite set, 260
Fundamental theorem of algebra, 111

G

Galois field, 108
Gauss, lemma, 91

Gaussian integers, 132
General associative law, 32
General commutative law, 32
General distributive law, 55
Generators:
   of a group, 48
   of a module, 160
   of a vector space, 152
Greater than relation, 73
Greatest common divisor (gcd), 16
   of polynomials, 85
   in a principal ideal domain, 124
Group, 165
   Abelian, 29
   cyclic, 48
   dihedral, 171
   divisible, 51
   permutation, 168
   power, 43
   Prüfer p^∞, 50
   quaternion, 181
   of rationals modulo 1, 39
   Sylow, 185
   symmetric, 168

H

Homogeneous system, 223
Homomorphism:
   of a group, 40, 167
   of a ring, 59
   of a vector space, 152

I

Ideal, 57, 191
   maximal, 86, 126
   principal, 58
   proper, 191
Idempotent operation, 246
Identity, mapping, 8
   element, 9
Image of a mapping, 5
Independent:
   submodules, 161
   subspaces, 144
   vectors, 145
Injection, 5
Inner product, of a vector space, 155

Integers, 11, 261
  negative, 13
  positive, 13, 263
Integers modulo n, 38
Integral domain, 65
  ordered, 71
Integral polynominal, 88
Intersection, 2
  in lattice, 245
  of submodules, 160
  of subspaces, 143
Inverse mapping, 6
  element, 9
Inversive operation, 9
Irrational numbers, 23
Isomorphism:
  group, 41
  poset, 244
  ring, 59
Isomorphism theorem:
  for Abelion groups, 46
  for groups, 183
  for rings, 61, 192

J

Jordan ring, 193

K

Kernel of a homomorphism:
  for Abelian groups, 46
  for groups, 183
  for rings, 60
Kronecker delta, 155

L

Lagrange's theorem, 39, 167
Lattice, 245
  complemented, 250
  complete, 247
  distributive, 252
  modular, 249
  semimodular, 251
Least common multiple (lcm), 16
  of polynomials, 85
  in a principal ideal domain, 124
Length, of a vector, 156
Lie ring, 193
Linear algebra, 196
Linear combination, of vectors, 149

Linear equation, 210
Linear ordering, 13, 244
Linear transformation, 194
  nonsingular, 205
  ring of, 205
  singular, 205
Linearly independent, 145
Lower bound, 21, 245
  greatest, 21, 245

M

Mapping, 4
  bijection, 5
  composite, 7
  domain, 5
  identity, 8
  image, 5
  injection, 5
  inverse, 6
  surjection, 5
Mathematical induction, 14, 257
Matrix, 200
  adjoint, 233
  augmented, 218
  diagonal, 204
  hermitian, 236
  rank, 220, 222
  ring, 202
  skew-hermitian, 236
  skew-symmetric, 236
  symmetric, 236
  trace, 204
Maximal ideal, 86, 126
Mersenne primes, 19
Minimal polynomial, 104, 107
Minor matrix, 229
Module, 160
  cyclic, 160
  finitely generated, 160
Monomorphism:
  group, 41
  ring, 59
Multiple, 16, 32
  of polynomial, 83

N

Natural numbers, 256
Negative, 30
  elements, 72
Nilpotent, 64

Nil ring, 208
Norm, 111, 132
Normalizer, 167
Normal orthogonal basis, 158
Normal subgroup, 180
nth roots, 116
Nullity, 206
Number of elements in a set, 261

O

Operation, 7
  associative, 9
  commutative, 9
  distributive, 10
  inversive, 9
Ordered field, 71
Order of an element, 48, 161, 166
  of a group, 166
  ideal, 161
Order-preserving mapping, 244

P

Partial fractions, 94
Partially ordered set, 243
Partial ordering, 243
Partition, 4
Permutation, 168
  even, 176
  group, 168
  odd, 176
Polynomial, 77
  function, 80
  homogeneous, 101
  integral, 88
  in n symbols, 98
  prime, 83
  rational, 88
  real, 88
  symmetric, 102
Poset, 243
Positive elements, 72
Power series ring, 97
Power set, 6
Prime number, 16
  element, 119
  polynomial, 83
Principal ideal domain, 122
Projection, 45
Prüfer p^∞ group, 50

Q

Quadratic field, 25
  domain, 131
Quaternions, 189
Quotient, 15
Quotient group, 37, 180
Quotient ring, 59, 192

R

Radical of an ideal, 64
Radical of a ring, 208, 209
Rank of a matrix, 222
Rank of a module, 161
Rational expression, 93
Rational numbers, 20
Rational polynomial, 88
Rationals modulo 1, 39
Rational zero theorem, 88
Real field, 24
Real numbers, 20
Real polynomial, 88
Reciprocal, 20
Recursion theorem, 257
Reflexive relation, 3
Regular ring, 207
Relation, 3
  antisymmetric, 3
  equivalence, 3
  reflexive, 3
  symmetric, 3
  transitive, 3
Relatively prime, 17, 125
Remainder, 15
  theorem, 87
Replacement property, 149
Ring, 188
  Boolean, 54
  commutative, 52
  convolution, 56
  division, 190
  Jordan, 193
  Lie, 193
  matrix, 200
  nil, 208
  of quaternions, 189
  regular, 207
  simple, 191
  zero, 58
Row rank of a matrix, 220

S

Scalar, 140
Scalar multiplication, 140, 160
Set, 1
  empty, 2
  intersection, 2
  ordered, 3
  power, 6
  union, 2
Sign of permutation, 226
Simple ring, 191
Solution set, 211
Square-free integer, 24
Subgroup, 34, 166
  commutator, 181
  normal, 180
  proper, 35
Sublattice, 248
Submodule, 160
Subring, 57
Subset, 1
  proper, 2
Subspace, 142
  minimal, 143
  proper, 143
Subtraction, 12, 31
Sum:
  of submodules, 160
  of subspaces, 143
Surjection, 5
Symmetric group, 168
Symmetric relation, 3
System of linear equations, 212
  compatible, 218
  echelon, 214
  equivalent, 213
  homogeneous, 223
  solution, 212

T

Torsion, 164
Trace, 111, 132
  of a matrix, 204

Transcendental element, 104
  extension of a field, 103
Transitive relation, 3
Transpose of a matrix, 227
Transposition, 174
Triangular form of a matrix, 231
Trigonometric form of complex number, 114

U

Union:
  of sets, 2
  in lattice, 245
Unique factorization domain, 119
Unit, 14
  of a ring, 56
Unitary space, 157
Upper bound, 21, 245
  least, 21, 245

V

Vectors, 140
  dependent, 147
  independent, 145
  linear combination, 149
Vector space, 140
  basis, 148
  dimension, 151
  Euclidean, 157
  normal orthogonal basis, 158
  unitary, 157

W

Well-ordered, 14, 73
Wilson's theorem, 68

Z

Zero:
  of a polynomial, 87
  ring, 58